A-Level

Mathematics

for Edexcel Statistics 2

The Complete Course for Edexcel S2

Contents

QA4
C20467961

About this book

In this book you'll find...

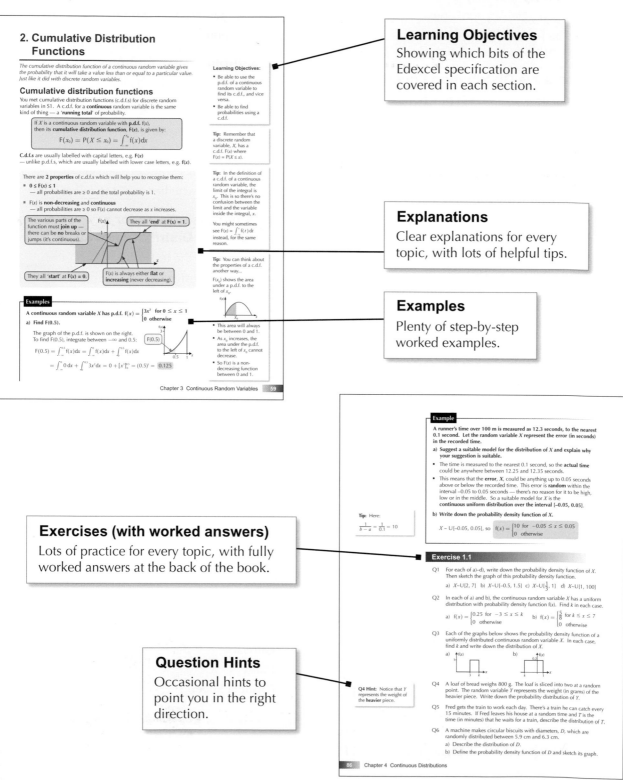

Learning Objectives
Showing which bits of the Edexcel specification are covered in each section.

Explanations
Clear explanations for every topic, with lots of helpful tips.

Examples
Plenty of step-by-step worked examples.

Exercises (with worked answers)
Lots of practice for every topic, with fully worked answers at the back of the book.

Question Hints
Occasional hints to point you in the right direction.

Review Exercise — Chapter 1

Q1 In how many different orders can the following be arranged?
   a) 15 identical red balls, plus 6 other balls, all of different colours.
   b) 4 red counters, 4 blue counters, 4 yellow counters and 4 green counters.
   c) 7 green counters and 5 blue counters.

Q2 Use the binomial probability function to find the probability of the following.
   a) Getting exactly 5 heads when you spin a fair coin 10 times.
   b) Getting exactly 9 heads when you spin a fair coin 10 times.

Q3 Which of the following would follow a binomial distribution? Explain your answers.
   a) The number of prime numbers you throw in 30 throws of a standard dice.
   b) The number of people in a particular class at a school who get 'heads'
      when they flip a coin.
   c) The number of aces in a 7-card hand dealt from a standard pack of 52 cards.
   d) The number of shots I have to take before I score from the free-throw line in basketball.

Q4 What is the probability of the following?
   a) Getting at least 5 heads when you spin a fair coin 10 times.
   b) Getting at least 9 heads when you spin a fair coin 10 times.

Q5 If $X \sim B(14, 0.27)$, find:
   a) $P(X = 4)$ b) $P(X < 2)$ c) $P(5 < X \leq 8)$

Q6 If $X \sim B(25, 0.15)$ and $Y \sim B(15, 0.65)$ find:
   a) $P(X \leq 3)$ b) $P(X \leq 7)$
   c) $P(X \leq 15)$ d) $P(Y \leq 3)$
   e) $P(Y \leq 7)$ f) $P(Y \leq 15)$

Q7 Find the required probability for each of the following binomial distributions.
   a) $P(X \leq 15)$ if $X \sim B(20, 0.4)$ b) $P(X < 4)$ if $X \sim B(40, 0.15)$
   c) $P(X > 7)$ if $X \sim B(25, 0.45)$ d) $P(X \geq 40)$ if $X \sim B(50, 0.8)$
   e) $P(X = 20)$ if $X \sim B(30, 0.7)$ f) $P(X = 7)$ if $X \sim B(10, 0.75)$

Q8 If $X \sim B(30, 0.35)$, find:
   a) a if $P(X \leq a) = 0.8737$ b) b if $P(X \geq b) = 0.8762$
   c) the maximum value c such that $P(X \leq c) < 0.05$.

Q9 Find the mean and variance of the following random variables.
   a) $X \sim B(20, 0.4)$ b) $X \sim B(25, 0.15)$
   c) $X \sim B(25, 0.45)$ d) $X \sim B(50, 0.8)$
   e) $X \sim B(30, 0.7)$ f) $X \sim B(45, 0.012)$

Review Exercises
Mixed questions covering the whole chapter, with fully worked answers.

Exam-Style Questions — Chapter 1

1 a) The random variable X follows the binomial distribution $B(12, 0.6)$. Find:
      (i) $P(X < 8)$,
                                                                        (2 marks)
      (ii) $P(X = 5)$,
                                                                        (2 marks)
      (iii) $P(3 < X \leq 7)$.
                                                                        (3 marks)
   b) If $Y \sim B(11, 0.8)$, find:
      (i) $P(Y = 4)$,
                                                                        (2 marks)
      (ii) $E(Y)$,
                                                                        (1 mark)
      (iii) $Var(Y)$.
                                                                        (1 mark)

2 The probability of an apple containing a maggot is 0.15.
   a) Find the probability that in a random sample of 40 apples there are:
      (i) fewer than 6 apples containing maggots,
                                                                        (2 marks)
      (ii) more than 2 apples containing maggots,
                                                                        (2 marks)
      (iii) exactly 12 apples containing maggots.
                                                                        (2 marks)
   b) These apples are sold in crates of 40. Ed buys 3 crates.
      Find the probability that more than 1 crate contains more than 2 apples with
      maggots.
                                                                        (3 marks)

3 Simon tries to solve the crossword puzzle in his newspaper every day for two weeks.
   He either succeeds in solving the puzzle, or he fails to solve it.
   a) Simon believes that this situation can be modelled by a random variable
      following a binomial distribution.
      (i) State two conditions needed for a binomial distribution to arise here.
                                                                        (2 marks)
      (ii) State which quantity would follow a binomial distribution (assuming the
           above conditions are satisfied).
                                                                        (1 mark)
   b) Simon believes a random variable X follows the distribution $B(18, p)$.
      If $P(X = 4) = P(X = 5)$, find p.
                                                                        (5 marks)

Exam-Style Questions
Questions in the same style as the ones you'll get in the exam, with worked solutions and mark schemes.

Formula Sheet and Statistical Tables
Containing all the formulas and statistical tables you'll be given in the S2 exam.

Glossary
All the definitions you need to know for the exam, plus other useful words.

Practice Exam Papers (on CD-ROM)
Two printable exam papers, with fully worked answers and mark schemes.

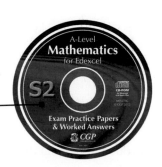

Published by CGP

Editors:
Ali Palin, Andy Park, Charlotte Whiteley.

Contributors:
Katharine Brown, Claire Creasor, Anna Gainey, Janet West.

ISBN: 978 1 84762 808 4

With thanks to Allan Graham and Glenn Rogers for the proofreading.
With thanks to Alastair Duncombe for the reviewing.

Groovy website: www.cgpbooks.co.uk

Printed by Elanders Ltd, Newcastle upon Tyne.
Jolly bits of clipart from CorelDRAW®

1. Binomial Distributions

The binomial distribution is a discrete probability distribution, and so describes discrete random variables (you saw these in S1). But before getting started with probability, you need to know all about binomial coefficients.

Binomial coefficients

It's really important in probability to be able to **count** the possible **arrangements** of various objects. This is because **different** arrangements of outcomes can sometimes correspond to the **same** event — there's more detail about this on the next few pages.

It's slightly easier to get your head round some of these ideas if you think about things that are less 'abstract' than outcomes. So first of all, think about arranging n **different** objects on a shelf.

> n **different** objects can be arranged in $n!$ ('n factorial') different orders, where $n! = n \times (n - 1) \times (n - 2) \times ... \times 3 \times 2 \times 1$.

Examples

a) **In how many orders can 4 different ornaments be arranged on a shelf?**
- Imagine placing the ornaments on the shelf one at a time, starting on the left. You have 4 choices for the first ornament, 3 choices for the second ornament, 2 choices for the third ornament, and 1 choice for the last ornament. So there are $4 \times 3 \times 2 \times 1 = 4! = \boxed{24}$ different orders.

b) **In how many orders can 8 different objects be arranged?**
- There are $8! = \boxed{40\,320}$ different orders.

Keep thinking about arranging n objects on a shelf — but this time, imagine that x of those objects are the **same**.

> n objects, of which x are **identical**, can be arranged in $\frac{n!}{x!}$ orders.

Examples

a) **In how many different orders can 5 objects be arranged if 2 of those objects are identical?**
- Imagine those 2 identical objects were actually different. Then there would be $5! = 120$ possible orders.
- But because those 2 objects are **identical**, you can **swap them round** without making a different arrangement. So there are really only $120 \div 2 = \boxed{60}$ different orders in which to arrange the objects.

Tip: 2 objects can be arranged in $2!$ (= 2) different orders.

Tip: This is $\frac{5!}{2!} = \frac{120}{2} = 60.$

Tip: If you had 7 objects where:

(i) 4 of those were identical to each other, and

(ii) 2 of the remaining objects were also identical to each other,

...then you'd have to divide 7! (= 5040) by 4! (= 24) **and** by 2! (= 2) to get 105 different arrangements.

Tip: Binomial coefficients can be written in different ways:
$$\binom{n}{x} = {}^nC_x = \frac{n!}{x!(n-x)!}$$

Tip: It doesn't matter whether x represents the number of green books or the number of blue books, since:
$$\binom{13}{5} = \binom{13}{8} = \frac{13!}{5!8!}$$

Tip: Notice how binomial coefficients get large very quickly. This is because $n!$ grows **very** quickly as n gets bigger.

b) In how many different orders can 7 objects be arranged if 4 of those objects are identical?

- If all 7 objects were different, there would be 7! possible orders.
- But those 4 identical objects can be swapped around in 4! ways (since there are 4! different ways to arrange 4 objects).
- So there are $\frac{n!}{x!} = \frac{7!}{4!} = \frac{5040}{24} = \boxed{210}$ possible orders for the 7 objects.

Now imagine that you have n objects, but x of these are identical to each other, and the other $n - x$ are also identical to each other (so there are really only two different types of object — x of one type, and $n - x$ of the other).

> x objects of one type and $(n - x)$ objects of another type can be arranged in $\dfrac{n!}{x!(n-x)!}$ different orders.

You've seen the expression $\dfrac{n!}{x!(n-x)!}$ before — it's a **binomial coefficient**.

Example

In how many different orders can 8 identical blue books and 5 identical green books be arranged on a shelf?

- You have two different types of object — so the number of possible orders is given by a binomial coefficient.
- $n = 13$ and $x = 8$ (or 5), so there are $\binom{13}{8} = \frac{13!}{8!5!} = \boxed{1287}$ orders.

Counting 'numbers of arrangements' crops up in all sorts of places.

Examples

a) How many ways are there to select 11 players from a squad of 16?
- This is basically a 'number of different arrangements' problem.
- Imagine the 16 players are lined up — then you could 'pick' or 'not pick' players by giving each of them a sign marked with a tick or a cross.
- So just find the number of ways to order 11 ticks and 5 crosses — this is $\binom{16}{11} = \frac{16!}{11!5!} = \boxed{4368}$.

b) How many ways are there to pick 6 lottery numbers from 49?
- Again, numbers are either 'picked' or 'unpicked', so there are $\binom{49}{6} = \frac{49!}{6!43!} = \boxed{13\,983\,816}$ possibilities.

Okay... it's time to get back to the subject of **probability**...

This chapter is all about **success** and **failure** — at least, there'll be a lot of situations where there are only **two** possible outcomes, and these outcomes are often **labelled** 'success' and 'failure'.

- For example, when you toss a coin, there are two possible outcomes — heads and tails. So 'success' could be heads, while 'failure' could be tails.

Tip: Or you could call tails 'success' and heads 'failure' — it doesn't matter which is which.

You're going to be working out the probability of getting x successes (in any order) when you try something n times in total (i.e. in n 'trials').

- For example, if you toss a coin 3 times, then you're going to find the probability of getting, say, 2 heads (so here, $n = 3$ and $x = 2$).

Tip: The 'in part' is explained on page 4.

But the probability of getting x successes in n trials depends **in part** on how many ways there are to arrange those x successes and $(n - x)$ failures.

- So to find the probability of getting 2 heads in 3 coin tosses, you'd need to find out how many ways there are to get 2 heads and 1 tail in any order.
- You could get:
  - (i)   heads on 1st and 2nd tosses, tails on the 3rd
  - (ii) heads on 1st and 3rd tosses, tails on the 2nd
  - (iii) heads on 2nd and 3rd tosses, tails on the 1st

Tip: These 3 possible arrangements of heads and tails are given by the binomial coefficient $\binom{3}{2} = \frac{3!}{2!1!} = 3$

These different arrangements of successes and failures are really important when you're finding the total probability of '2 heads and 1 tail'.

Tip: See the next page for finding probabilities.

Examples

15 coins are tossed. How many ways are there to get:

a) 9 heads and 6 tails?

- This is $\binom{15}{9} = \frac{15!}{9!(15-9)!} = \frac{15!}{9! \times 6!} = \boxed{5005}$

b) 6 heads and 9 tails?

- This is $\binom{15}{6} = \frac{15!}{6!(15-6)!} = \frac{15!}{6! \times 9!} = \boxed{5005}$

Tip: You get the same answer for '9 heads and 6 tails' and '6 heads and 9 tails'.

This is why it doesn't matter whether you call heads 'success' or 'failure' — there are just as many ways to arrange '9 successes and 6 failures' as there are ways to arrange '6 successes and 9 failures'.

In fact, $\binom{n}{x} = \binom{n}{n-x}$ for any n and x.

Exercise 1.1

Q1 a) In how many ways can the letters of STARLING be arranged?

b) In how many ways can the letters of STARLINGS be arranged?

c) In how many ways can the letters of STARTER be arranged?

Q2 A school football squad consists of 20 players.
The coach has to choose 11 of these players to make up the team.
How many different ways are there to choose 11 players out of 20?

Tip: A **trial** means a situation where there are different possible outcomes. So tossing a coin is a trial, because there are two different possible outcomes. Rolling a dice is also a trial, because there are six different possible outcomes.

Q3 Ten 'success or failure' trials are carried out. In how many different ways can the following be arranged:

a) 3 successes and 7 failures?   b) 5 successes and 5 failures?

Q4 Eleven 'success or failure' trials are carried out.
In how many different ways can the results be arranged if there are:

a) 4 successes?   b) 6 successes?   c) 8 successes?

The binomial distribution

I said on page 3 that the probability of getting x successes in n trials depended **in part** on the number of ways those x successes could be arranged.

But there's another factor as well — the **probability of success** in any of those trials. The examples below both involve finding the probability of getting 3 successes in 4 trials.

Examples

a) I roll a fair dice 4 times.
   Find the probability of getting a five or a six on 3 of those rolls.

- First, note that each roll of the dice is **independent** of the others. That means you can **multiply** individual probabilities together.

- Now... '**success**' here means rolling a 5 or a 6.
  This has a probability of $\frac{2}{6}$, or $\frac{1}{3}$.
  So '**failure**' means rolling a 1, 2, 3 or 4 — with probability $1 - \frac{1}{3} = \frac{2}{3}$.

- There are $\binom{4}{3}$ = 4 different possible orders that these 3 'successes' and 1 'failure' could happen in.

  So P(3 successes) = P(success) × P(success) × P(success) × P(failure)
  + P(success) × P(success) × P(failure) × P(success)
  + P(success) × P(failure) × P(success) × P(success)
  + P(failure) × P(success) × P(success) × P(success)

- Each line above contains the same probabilities — each line will equal [P(success)]³ × P(failure) = $\left(\frac{1}{3}\right)^3 \times \frac{2}{3}$.

- So if you add up all four lines, you find:
  P(3 successes) = 4 × [P(success)]³ × P(failure)

  $$= 4 \times \left(\frac{1}{3}\right)^3 \times \frac{2}{3} = \frac{8}{81} = \boxed{0.0988 \text{ (to 3 sig. fig.)}}$$

b) I roll a fair dice 4 times.
   Find the probability of getting a six on 3 of those rolls.

- This time, '**success**' means rolling a 6 — this has probability $\frac{1}{6}$.
  And '**failure**' means a 1, 2, 3, 4 or 5 — this has probability $1 - \frac{1}{6} = \frac{5}{6}$.

- You could go through exactly the same process as in a) — you still have $n = 4$ and $x = 3$, so there are still 4 ways to arrange the 3 successes and 1 failure — the only difference would be the probabilities.

- So this time:
  P(3 successes) = 4 × [P(success)]³ × P(failure)

  $$= 4 \times \left(\frac{1}{6}\right)^3 \times \frac{5}{6} = \frac{4 \times 5}{6^4} = \frac{20}{1296} = \boxed{0.0154 \text{ (to 3 sig. fig.)}}$$

Tip: If the probability of an event (X) happening is p (i.e. P(X) = p), then the probability that X doesn't happen is $1 - p$ (i.e. P(X′) = $1 - p$, where X′ is the event "not X", i.e. X doesn't happen).

Tip: The 4 different arrangements shown are the $\binom{4}{3} = \frac{4!}{3! \times 1!} = 4$ ways to arrange 3 successes and 1 failure.

Tip: Remember... if events A and B are mutually exclusive, then P(A or B) = P(A) + P(B).

Tip: Remember... if events A and B are independent, then P(A and B) = P(A) × P(B).

Tip: Notice how, although the final probability is different for these two examples, the formula for working it out is the same:

P(3 successes)
   = 4 × [P(success)]³
      × P(failure)

You could use exactly the same logic to work out the formula for the probability of x successes in n trials, for any values of x and n.
This is what you'd get:

$$P(x \text{ successes in } n \text{ trials}) = \binom{n}{x} \times [P(\text{success})]^x \times [P(\text{failure})]^{n-x}$$

This is the **probability function** for the **binomial distribution**.
It tells you the probability that in a total of n separate trials, there will be x successes, for any value of x from 0 to n.

There are **5 conditions** that lead to a binomial distribution.
If just one of these conditions is **not met**, then the logic you've just seen to get the above formula won't hold, and you **won't** have a binomial distribution.

Tip: Remember... a **probability function** lets you work out the probability of a discrete random variable taking its possible values.

A random variable X follows a **binomial distribution** as long as these 5 conditions are satisfied:

1) There is a **fixed** number (n) of trials.
2) Each trial involves either '**success**' or '**failure**'.
3) All the trials are **independent**.
4) The probability of 'success' (p) is the **same** in each trial.
5) The variable is the **total** number of **successes** in the n trials.

In this case, $P(X = x) = \binom{n}{x} \times p^x \times (1-p)^{n-x}$ for $x = 0, 1, 2,..., n$,

and you can write $X \sim B(n, p)$.

Tip: Binomial random variables are **discrete**, since they only take values 0, 1, 2,..., n.

Tip: n and p are the two **parameters** of the binomial distribution. (Or n is sometimes called the '**index**'.)

Examples

Which of the random variables described below would follow a binomial distribution? For those that do, state the distribution's parameters.

a) **The number of faulty items (T) produced in a factory per day, if the probability of each item being faulty is 0.01 and there are 10 000 items produced every day.**
Binomial — there's a fixed number (10 000) of trials with two possible results ('faulty' or 'not faulty'), a constant probability of 'success', and T is the total number of 'faulty' items.
So (as long as faulty items occur independently) $T \sim B(10\,000, 0.01)$.

b) **The number of red cards (R) drawn from a standard, shuffled 52-card pack in 10 picks, not replacing the cards each time.**
Not binomial, since the probability of 'success' changes each time (as the cards are not replaced).

c) **The number of red cards (R) drawn from a standard, shuffled 52-card pack in 10 picks, replacing the cards each time.**
Binomial — there's a fixed number (10) of independent trials with two possible results ('red' or 'black/not red'), a constant probability of success (as the cards are replaced), and R is the number of red cards drawn. So $R \sim B(10, 0.5)$.

d) The number of times (T) I have to toss a coin before I get heads.
Not binomial, since the number of trials isn't fixed.

e) The number of left-handed people (L) in a sample of 500 randomly chosen people if the fraction of left-handed people in the population as a whole is 0.13.
Binomial — there's a fixed number (500) of independent trials with two possible results ('left-handed' or 'not left-handed'), a constant probability of success (0.13), and L is the number of left-handers. So $L \sim B(500, 0.13)$.

Sometimes you might need to make an **assumption** in order to justify using a binomial distribution. Any assumption you need to make will be in order to satisfy one of the 5 conditions for a binomial distribution on the previous page.

Examples

State any assumptions you need to make for the random variables described below to follow a binomial distribution.

a) The total number of defective widgets (N) produced by a machine in a day, if it produces 5000 widgets every day.

- There's a fixed number (5000) of trials, and each trial has two possible results ('defective' or 'not defective'). N is the number of 'successes' over the 5000 trials.

- That leaves two conditions to satisfy. So you'd need to assume that the trials are **independent** (e.g. that one defective widget doesn't lead to another), and that the probability of a defective widget being produced is **always the same** (if the machine needed to 'warm up' every morning before it started working properly, then this might not be true).

b) The number of games of chess Tina wins against Mihir (X) if they play 6 games, where in the past Tina has won 60% of their games.

- There's a fixed number (6) of trials, and each trial has two possible results ('Tina wins' or 'Tina doesn't win'). X is the number of 'successes' over the 6 games.

- So you'd need to assume that the trials are **independent** (e.g. that Tina losing one game won't lead to her getting disheartened and losing another as a result), and that the probability of Tina winning remains **constant** (which it might not if one of them practises lots between games and improves, for example).

Q1 In each of the following situations, explain whether or not the random variable follows a binomial distribution. For those that follow a binomial distribution, state the parameters n and p.

a) The number of spins (X) of a five-sided spinner (numbered 1-5) until a 3 is obtained.

b) The number of defective light bulbs (X) in a batch of 2000 bulbs that have been recently produced, where the production process randomly produces 0.5% defective light bulbs.

c) The number of boys (Y) out of the next 10 children born in a hospital, assuming each birth is equally likely to produce a girl or a boy.

Q2 Based on previous experience, a circus performer successfully completes his circus act on 95% of occasions. Over the next few weeks, he will perform his circus act on 15 occasions and X is the number of occasions on which he successfully completes the act.

State the assumptions that would need to be made in order for X to be modelled by a binomial distribution.

Q3 Ahmed picks 10 cards from a standard, shuffled pack of 52 cards, and counts the number of picture cards (i.e. jacks, queens or kings). State the conditions under which the number of picture cards (X) would follow a binomial distribution, and give the parameters of this distribution.

Q4 A sewing machine operator sews buttons onto jackets. The probability that a button sewed by this operator falls off a jacket before it leaves the factory is 0.001. On one particular day, the sewing machine operator sews 650 buttons, and X is the number of these buttons that fall off a jacket before it leaves the factory.

Can X be modelled by a binomial distribution? State any assumptions you make and state the value of any parameters.

Using the binomial probability function

You've seen the conditions that give rise to a binomial probability distribution. And you've seen where the binomial probability function (below) comes from.

> For a random variable X, where $X \sim B(n, p)$:
> $$P(X = x) = \binom{n}{x} \times p^x \times (1 - p)^{n-x} \quad \text{for } x = 0, 1, 2,..., n.$$

Now you need to make sure you know how to use it.

Examples

If $X \sim B(12, 0.16)$, find:

a) $P(X = 0)$

- Use the formula with $n = 12$, $p = 0.16$ and $x = 0$:

$$P(X = 0) = \binom{n}{x} \times p^x \times (1 - p)^{n-x} = \binom{12}{0} \times 0.16^0 \times (1 - 0.16)^{12-0}$$

$$= \frac{12!}{0!12!} \times 0.16^0 \times 0.84^{12}$$

$$= 0.123 \text{ (to 3 sig. fig.)}$$

b) $P(X = 2)$

- Use the formula with $n = 12$, $p = 0.16$ and $x = 2$:

$$P(X = 2) = \binom{n}{x} \times p^x \times (1 - p)^{n-x} = \binom{12}{2} \times 0.16^2 \times (1 - 0.16)^{12-2}$$

$$= \frac{12!}{2!10!} \times 0.16^2 \times 0.84^{10}$$

$$= 0.296 \text{ (to 3 sig. fig.)}$$

Tip: Remember... $a^0 = 1$ for any number a.

Don't be put off if the question is asked in some kind of context.

Examples

I spin the fair spinner on the right 7 times. Find the probability that I roll:

a) 2 fives

- For this part, call 'roll a five' a success, and 'roll anything other than a five' a failure.

- Then $P(\text{roll 2 fives}) = \binom{7}{2} \times \left(\frac{1}{5}\right)^2 \times \left(\frac{4}{5}\right)^5$

$$= \frac{7!}{2!5!} \times \frac{1}{25} \times \frac{1024}{3125} = 0.275 \text{ (to 3 sig. fig.)}$$

b) 3 fives

- Again, call 'roll a five' a success, and 'roll anything other than a five' a failure.

- Then $P(\text{roll 3 fives}) = \binom{7}{3} \times \left(\frac{1}{5}\right)^3 \times \left(\frac{4}{5}\right)^4$

$$= \frac{7!}{3!4!} \times \frac{1}{125} \times \frac{256}{625} = 0.115 \text{ (to 3 sig. fig.)}$$

Tip: $p = P(\text{roll a five})$
$= \frac{1}{5}$

c) 4 numbers less than three

- This time, success means 'roll a one or a two', while failure is now 'roll a three, four or five'.

- So

$$P(\text{roll 4 numbers less than three}) = \binom{7}{4} \times \left(\frac{2}{5}\right)^4 \times \left(\frac{3}{5}\right)^3$$

$$= \frac{7!}{4!3!} \times \frac{16}{625} \times \frac{27}{125} = \boxed{0.194} \text{ (to 3 sig. fig.)}$$

Tip: $p = $ P(roll a one or a two)

$$= \frac{2}{5}$$

Sometimes you might need to find several individual probabilities, and then add the results together.

Examples

If $X \sim B(6, 0.32)$, find:

a) $P(X \le 2)$

- If $X \le 2$, then X can be 0, 1 or 2.
- So use the formula to find $P(X = 0)$, $P(X = 1)$ and $P(X = 2)$, and then add the results together.
- This time, $n = 6$ and $p = 0.32$.

- $P(X = 0) = \binom{n}{x} \times p^x \times (1-p)^{n-x} = \binom{6}{0} \times 0.32^0 \times (1-0.32)^{6-0}$

$$= \frac{6!}{0!6!} \times 0.32^0 \times 0.68^6$$

$$= \mathbf{0.0988...}$$

- $P(X = 1) = \binom{n}{x} \times p^x \times (1-p)^{n-x} = \binom{6}{1} \times 0.32^1 \times (1-0.32)^{6-1}$

$$= \frac{6!}{1!5!} \times 0.32^1 \times 0.68^5$$

$$= \mathbf{0.2791...}$$

- $P(X = 2) = \binom{n}{x} \times p^x \times (1-p)^{n-x} = \binom{6}{2} \times 0.32^2 \times (1-0.32)^{6-2}$

$$= \frac{6!}{2!4!} \times 0.32^2 \times 0.68^4$$

$$= \mathbf{0.3284...}$$

- So $P(X \le 2) = P(X = 0) + P(X = 1) + P(X = 2)$
$$= 0.0988... + 0.2791... + 0.3284... = \boxed{0.706 \text{ (to 3 sig. fig.)}}$$

b) $P(2 \le X < 4)$

- If $2 \le X < 4$, then X can be 2 or 3.
- You've already found $P(X = 2)$, so you just need to find $P(X = 3)$ now.

- $P(X = 3) = \binom{n}{x} \times p^x \times (1-p)^{n-x} = \binom{6}{3} \times 0.32^3 \times (1-0.32)^{6-3}$

$$= \frac{6!}{3!3!} \times 0.32^3 \times 0.68^3$$

$$= \mathbf{0.2060...}$$

- So $P(2 \le X < 4) = P(X = 2) + P(X = 3)$
$$= 0.3284... + 0.2060... = \boxed{0.534 \text{ (to 3 sig. fig.)}}$$

Tip: Remember... if $X \sim B(n, p)$, then X can only take integer values from 0 to n.

Tip: Remember... if events A and B are mutually exclusive then you **add** their probabilities to find the probability of **either** A **or** B happening.

Sometimes you're better off using a bit of cunning and coming at things from a different direction entirely.

Example

If $X \sim B(8, 0.83)$, find $P(X \leq 6)$:

- You could use the method in the previous examples, and find $P(X \leq 6)$ by working out $P(X = 0) + P(X = 1) + ... + P(X = 6)$.
- But remember... $P(X \leq 6) = 1 - P(X > 6) = 1 - P(X = 7) - P(X = 8)$.
- So instead, use the formula to find $P(X = 7)$ and $P(X = 8)$, and then subtract them both from 1.
- So using $n = 8$ and $p = 0.83$.

- $P(X = 7) = \binom{n}{x} \times p^x \times (1 - p)^{n-x} = \binom{8}{7} \times 0.83^7 \times (1 - 0.83)^{8-7}$

$$= \frac{8!}{7!1!} \times 0.83^7 \times 0.17^1$$

$$= \mathbf{0.3690...}$$

- $P(X = 8) = \binom{n}{x} \times p^x \times (1 - p)^{n-x} = \binom{8}{8} \times 0.83^8 \times (1 - 0.83)^{8-8}$

$$= \frac{8!}{8!0!} \times 0.83^8 \times 0.17^0$$

$$= \mathbf{0.2252...}$$

- So $P(X \leq 6) = 1 - P(X = 7) - P(X = 8) = 1 - 0.3690... - 0.2252...$

$$= \boxed{0.406 \text{ (to 3 sig. fig.)}}$$

Example

When I toss a grape in the air and try to catch it in my mouth, my probability of success is always 0.8. The number of grapes I catch in 10 throws is described by the discrete random variable X.

a) How is X distributed? Name the type of distribution, and give the values of any parameters.

- There's a fixed number (10) of independent trials with two possible results ('catch' and 'not catch'), a constant probability of success (0.8), and X is the total number of catches.
- Therefore X follows a binomial distribution, $\boxed{X \sim B(10, 0.8)}$

b) Find the probability of me catching at least 9 grapes in 10 throws.

- $P(\text{at least 9 catches}) = P(9 \text{ catches}) + P(10 \text{ catches})$

$$= \left\{ \binom{10}{9} \times 0.8^9 \times 0.2^1 \right\} + \left\{ \binom{10}{10} \times 0.8^{10} \times 0.2^0 \right\}$$

$$= 0.2684... + 0.1073... = \boxed{0.376 \text{ (to 3 sig. fig.)}}$$

Exercise 1.3

Q1 Find the probabilities below.
Give your answers to 3 significant figures.

a) For $X \sim B(10, 0.14)$:

   (i) $P(X = 2)$ (ii) $P(X = 4)$ (iii) $P(X = 5)$

b) For $X \sim B(8, 0.27)$:

   (i) $P(X = 3)$ (ii) $P(X = 5)$ (iii) $P(X = 7)$

Q2 Find the probabilities below.
Give your answers to 3 significant figures.

a) For $X \sim B(20, 0.16)$:

   (i) $P(X < 2)$ (ii) $P(X \leq 3)$ (iii) $P(1 < X \leq 4)$

b) For $X \sim B(30, 0.88)$:

   (i) $P(X > 28)$ (ii) $P(25 < X < 28)$ (iii) $P(X \geq 27)$

Q3 Find the probabilities below.
Give your answers to 3 significant figures.

a) For $X \sim B(5, \frac{1}{2})$:

   (i) $P(X \leq 4)$ (ii) $P(X > 1)$ (iii) $P(1 \leq X \leq 4)$

b) For $X \sim B(8, \frac{2}{3})$:

   (i) $P(X < 7)$ (ii) $P(X \geq 2)$ (iii) $P(0 \leq X \leq 8)$

Q4 A fair, six-sided dice is rolled 5 times.
What is the probability of obtaining exactly 2 sixes?

Q5 A multiple-choice test has three possible answers to each question,
only one of which is correct. A student guesses the answer to each
of the twelve questions at random. The random variable X is the
number of correct answers.

a) State the distribution of X.

b) Find the probability that the student gets
fewer than three questions correct.

Q6 A biased coin is tossed ten times.
The probability of it landing on heads is 0.65 for each toss.

a) State the distribution of X, where X is the total number
of heads obtained.

b) Find $P(4 < X \leq 7)$.

Q7 5% of the items made using a particular production process are
defective. A quality control manager samples 15 items at random.
What is the probability that there are between 1 and 3 defective
items (inclusive)?

2. Using Binomial Tables

Learning Objectives:

- Be able to use binomial tables to find probabilities.
- Be able to use binomial tables to find values for a random variable given a probability.

Doing one calculation to work out a probability using the binomial probability function is bad enough. Doing lots of them and adding the results together is worse... potentially much worse. Fortunately, there are binomial tables.

Using tables to find probabilities

Binomial tables reduce the amount of 'calculator work' you have to do to answer questions on the binomial distribution.

Here's an example of a problem solved **without** binomial tables.

Example 1

I have an unfair coin. When I toss this coin, the probability of getting heads is 0.35. Find the probability that it will land on heads fewer than 3 times when I toss it 12 times in total.

- If the random variable X represents the number of heads I get in 12 tosses, then $X \sim B(12, 0.35)$. You need to find $P(X \le 2)$.

- $P(X \le 2) = P(X = 0) + P(X = 1) + P(X = 2)$

$$= \left\{ \binom{12}{0} \times 0.35^0 \times 0.65^{12} \right\} + \left\{ \binom{12}{1} \times 0.35^1 \times 0.65^{11} \right\}$$

$$+ \left\{ \binom{12}{2} \times 0.35^2 \times 0.65^{10} \right\}$$

$$= 0.005688... + 0.036753... + 0.108846...$$

$$= 0.1513 \text{ (to 4 sig. fig.)}$$

But it's much quicker to use tables of the binomial **cumulative distribution function** (c.d.f.). These tables show $P(X \le x)$, for $X \sim B(n, p)$.

So have another look at the problem in the previous example.
Here, $X \sim B(12, 0.35)$, and you need to find $P(X \le 2)$.

- First find the table for the correct value of n. The table below is for $n = 12$.
- Then find the right value of p across the top of the table — here, $p = 0.35$.

Binomial Cumulative Distribution Function
Values show $P(X \le x)$, where $X \sim B(n, p)$

② ...then find p.

$p =$	0.05	0.10	0.15	0.20	0.25	0.30	0.35	0.40	0.45	0.50
$n = 12$ $x = $ 0	0.5404	0.2824	0.1422	0.0687	0.0317	0.0138	0.0057	0.0022	0.0008	0.0002
1	0.8816	0.6590	0.4435	0.2749	0.1584	0.0850	0.0424	0.0196	0.0083	0.0032
2	0.9804	0.8891	0.7358	0.5583	0.3907	0.2528	0.1513	0.0834	0.0421	0.0193
3	0.9978	0.9744	0.9078	0.7946	0.6488	0.4925	0.3467	0.2253	0.1345	0.0730
4	0.9998	0.9957	0.9761	0.9274	0.8424	0.7237	0.5833	0.4382	0.3044	0.1938
5	1.0000	0.9995	0.9954	0.9806	0.9456	0.8822	0.7873	0.6652	0.5269	0.3872
6	1.0000	0.9999	0.9993	0.9961	0.9857	0.9614	0.9154	0.8418	0.7393	0.6128
7	1.0000	1.0000	0.9999	0.9994	0.9972	0.9905	0.9745	0.9427	0.8883	0.8062
8	1.0000	1.0000	1.0000	0.9999	0.9996	0.9983	0.9944	0.9847	0.9644	0.9270
9	1.0000	1.0000	1.0000	1.0000	1.0000	0.9998	0.9992	0.9972	0.9921	0.9807
10	1.0000	1.0000	1.0000	1.0000	1.0000	1.0000	0.9999	0.9997	0.9989	0.9968
11	1.0000	1.0000	1.0000	1.0000	1.0000	1.0000	1.0000	1.0000	0.9999	0.9998

① Find n...

- The numbers underneath your value of p then tell you $P(X \le x)$ for all the different values of x down the left-hand side of the table. Here, you need $P(X \le 2)$.
- So reading across, the table tells you $P(X \le 2) = \mathbf{0.1513}$.

Tip: The full set of binomial tables is on pages 159-163.

These tables are the same ones that'll be in the formula booklet you'll get in your exam.

Only tables for certain values of n are included (the biggest value included is $n = 50$). The table on the right shows the table for $n = 12$.

So sometimes you still have to find probabilities in other ways (e.g. using the probability function).

Example 2

I have an unfair coin. When I toss this coin, the probability of getting heads is 0.35. Find the probability that it will land on heads fewer than 6 times when I toss it 12 times in total.

- Since $n = 12$ again, you can use the table at the bottom of the previous page.
- And since $p = 0.35$, the probability you need will also be in the highlighted column.
- But this time, you need to find $P(X \leq 5)$, so find $x = 5$ down the left-hand side of the table, and then read across.
- This tells you that $P(X \leq 5) = \boxed{0.7873}$.

Tip: You could work out all the individual probabilities and add them together, but it would take a lot longer.

For these next examples, the value of n is also 12, so you can still use the table on the previous page. The value of p is different, though — so you'll need to use a different column.

But be warned... in these examples, looking up the value in the table is just the start of the solution.

Example 3

I have a different unfair coin. When I toss this coin, the probability of getting heads is 0.4. Find the probability that it will land on heads more than 4 times when I toss it 12 times in total.

- This time, $p = 0.4$ — so find $p = 0.4$ along the top of the table, and look at the entries in that column.
- The tables only show $P(X \leq x)$, whereas you need to find $P(X > 4)$. But $P(X > 4) = 1 - P(X \leq 4)$ — so you can still use the information in the table to quickly find the answer.
- Find the entry for $x = 4$ — this tells you $P(X \leq 4) = \mathbf{0.4382}$.
- So $P(X > 4) = 1 - P(X \leq 4) = 1 - 0.4382 = \boxed{0.5618}$.

With a bit of cunning, you can get binomial tables to tell you almost anything you want to know...

Example 4

The probability of getting heads when I toss my unfair coin is 0.4. When I toss this coin 12 times in total, find the probability that:

a) it will land on heads exactly 6 times.

- Again, $p = 0.4$ — so use the '$p = 0.4$' column in the table for $n = 12$.
- To find $P(X = 6)$, use the fact that $P(X \leq 6) = P(X \leq 5) + P(X = 6)$. This means $P(X = 6) = P(X \leq 6) - P(X \leq 5)$ — and you can find both $P(X \leq 6)$ and $P(X \leq 5)$ from the table.
- So $P(X = 6) = P(X \leq 6) - P(X \leq 5) = 0.8418 - 0.6652 = \boxed{0.1766}$.

Tip: Remember... if A and B are mutually exclusive events, then $P(A \text{ or } B) = P(A) + P(B)$.

If you call A the event '$X \leq 5$', and B the event '$X = 6$', then:
$P(A \text{ or } B)$
  $= P(X \leq 5 \text{ or } X = 6)$
  $= P(X \leq 6)$.

And so using the rule above:
$P(X = 6)$
  $= P(X \leq 6) - P(X \leq 5)$

b) it will land on heads more than 3 times but fewer than 6 times.

- This time you need to find $P(3 < X < 6)$.
  This is the same as $P(3 < X \leq 5)$.
- But $P(X \leq 5) = P(X \leq 3) + P(3 < X \leq 5)$.
  This means $P(3 < X \leq 5) = P(X \leq 5) - P(X \leq 3)$
  — and you can find both $P(X \leq 5)$ and $P(X \leq 3)$ from the table.
- So $P(3 < X < 6) = P(X \leq 5) - P(X \leq 3) = 0.6652 - 0.2253 = \boxed{0.4399}$.

There's an easy way to remember which probability to subtract from which other probability. For example, suppose you need to find $P(a < X \leq b)$.

- Use the table to find **$P(X \leq b)$** — the probability that X is less than or equal to the largest value satisfying the inequality '$a < X \leq b$'...

- ...**and subtract $P(X \leq a)$** to 'remove' the probability that X takes one of the smaller values not satisfying the inequality '$a < X \leq b$'.

Examples

If $X \sim B(12, 0.45)$, find:

a) $P(5 < X \leq 8)$

- The largest value satisfying the inequality $5 < X \leq 8$ is $X = 8$.
  So you need to find $P(X \leq 8)$.
- Using the table for $n = 12$ and $p = 0.45$, $P(X \leq 8) = \textbf{0.9644}$.
- You need to subtract the probability $P(X \leq 5)$, since $X = 5$ doesn't satisfy the inequality $5 < X \leq 8$, and neither does any value smaller than 5.
- From the table, $P(X \leq 5) = \textbf{0.5269}$.
- So $P(5 < X \leq 8) = P(X \leq 8) - P(X \leq 5) = 0.9644 - 0.5269 = \boxed{0.4375}$

b) $P(4 \leq X < 10)$

- The largest value satisfying the inequality $4 \leq X < 10$ is $X = 9$.
  So you need to find $P(X \leq 9)$.
- Using the table for $n = 12$ and $p = 0.45$, $P(X \leq 9) = \textbf{0.9921}$.
- Now subtract the probability $P(X \leq 3)$, since $X = 3$ doesn't satisfy the inequality $4 \leq X < 10$, and neither does any value smaller than 3.
- From the table, $P(X \leq 3) = \textbf{0.1345}$.
- So $P(4 \leq X < 10) = P(X \leq 9) - P(X \leq 3) = 0.9921 - 0.1345 = \boxed{0.8576}$

Using the tables is relatively straightforward as long as you can find the value of p you need. But the values of p only go as high as $p = 0.5$ — so if $p > 0.5$, you need to think about things slightly differently.

- Suppose $X \sim B(12, 0.65)$, and you need to find $P(X \leq 5)$.
- This means you need to find the probability of 5 or fewer 'successes', when the probability of 'success' is $p = 0.65$.
- But you can switch things round and say you need to find the probability of 7 or more 'failures', where the probability of 'failure' is $1 - p = 0.35$.
- It's easiest if you rewrite the problem using a new variable, Y, say. Y will represent the number of 'failures' in 12 trials, so $Y \sim B(12, 0.35)$.

Tip: This time, call A the event '$X \leq 3$', and B the event '$3 < X \leq 5$' — then A and B are mutually exclusive, with
$P(A \text{ or } B)$
$= P(X \leq 3 \text{ or } 3 < X \leq 5)$
$= P(X \leq 5)$

Then using the formula $P(A \text{ or } B) = P(A) + P(B)$ for mutually exclusive events, you get:
$P(X \leq 5)$
$= P(X \leq 3) + P(3 < X \leq 5)$

Tip: This is very similar to what you did in S1 when you were using Z-tables to find $P(a < Z < b)$ — this was $P(Z < b) - P(Z \leq a)$.

Tip: $n = 12$ again — so you can either use the table on p12, or refer to the tables on p159-163.

Tip: The inequality $4 \leq X < 10$ can be written as $3 < X \leq 9$.

- You can use tables to find $P(Y \geq 7) = 1 - P(Y < 7)$
$$= 1 - P(Y \leq 6)$$
$$= 1 - 0.9154 = \mathbf{0.0846}$$

Tip: $n = 12$ again — so you can either use the table on p12, or refer to the tables on p159-163.

- So the probability of 7 or more 'failures' if the probability of 'failure' is 0.35 is 0.0846. This must equal the probability of 5 or fewer 'successes' if the probability of 'success' is 0.65.
- So if $X \sim B(12, 0.65)$, then $P(X \leq 5) = \mathbf{0.0846}$.

Where $X \sim B(n, p)$, but $p > 0.5$...
First define $Y = n - X$, where $Y \sim B(n, 1 - p)$.
Then, for constants k and h:
- $P(X \leq k) = P(Y \geq n - k)$ and $P(X < k) = P(Y > n - k)$
- $P(X \geq k) = P(Y \leq n - k)$ and $P(X > k) = P(Y < n - k)$
- $P(h < X \leq k) = P(n - k \leq Y < n - h)$

Tip: $h < X \leq k$ means that $X > h$ and $X \leq k$.

So $Y < n - h$ and $Y \geq n - k$.

In other words:
$n - k \leq Y < n - h$.

Notice that, as well as having been subtracted from n, both k and h have 'swapped sides' in the inequality, and the $\leq$ and $<$ signs have moved with them.

Examples

The probability of this spinner landing on blue is 0.7. The spinner is spun 12 times, and the random variable X represents the number of times the spinner lands on blue.

a) Find $P(X > 8)$.

- Since X represents the number of 'blues' in 12 spins, $X \sim B(12, 0.7)$.
- Because $p = 0.7$, you won't be able to use the tables directly. So define a new random variable Y, where Y represents the number of 'reds' in 12 spins. Since the spinner can only land on either red or blue, $P(red) = 1 - P(blue) = 1 - 0.7 = 0.3$. This means $Y \sim B(12, 0.3)$.
- Then $P(X > 8) = P(Y < 4) = P(Y \leq 3) = \boxed{0.4925}$

b) Find $P(X \leq 4)$.

- $P(X \leq 4) = P(Y \geq 8) = 1 - P(Y < 8) = 1 - P(Y \leq 7) = 1 - 0.9905 = \boxed{0.0095}$

c) Find $P(5 \leq X < 8)$.

- $P(5 \leq X < 8) = P(4 < Y \leq 7) = P(Y \leq 7) - P(Y \leq 4)$
$$= 0.9905 - 0.7237 = \boxed{0.2668}$$

Exercise 2.1

Q1 The random variable $X \sim B(10, 0.25)$.
Use the binomial table for $n = 10$ to find:

Q1 Hint: The binomial tables start on page 159.

a) $P(X \leq 2)$ b) $P(X \leq 7)$ c) $P(X \leq 9)$

d) $P(X < 5)$ e) $P(X < 4)$ f) $P(X < 6)$

Q2 The random variable $X \sim B(15, 0.4)$.
Use the appropriate binomial table to find:

a) $P(X > 3)$ b) $P(X > 6)$ c) $P(X > 10)$

d) $P(X \geq 5)$ e) $P(X \geq 3)$ f) $P(X \geq 13)$

Q3 The random variable $X \sim B(20, 0.35)$.
Use the appropriate binomial table to find:

a) $P(X = 7)$ b) $P(X = 12)$ c) $P(2 < X \leq 4)$

d) $P(10 < X \leq 15)$ e) $P(7 \leq X \leq 10)$ f) $P(3 \leq X < 11)$

Q4 The random variable $X \sim B(25, 0.8)$.
Use the appropriate binomial table to find:

a) $P(X \geq 17)$ b) $P(X \geq 20)$ c) $P(X > 14)$

d) $P(X = 21)$ e) $P(3 \leq X < 14)$ f) $P(12 \leq X < 18)$

Q5 Seven fair coins are tossed. What is the probability of tossing more than four heads?

Q6 In a production process it is known that approximately 5% of items are faulty. In a random sample of 25 objects, estimate the probability that fewer than 6 are faulty.

Using binomial tables 'backwards'

Sometimes, you'll need to use the tables 'the other way round'.

- So far you've been given a value for x, and you've had to find a probability such as $P(X \leq x)$, $P(X > x)$, $P(X = x)$,... and so on.
- But you could be given a probability (c, say) and asked to find a value of x.
- These kinds of questions can get quite complicated.

Examples

If $X \sim B(25, 0.2)$, find:

a) c if $P(X \leq c) = 0.7800$

- Use the binomial table for $n = 25$, and the column for $p = 0.2$.
- Going down the column, you can see that $P(X \leq 6) = 0.7800$, so $c = 6$.

b) d if $P(X \geq d) = 0.7660$

- If $P(X \geq d) = 0.7660$, then $P(X < d) = P(X \leq d - 1)$
$$= 1 - 0.7660 = 0.2340.$$
- Using the table, you can see that $P(X \leq 3) = 0.2340$.
- This means that $d - 1 = 3$, which gives $d = 4$.

Here are some slightly trickier examples.

Examples

If $X \sim B(30, 0.4)$, find:

a) the maximum value a such that $P(X \leq a) < 0.05$.

- Use the binomial table for $n = 30$, and the column for $p = 0.4$.
- You can see that $P(X \leq 7) = 0.0435$ and $P(X \leq 8) = 0.0940$.
- So the maximum value a such that $P(X \leq a) < 0.05$ is $a = 7$.

b) the minimum value b such that $P(X > b) < 0.05$.

- This time you need the smallest value of b with $P(X > b) < 0.05$.
  But if $P(X > b) < 0.05$, then $P(X \le b) > 0.95$.
  So you need the smallest value of b with $P(X \le b) > 0.95$.

- Using the same binomial table as before, you can see that
  $P(X \le 15) = 0.9029$ and $P(X \le 16) = 0.9519$.

- So the minimum value of b with $P(X \le b) > 0.95$ is $b = 16$. This means
  that the minimum value of b with $P(X > b) < 0.05$ must also be $\boxed{b = 16}$.

Tip: Remember...
$P(X \le b) = 1 - P(X > b)$.

So if $P(X > b) < 0.05$,
then $P(X \le b) > 0.95$.

This kind of question occurs in real-life situations.

Example

A teacher sets her class a multiple-choice test. In this test there are 20 questions, and each question has 5 possible answers.
The teacher wants to make it very unlikely that a student who guesses the answer to every question would pass the test.
How high should the pass mark be to give a student guessing the answer to every question less than a 10% probability of passing the test?

- Since each question has 5 possible answers, the probability of correctly guessing the answer to each question must be 0.2.

- There are 20 questions altogether, so if the random variable X is the overall score of a student who always guesses, then $X \sim B(20, 0.2)$.

- You need to find the minimum value m such that $P(X \ge m) < 0.1$,
  i.e. the minimum value m with $P(X < m) > 0.9$ or $P(X \le m - 1) > 0.9$.

- From tables, $P(X \le 5) = 0.8042$, but $P(X \le 6) = 0.9133$.

- So the probability of a student who always guesses getting more than 5 answers correct is $P(X > 5) = 1 - P(X \le 5) = 1 - 0.8042 = 0.1958$.
  But the probability of a student who always guesses getting more than 6 answers correct is $P(X > 6) = 1 - P(X \le 6) = 1 - 0.9133 = 0.0867$.

- So the pass mark should be set at $\boxed{\text{7 or more}}$. Then the probability that a student who always guesses will pass the test is less than 10%.

Tip: This situation satisfies the conditions for a binomial distribution, since:

(i) there are a fixed number (20) of trials (i.e. each question is a trial),

(ii) the only possible outcomes of each trial are success or failure,

(iii) the trials are all independent — guessing the correct answer to one question doesn't make a student any more or less likely to guess the next answer correctly,

(iv) the probability of success in each trial is always 0.2,

(iv) the variable X is the total number of successes in the 20 trials.

Exercise 2.2

For all the questions below, use binomial tables to find your answers.

Q1 The random variable $X \sim B(8, 0.35)$.
Find the values of a, b, c and d such that:

a) $P(X \le a) = 0.4278$ b) $P(X < b) = 0.9747$

c) $P(X > c) = 0.8309$ d) $P(X \ge d) = 0.1061$

Q2 A teacher is writing a multiple-choice test, with 4 options for each of the 30 questions. He wants the probability of someone passing the test by guessing the answer to each question to be 10% or less.

a) What is the lowest score that should be set as the pass mark?

b) Another teacher says the probability of passing by guessing should be less than 1%. What should the minimum pass score be now?

Q3 In a fairground competition, a fair coin is tossed 20 times by a contestant. If the contestant scores x heads or more, they win a prize. If the random variable X represents the number of heads obtained, find the minimum number of heads that are needed to win if the probability of winning is to be kept below 0.05.

Q2 & Q3 Hint: With these wordy questions, read everything carefully and be very careful with the inequality signs.

3. Mean and Variance

Learning Objectives:

- Be able to calculate the mean and variance of a binomial distribution.
- Be able to find n or p given values for $E(X)$ or $Var(X)$.

You saw the mean and variance of a discrete random variable in S1. In this section, you're going to work out the mean and variance of a discrete random variable following a binomial distribution.

Mean and variance of the binomial distribution

The mean

The **mean** of a random variable is also called its **expected value**. It's a kind of 'theoretical mean' — what you'd expect the mean to be if you gathered a large number of observations of the random variable.

So suppose you have a random variable $X \sim B(n, p)$. The mean of X would be the 'average' number of successes if you performed lots of sets of n trials.

The mean (expected value) of X can be written either as μ or $E(X)$, and is given by the formula below.

> If $X \sim B(n, p)$, then:
>
> **Mean (or Expected Value) $= \mu = E(X) = np$**

Tip: This formula will be in your formula booklet. But it's worth committing to memory, because it's so important.

Remember... this is a 'theoretical mean' — the mean of experimental results is unlikely to match it **exactly**.

Tip: Greek letters (e.g. μ) often show something based purely on theory rather than experimental results.

Examples

Find the expected values of the following random variables.

a) $X \sim B(20, 0.2)$
- Just put the parameters of the distribution into the formula. $E(X) = np = 20 \times 0.2 = \boxed{4}$

b) $X \sim B(155, 0.37)$
- Again, just use the formula. $E(X) = np = 155 \times 0.37 = \boxed{57.35}$

Tip: Notice that the probability of getting exactly 5 sixes on my next set of 30 rolls

$$= \binom{30}{5} \times \left(\tfrac{1}{6}\right)^5 \times \left(\tfrac{5}{6}\right)^{25}$$

$= 0.192$ (to 3 sig. fig.)

So I'm much more likely **not** to get exactly 5 sixes ($= 1 - 0.192 = 0.808$).

This is why it only makes sense to talk about the mean as a 'long-term average', and not as 'what I expect to happen next'.

Example

What's the expected number of sixes when I roll a fair dice 30 times? Interpret your answer.

- If the random variable X represents the number of sixes in 30 rolls, then $X \sim B(30, \tfrac{1}{6})$.
- So the expected value of X is $E(X) = 30 \times \dfrac{1}{6} = \boxed{5}$
- If I were to repeatedly roll the dice 30 times, and find the **average** number of sixes in each set of 30 rolls, then I would expect it to end up pretty close to 5. And the more sets of 30 rolls I did, the closer to 5 I'd expect the average to be.

The variance and standard deviation

The **variance** of a random variable is a kind of 'theoretical variance' — again, it's what you'd expect the variance to be if you gathered a large number of observations of the random variable.

So the variance of a random variable $X \sim B(n, p)$ would be the expected variance if you performed lots of sets of n trials.

The variance of a random variable can be written either as σ^2 or $\text{Var}(X)$.

The **standard deviation** of a random variable is the positive square root of the variance, and is usually written σ.

> If $X \sim B(n, p)$, then:
>
> **Variance = Var$(X) = \sigma^2 = np(1 - p) = npq$**
>
> **Standard Deviation $= \sigma = \sqrt{np(1 - p)} = \sqrt{npq}$**

Tip: For a binomial distribution, P(success) is usually called p, and P(failure) is sometimes called q $(= 1 - p)$.

Like with the mean... the variance of experimental results is unlikely to match this 'theoretical variance' **exactly**.

Examples

Find the variance and standard deviation of these random variables.

a) $X \sim B(400, 0.1)$

- First find $q = 1 - p$.   Since $p = 0.1$, $q = 1 - 0.1 = $ **0.9**.
- Then use the formula $\text{Var}(X) = \sigma^2 = npq$
  for the variance. $= 400 \times 0.1 \times 0.9 = \boxed{36}$
- Take the square root to find   Standard deviation $= \sigma = \sqrt{36} = \boxed{6}$
  the standard deviation.

b) $X \sim B(155, 0.37)$

- Find $q = 1 - p$.   Since $p = 0.37$, $q = 1 - 0.37 = $ **0.63**.
- Calculate the variance. $\text{Var}(X) = \sigma^2 = npq$
                                                       $= 155 \times 0.37 \times 0.63$
                                                       $= \boxed{36.1305}$
- Find the standard deviation.   Standard deviation $= \sigma = \sqrt{36.1305}$
                                                       $= \boxed{6.01}$ (to 3 sig. fig.)

Examples

If $X \sim B(25, 0.2)$, find:

a) $P(X \le \mu)$

- Find the mean. $\mu = 25 \times 0.2 = 5$
- Use tables to find $P(X \le \mu)$. $P(X \le \mu) = P(X \le 5) = \boxed{0.6167}$

Tip: See p12 for more about using binomial tables.

b) $P(X \le \mu - \sigma)$

- Find the variance, and then the $\sigma^2 = 25 \times 0.2 \times 0.8 = 4$,
  standard deviation.   which gives $\sigma = 2$.
- Use tables to find $P(X \le \mu - \sigma)$. $P(X \le \mu - \sigma) = P(X \le 3) = \boxed{0.2340}$

c) $P(X \le \mu - 2\sigma)$

- You'll need to use tables again. $P(X \le \mu - 2\sigma) = P(X \le 1) = \boxed{0.0274}$

You could be given E(X) and/or Var(X), and asked to find n and/or p.

Example 1

If $X \sim B(200, p)$ and E(X) = 60, find p.

E(X) = 200 × p = 60, so $p = \dfrac{60}{200} = \boxed{0.3}$

Example 2

A random variable $X \sim B(n, p)$.
If E(X) = 10 and Var(X) = 9, find n and p.

- Write down what you know about E(X) and Var(X). This gives you two equations involving n and p.

$$E(X) = np = 10$$
$$Var(X) = np(1 - p) = 9$$

- Divide Var(X) by E(X) — this will give you an equation just involving p, since the n's cancel.

$$\frac{Var(X)}{E(X)} = \frac{np(1 - p)}{np} = 1 - p$$
$$\frac{Var(X)}{E(X)} = \frac{9}{10} = 0.9$$

- Solve to find p.

So $1 - p = 0.9$, which means $\boxed{p = 0.1}$

- Use your value for p to find n.

E(X) = np = 10, so $\boxed{n = 10 \div 0.1 = 100}$

Exercise 3.1

Q1 For each of the following random variables, find:
  (i)   the mean (μ)
  (ii) the variance (σ^2)
  (iii) the standard deviation (σ)

  a) $X \sim B(10, 0.9)$ b) $X \sim B(25, 0.7)$ c) $X \sim B(50, 0.05)$
  d) $X \sim B(70, 0.85)$ e) $X \sim B(15, 0.1)$ f) $X \sim B(100, 0.35)$

Q2 A biased coin has a probability of 0.6 of landing on heads. The random variable X represents the number of heads obtained in 60 tosses of the coin.

  a) State the distribution of X.

  b) Find the mean and the variance of X.

Q3 The random variable Y represents the number of times a biased coin lands on heads when it is tossed 150 times.
  If E(Y) = 30, find:
  a) the probability (p) of this coin landing on heads,

  b) the variance of Y.

Q4 In a raffle, each ticket sold has a probability of 0.1 of winning a prize.

  a) If 1600 tickets are sold in total and X represents the number of winning tickets sold, find the expected number of winning tickets (E(X)).

  b) Calculate σ^2, the variance of X.

4. Modelling Real Problems

Exam questions often involve a 'realistic-sounding' situation.
So it's not enough just to know everything about the binomial distribution
— you have to know how to apply that knowledge in real life as well.

Modelling real problems with B(*n*, *p*)

The first step with a real-world problem is to **model** it using a sensible probability distribution. If the situation satisfies all the conditions on page 5, then you'll need to use a **binomial distribution**.

When you've decided how to model the situation, you can 'do the maths'. Don't forget to include units in your answer where necessary.

You may then need to **interpret** your solution — saying what your answer means in the **context** of the question.

Tip: You might need to make some **assumptions** before using a binomial distribution. If so, you should write down what those assumptions are (unless you've already been told in the question to assume that those things are true).

Example 1

A double-glazing salesman is handing out leaflets in a busy shopping centre. He knows that the probability of a passing person taking a leaflet is always 0.3. During a randomly chosen one-minute interval, 30 people passed him.

a) **Suggest a suitable model to describe the number of people (*X*) who take a leaflet.**

- During this one-minute interval:
  (i)   there's a **fixed number** (30) of trials,
  (ii) all the trials are **independent**,
  (iii) there are **two possible results** ('take a leaflet' and 'do not take a leaflet'),
  (iv) there's a **constant** probability of success (0.3),
  (v)   *X* is the **total number** of people taking leaflets.

All the conditions for a binomial distribution are satisfied.

In fact, $X \sim B(30, 0.3)$.

Tip: The information in the question will make clear that some of these conditions are satisfied.

For example, you're told in the question that 'the probability of a passing person taking a leaflet is **always** 0.3' — this is the examiner's way of telling you that there's a constant probability of success, and that the trials are independent (so you don't have to worry about some people taking leaflets because they see other people taking one).

b) **What is the probability that more than 10 people take a leaflet?**

- You know it's a binomial distribution, so you can get this probability from the binomial tables.

$P(X > 10) = 1 - P(X \le 10)$
$= 1 - 0.7304$
$= 0.2696$

Tip: See p12 for more about binomial tables.

c) **How many people would the salesman expect to take a leaflet?**

- Use the formula for the mean (expected value) of a binomial distribution.

$E(X) = np = 30 \times 0.3 = 9$

So the salesman could expect 9 people to take a leaflet.

d) **Find the standard deviation of *X*.**

- First use the formula for the variance of a binomial distribution.

Variance = $np(1 - p)$
$= 30 \times 0.3 \times (1 - 0.3)$
$= \mathbf{6.3}$

- Then take the square root to find the standard deviation.

Standard deviation = $\sqrt{6.3}$
$= 2.51$ people (to 3 sig. fig.)

Example 2

A student has to take a 50-question multiple-choice exam. Each question has five possible answers of which only one is correct.

He believes he can pass the exam by guessing answers at random.

a) **How many questions could the student be expected to guess correctly?**

- Define your random variable first, and say how it will be distributed.

  Let X be the number of correct guesses in 50 questions. Then $X \sim B(50, 0.2)$.

- Then you can use the formula for the mean (expected value).

  $E(X) = np = 50 \times 0.2$
  $= \boxed{10 \text{ questions}}$

b) **If the pass mark is 15, what is the probability that the student will pass the exam?**

- You need to find $P(X \geq 15)$.

- Remember... the tables only tell you $P(X \leq x)$.

  $P(X \geq 15) = 1 - P(X < 15)$
  $= 1 - P(X \leq 14)$
  $= 1 - 0.9393 = \boxed{0.0607}$

c) **The examiner decides to set the pass mark so that it is at least 3 standard deviations above the expected number of correct guesses. What should the minimum pass mark be?**

- You need the standard deviation of X — so start by finding the variance.

  $Var(X) = np(1 - p)$
  $= 50 \times 0.2 \times 0.8 = 8$

  So the standard deviation $= \sqrt{8}$
  $= \mathbf{2.828...}$

- Now you need to think about what the question is actually asking.

  This means the pass mark needs to be at least $10 + (3 \times 2.828...) \approx 18.5$ — i.e. $\boxed{\text{the minimum pass mark should be 19}}$.

Example 3

I am spinning a coin that I know is three times as likely to land on heads as it is on tails.

a) **What is the probability that it lands on tails for the first time on the third spin?**

- First you need to know the probabilities for heads and tails.

  $P(\text{heads}) = 3 \times P(\text{tails})$.
  But $P(\text{heads}) + P(\text{tails}) = 1$.

  This means that $P(\text{heads}) = 0.75$ and $P(\text{tails}) = 0.25$.

- If it lands on tails for the first time on the third spin, then the first two spins must have been heads.

  $P(\text{lands on tails for the first time on the third spin})$
  $= 0.75 \times 0.75 \times 0.25$
  $= \boxed{0.141 \text{ (to 3 sig. fig.)}}$

- Since all the spins are independent, you know that:

  $P(\text{heads } \underline{\text{then}} \text{ heads } \underline{\text{then}} \text{ tails})$
  $= P(\text{heads}) \times P(\text{heads}) \times P(\text{tails})$

b) What is the probability that in 10 spins, it lands on heads at least 7 times?

- First define your random variable, and state how it is distributed.

  If X represents the number of heads in 10 spins, then $X \sim B(10, 0.75)$.

- $p = 0.75$ isn't in your tables, so define a new binomial random variable Y with probability of success $p = 0.25$.

  The number of tails in 10 spins can be described by the random variable $Y = 10 - X$, where $Y \sim B(10, 0.25)$.

- You need the probability of 'at least 7 heads' — this is the same as the probability of '3 or fewer tails'.

  $P(X \geq 7) = P(Y \leq 3) = \boxed{0.7759}$

Exercise 4.1

Q1 A hairdresser hands out leaflets. She knows there is always a probability of 0.25 that a passer-by will take a leaflet. During a five-minute period, 50 people pass the hairdresser.

a) Suggest a suitable model for X, the number of passers-by who take a leaflet in the five-minute period. Explain why this is a suitable model.

b) What is the probability that more than 4 people take a leaflet?

c) What is the probability that exactly 10 people take a leaflet?

d) What is the expected number of people who will take a leaflet in this period?

e) Find the standard deviation (σ) of X.

Q2 Jasmine plants 15 randomly selected seeds in each of her plant trays. She knows that 35% of this type of plant grow with yellow flowers, while the remainder grow with white flowers. All her seeds grow successfully, and Jasmine counts how many plants in each tray grow with yellow flowers.

a) Find the probability that a randomly selected tray has exactly 5 plants with yellow flowers.

b) Find the probability that a randomly selected tray contains more plants with yellow flowers than plants with white flowers.

Q3 In the UK, the probability of any particular person in a random sample having hazel eyes is 0.15. A random sample of size n is taken, and X represents the number of people in this sample with hazel eyes. It is known that $E(X) = 6$.

a) Find the value of n.

b) Find the probability that fewer than 6 people have hazel eyes in this sample.

c) In a random sample of a different size, the expected number of people with hazel eyes is calculated to be 24. If Y represents the number of people in this sample with hazel eyes, find $Var(Y)$.

Review Exercise — Chapter 1

Q1 In how many different orders can the following be arranged?
   a) 15 identical red balls, plus 6 other balls, all of different colours.
   b) 4 red counters, 4 blue counters, 4 yellow counters and 4 green counters.
   c) 7 green counters and 5 blue counters.

Q2 Use the binomial probability function to find the probability of the following.
   a) Getting exactly 5 heads when you spin a fair coin 10 times.
   b) Getting exactly 9 heads when you spin a fair coin 10 times.

Q3 Which of the following would follow a binomial distribution? Explain your answers.
   a) The number of prime numbers you throw in 30 throws of a standard dice.
   b) The number of people in a particular class at a school who get 'heads' when they flip a coin.
   c) The number of aces in a 7-card hand dealt from a standard pack of 52 cards.
   d) The number of shots I have to take before I score from the free-throw line in basketball.

Q4 What is the probability of the following?
   a) Getting at least 5 heads when you spin a fair coin 10 times.
   b) Getting at least 9 heads when you spin a fair coin 10 times.

Q5 If $X \sim B(14, 0.27)$, find:
   a) $P(X = 4)$
   b) $P(X < 2)$
   c) $P(5 < X \leq 8)$

Q6 If $X \sim B(25, 0.15)$ and $Y \sim B(15, 0.65)$ find:
   a) $P(X \leq 3)$
   b) $P(X \leq 7)$
   c) $P(X \leq 15)$
   d) $P(Y \leq 3)$
   e) $P(Y \leq 7)$
   f) $P(Y \leq 15)$

Q7 Find the required probability for each of the following binomial distributions.
   a) $P(X \leq 15)$ if $X \sim B(20, 0.4)$
   b) $P(X < 4)$ if $X \sim B(40, 0.15)$
   c) $P(X > 7)$ if $X \sim B(25, 0.45)$
   d) $P(X \geq 40)$ if $X \sim B(50, 0.8)$
   e) $P(X = 20)$ if $X \sim B(30, 0.7)$
   f) $P(X = 7)$ if $X \sim B(10, 0.75)$

Q8 If $X \sim B(30, 0.35)$, find:
   a) a if $P(X \leq a) = 0.8737$
   b) b if $P(X \geq b) = 0.8762$
   c) the maximum value c such that $P(X \leq c) < 0.05$.

Q9 Find the mean and variance of the following random variables.
   a) $X \sim B(20, 0.4)$
   b) $X \sim B(40, 0.15)$
   c) $X \sim B(25, 0.45)$
   d) $X \sim B(50, 0.8)$
   e) $X \sim B(30, 0.7)$
   f) $X \sim B(45, 0.012)$

1   a)   The random variable X follows the binomial distribution B(12, 0.6). Find:

   (i)   P($X < 8$),

(2 marks)

   (ii)   P($X = 5$),

(2 marks)

   (iii) P($3 < X \leq 7$).

(3 marks)

   b)   If $Y \sim$ B(11, 0.8), find:

   (i)   P($Y = 4$),

(2 marks)

   (ii)   E(Y),

(1 mark)

   (iii) Var(Y).

(1 mark)

2   The probability of an apple containing a maggot is 0.15.

   a)   Find the probability that in a random sample of 40 apples there are:

   (i)   fewer than 6 apples containing maggots,

(2 marks)

   (ii)   more than 2 apples containing maggots,

(2 marks)

   (iii) exactly 12 apples containing maggots.

(2 marks)

   b)   These apples are sold in crates of 40. Ed buys 3 crates.

   Find the probability that more than 1 crate contains more than 2 apples with maggots.

(3 marks)

3   Simon tries to solve the crossword puzzle in his newspaper every day for two weeks.
   He either succeeds in solving the puzzle, or he fails to solve it.

   a)   Simon believes that this situation can be modelled by a random variable
   following a binomial distribution.

   (i)   State two conditions needed for a binomial distribution to arise here.

(2 marks)

   (ii)   State which quantity would follow a binomial distribution (assuming the
   above conditions are satisfied).

(1 mark)

   b)   Simon believes a random variable X follows the distribution B(18, p).
   If P($X = 4$) = P($X = 5$), find p.

(5 marks)

4   A darts player gets a 'treble-20' with each dart with a probability of 0.75.

   a)   The player throws 3 darts.

        Find the probability that he gets a 'treble-20' with at least 2 of the darts.

        (2 marks)

   b)   He throws another 5 sets of 3 darts.

        In how many sets would he be expected to get a 'treble-20'
        with at least 2 darts?

        (2 marks)

   c)   He now throws another 30 darts for a charity challenge.

        (i)   If he gets a 'treble-20' with at least 26 of the darts, he wins a major prize
              for the charity.

              What is the probability that he wins the major prize?

              (2 marks)

        (ii) If he gets a 'treble-20' with between 22 and 25 of the darts (inclusive),
              he wins a minor prize for the charity.

              What is the probability that he wins the minor prize?

              (3 marks)

5   Jessica has a bag of coins. Some of the coins are bronze and some are silver.

     Jessica picks a coin at random, makes a note of whether it is bronze or silver, replaces it in
     the bag and then gives the bag a shake. She repeats this process n times in total.

     The probability of her picking a bronze coin each time is 0.3.

   a)   Given that the expected number of bronze coins she obtains is 7.5, find n.

        (2 marks)

   b)   Using this value of n, find the probability that Jessica picks bronze and silver
        coins in the ratio $1:4$.

        (2 marks)

6   The probability that any egg from a particular farm will be cracked by the time
     it reaches the supermarket shelves is 0.06. These eggs are sold in boxes of 12.

   a)   If X represents the number of cracked eggs in a randomly selected
        box of 12, find:

        (i)   the probability that there will be no cracked eggs,

              (2 marks)

        (ii) the probability that there will be more than 2 cracked eggs.

              (3 marks)

   b)   A supermarket always orders 50 boxes of 12 eggs at a time.

        (i)   State how Y will be distributed, where Y is the number of boxes per order
              containing more than 2 cracked eggs.

              (1 mark)

        (ii) Find the probability that at least one box in an order contains
              more than 2 cracked eggs.

              (2 marks)

1. Poisson Distributions

The Poisson distribution is another really common discrete probability distribution. It crops up all over the place when things happen at random — such as when radioactive atoms decay or errors occur in an industrial process.

The Poisson distribution

Like the binomial distribution, the Poisson distribution is a **discrete** probability distribution (and so there are 'gaps' between the possible values that a Poisson random variable can take).

- A random variable X following a Poisson distribution can only take **non-negative integer** values (although there's no upper limit).
- So if X follows a Poisson distribution, then the possible values for X are 0, 1, 2, 3, 4, 5... and so on.

The Poisson distribution occurs quite a lot in everyday life.

- For example, a Poisson distribution can be used to describe:
  - the number of cars that will pass a point in a minute,
  - the number of radioactive atoms that will decay in an hour,
  - the number of misprints that will occur on a page of a book,
  - the number of plants that grow in 1 m² of a field,
  - the number of a certain type of cell in 1 cm³ of blood.

All of the examples above are kinds of **rates**. They tell you **how often** an event **happens** (or **how often** something **is present**) in one minute / in one hour / on one page / in 1 m² of field / in 1 cm³ of blood.

- This rate is the **parameter** of the Poisson distribution — and is usually called λ (the Greek letter 'lambda').
- λ represents the **average** number of events or things that occur/are present in a particular **period** — either a period of **time** (e.g. minute / hour etc.), or a period of **space** (e.g. page / m² / cm³ etc.)
- If X is a random variable that follows a Poisson distribution with parameter λ, then you can write $X \sim \text{Po}(\lambda)$.

There are **three conditions** that need to be met for a random variable to follow a Poisson distribution.

> If X represents the number of events that occur in a particular space or time, then X will follow a Poisson distribution as long as:
>
> 1) The events occur **randomly**, and are all **independent** of each other.
> 2) The events happen **singly** (i.e. 'one at a time').
> 3) The events happen (on average) at a **constant rate** (λ).
>
> If $X \sim \text{Po}(\lambda)$, then X can take values 0, 1, 2, 3... with probability:
>
> $$P(X = x) = \frac{e^{-\lambda}\lambda^x}{x!}$$

Learning Objectives:

- Be able to recognise the conditions that give rise to a Poisson distribution.
- Be able to find probabilities for the Poisson distribution using the Poisson probability function.
- Be able to use the additive property of the Poisson distribution.

Tip: The events need to happen at a constant average rate, but this could be a rate in either **time** or **space**.

Tip: This is the Poisson **probability function**. There's lots more about it on page 29.

Which of the random variables below would follow a Poisson distribution?

a) **The random variable X represents the number of sixes thrown in 20 minutes of dice-throwing.**

- Sixes will occur **randomly**, **independently** and **singly** and at a **constant rate** (on average), so X will follow a Poisson distribution.

b) **The random variable A represents the number of grains of sand in 1 cm³ of a large beaker full of water. On average, there are 750 grains of sand per litre, but the beaker has been standing for a few minutes.**

- This is **not** Poisson, since the grains of sand will all have sunk to the bottom, and so they **won't** be distributed **independently** or **randomly**.

c) **The random variable B represents the number of tiny soil particles in 1 cm³ of a large beaker full of water. On average, there are 750 soil particles per litre, and the water has just been well stirred.**

- This is Poisson, since the soil particles will occur **singly** and should be distributed **randomly** and **independently** of each other because of the stirring (i.e. they shouldn't be in large clusters).

Tip: In exam questions, there are usually hints about whether it's reasonable to **assume** something.
For example, this question is about wedding dresses — and these are usually sold one at a time (i.e. singly).

But you **wouldn't** be able to make the same assumption about books (because people often buy more than one book at a time).

Example

A shop sells wedding dresses at an average rate of 1.5 per week. The random variable X represents the number of wedding dresses sold by the shop in a given week. State the probability distribution of X.

- Wedding dresses are likely to be sold **randomly** and **singly**, and you're told they're sold at a constant average rate. So X will follow a Poisson distribution.

- The **parameter** of this distribution is the average number of wedding dresses sold per week — this is 1.5. So $X \sim \text{Po}(1.5)$.

Exercise 1.1

Q1 In each of the following situations, explain whether or not the random variable follows a Poisson distribution. If it does follow a Poisson distribution, state the parameter of its distribution.

a) The number of daisies (D) in 1 m² of a field where they grow randomly with an average density of 10 daisies per square metre.

b) The number of randomly scattered flaws (F) in 1 m of a roll of cloth, where on average there are 0.5 flaws per metre.

c) The number of gravel particles (P) in 1 litre of a large container full of water which has been standing for 24 hours, and which contains an average of 40 gravel particles per litre .

d) The number of micro-organisms (M) in 1 litre of a large container full of water which has just been vigorously stirred up, and which contains an average of 40 micro-organisms per litre.

Q2 A farmer keeps 100 sheep in a field of area 7000 m². The farmer puts food into the corner of the field at 7 am. The random variable X is the number of sheep in a randomly chosen square metre of field at 7:30 am. Will X follow a Poisson distribution? Explain your answer.

Using the Poisson probability function

Remember... a Poisson distribution has just one parameter: λ.

It appears twice in the **probability function** for the Poisson distribution.

Tip: The Greek letter 'lambda' (λ) is often used for the Poisson parameter.

> If $X \sim Po(\lambda)$, then X takes values 0, 1, 2, 3... with probability:
> $$P(X = x) = \frac{e^{-\lambda}\lambda^{x}}{x!}$$

Examples

If $X \sim Po(2.8)$, find:

a) $P(X = 0)$

- Use the formula: $P(X = 0) = \dfrac{e^{-2.8} \times 2.8^{0}}{0!}$

$$= e^{-2.8}$$
$$= 0.06081... = \boxed{0.0608} \text{ (to 3 sig. fig.)}$$

Tip: Remember...
- $0! = 1$
- $a^{0} = 1$, for any number a.

b) $P(X = 1)$

- Again, just use the formula: $P(X = 1) = \dfrac{e^{-2.8} \times 2.8^{1}}{1!}$

$$= e^{-2.8} \times 2.8$$
$$= 0.17026... = \boxed{0.170} \text{ (to 3 sig. fig.)}$$

c) $P(X = 2)$

- And again... $P(X = 2) = \dfrac{e^{-2.8} \times 2.8^{2}}{2!}$

$$= \frac{e^{-2.8} \times 2.8^{2}}{2 \times 1}$$
$$= 0.23837... = \boxed{0.238} \text{ (to 3 sig. fig.)}$$

You might need to do a little bit more than just plug numbers into a formula.

Examples

If $X \sim Po(2.8)$, find:

a) $P(X < 3)$

- A Poisson distribution only allows whole-number values. So $P(X < 3)$ is the same as $P(X \leq 2)$.

$P(X < 3) = P(X \leq 2)$
$= P(X = 0) + P(X = 1) + P(X = 2)$
$= 0.06081... + 0.17026... + 0.23837...$
$= 0.4694... = \boxed{0.469} \text{ (to 3 sig. fig.)}$

Tip: Use the probability function to find the probabilities $P(X = 0)$, $P(X = 1)$ and $P(X = 2)$... and then add the results together.

b) $P(X \geq 3)$

- All the normal probability rules still apply.

$P(X \geq 3) = 1 - P(X < 3) = 1 - 0.4694...$
$= 0.5305... = \boxed{0.531} \text{ (to 3 sig. fig.)}$

Tip: Remember... $P(X \geq k) = 1 - P(X < k)$.

Example

The number of wedding dresses (X) sold in a week by a particular shop follows the Poisson distribution Po(1.5).

a) Find the probability that in a particular week the shop sells 2 dresses.

- Use the formula with $\lambda = 1.5$ and $x = 2$.

$$P(X = 2) = \frac{e^{-\lambda}\lambda^x}{x!}$$

$$= \frac{e^{-1.5} \times 1.5^2}{2!}$$

$$= 0.25102\ldots = \boxed{0.251} \text{ (to 3 sig. fig.)}$$

b) Find the probability that in a particular week the shop sells fewer than 2 dresses.

- $P(X < 2) = P(X \le 1)$
  $= P(X = 0) + P(X = 1)$

$$P(X < 2) = P(X = 0) + P(X = 1)$$

$$= \frac{e^{-1.5} \times 1.5^0}{0!} + \frac{e^{-1.5} \times 1.5^1}{1!}$$

$$= 0.22313\ldots + 0.33469\ldots$$

$$= 0.55782\ldots = \boxed{0.558} \text{ (to 3 sig. fig.)}$$

Exercise 1.2

Give your answers to 3 significant figures in this exercise.

Q1 The random variable X has distribution $X \sim$ Po(2). Find:
    a) $P(X = 1)$ b) $P(X = 0)$ c) $P(X = 4)$

Q2 The random variable X has distribution $X \sim$ Po(3). Find:
    a) $P(X = 4)$ b) $P(X \le 1)$ c) $P(4 \le X \le 6)$

Q3 If $X \sim$ Po(3.8), find:
    a) $P(X = 3)$ b) $P(X < 3)$ c) $P(X \ge 3)$

Q4 For the random variable $X \sim$ Po(1.4), find $P(X > 3)$.

Q5 Flaws occur randomly in a length of fabric at an average rate of 0.2 flaws per metre.
    a) State an appropriate statistical model to represent the random variable X, the number of flaws in a given metre of fabric. Explain your answer.
    b) In a randomly chosen metre of fabric, find the probability of obtaining:
        (i) no flaws,
        (ii) fewer than 2 flaws.

Q6 Telephone calls arrive at a switchboard at an average rate of 12 per minute. In a randomly chosen minute, find the probability of receiving:
    a) exactly 12 phone calls,
    b) between 10 and 13 calls inclusive.

Mean and variance of a Poisson distribution

For a Poisson distribution, the **mean** and the **variance** are the same
— they both equal λ, the Poisson parameter.

> If $X \sim \text{Po}(\lambda)$: **Mean ($\mu$) of X = E(X) = λ**
> **Variance (σ^2) of X = Var(X) = λ**

This means that the **standard deviation** (σ) is given by: $\sigma = \sqrt{\lambda}$

Examples

If $X \sim \text{Po}(7)$, find:

a) E(X)

- It's Poisson, so E(X) equals λ. $E(X) = \lambda = \boxed{7}$

b) Var(X)

- It's Poisson, so Var(X) also equals λ. $\text{Var}(X) = \lambda = \boxed{7}$

c) The standard deviation of X.

- Take the square root of the variance to find the standard deviation.

$$\text{Standard deviation of } X = \sqrt{\text{Var}(X)}$$
$$= \sqrt{\lambda}$$
$$= \boxed{\sqrt{7}}$$

Examples

If $X \sim \text{Po}(1)$, find:

a) $P(X \le \mu)$

- $\mu = \lambda = 1$.

$$P(X \le \mu) = P(X \le 1) = P(X = 0) + P(X = 1)$$
$$= \frac{e^{-1} \times 1^0}{0!} + \frac{e^{-1} \times 1^1}{1!}$$
$$= e^{-1} + e^{-1}$$
$$= 0.735758... = \boxed{0.736} \text{ (to 3 sig. fig.)}$$

b) $P(X \le \mu - \sigma)$

- $\sigma^2 = \lambda = 1$.
  So $\sigma = 1$ too.
- So $\mu - \sigma = 0$.

$$P(X \le \mu - \sigma) = P(X \le 0)$$
$$= P(X = 0)$$
$$= \frac{e^{-1} \times 1^0}{0!}$$
$$= 0.367879... = \boxed{0.368} \text{ (to 3 sig. fig.)}$$

Example

**The number of injuries each week (x) during a school's PE lessons was
recorded. After 33 weeks, the following results had been obtained:**

$$\sum x = 16 \qquad\qquad \sum x^2 = 24$$

a) Calculate the mean number of injuries per week.

- Use the formula for the mean.

$$\bar{x} = \frac{\sum x}{n} = \frac{16}{33} = 0.484848...$$
$$= \boxed{0.485} \text{ (to 3 sig. fig.)}$$

b) Calculate the variance of the number of injuries per week.

- The variance is the mean of the squares $\left(\frac{\sum x^2}{n}\right)$ minus the square of the mean $\left(\frac{\sum x}{n}\right)^2$.

$$\frac{\sum x^2}{n} - \left(\frac{\sum x}{n}\right)^2 = \frac{24}{33} - \left(\frac{16}{33}\right)^2$$
$$= 0.492194...$$
$$= \boxed{0.492 \text{ (to 3 sig. fig.)}}$$

Tip: Whenever you come across a distribution where the mean and the variance are the same (or very nearly the same), then think Poisson.

c) Explain why this data supports the choice of a Poisson distribution as a model for the number of injuries (X) per week.

- For this data, the mean and the variance are almost equal.
- Since the mean and variance of a Poisson distribution are equal, this suggests that this data may follow a Poisson distribution.

Tip: You choose the parameter λ by using the mean of your data.

d) If $X \sim Po(\lambda)$, what value should be chosen for λ?

- The parameter of a Poisson distribution equals the mean for a given period.

Since X is the number of injuries per week, $\boxed{X \sim Po(0.485)}$.

e) Find the probability of there being at least 1 injury in a given week.

- Use the Poisson probability function.

$$P(X > 0) = 1 - P(X = 0)$$
$$= 1 - \frac{e^{-0.485} \times 0.485^0}{0!}$$
$$= 1 - 0.61569...$$
$$= \boxed{0.384 \text{ (to 3 sig. fig.)}}$$

Exercise 1.3

Q1   For each of the following random variables, state:
- (i) the mean
- (ii) the variance

    a) $X \sim Po(9)$ b) $Y \sim Po(12)$ c) $M \sim Po(4.3)$

Q2   The discrete random variable $X \sim Po(9)$.
- a) State the mean (μ) and variance (σ^2) of X.
- b) Find the standard deviation (σ) of X.
- c) Find $P(X = \mu + \sigma)$

Q3   A discrete random variable X follows a Poisson distribution with $\lambda = 16$.
- a) State the mean (μ) and variance (σ^2) of X.
- b) Find the standard deviation (σ) of X.
- c) Find $P(X \leq \sigma)$. Give your answer to 4 decimal places.

Q4   A company rents out video cameras. In their current shop,
the weekly rentals (X) occur at an average rate of 10 per week,
and follow a Poisson distribution.

The owners decide to open a new shop in a nearby town and assume
that the rentals will also follow a Poisson distribution. During the
first year, the weekly rentals were as follows:

Rentals per week (x)	5	6	7	8	9	10	11	12	13
Frequency (f)	4	6	3	8	16	9	3	2	1

a) Calculate the mean and variance of this data

b) Comment on the assumption that the sales follow a Poisson
distribution.

Additive property of the Poisson distribution

The Poisson parameter is **additive**. That sounds complicated, but there are
just two things you need to know. This is the **first** one:

> If X represents the number of events in **1 unit** of time or space
> (e.g. 1 minute / hour / m² / m³), and $X \sim \textbf{Po}(\lambda)$, then the number
> of events in **t units** of time or space follows the distribution **Po($t\lambda$)**.

That sounds trickier than it really is.
Think of it this way:

- If X describes the number of events in a day, and $X \sim Po(4)$, then...
- ...this means that the event happens 4 times a day, on average...
- ...so in a week, the event will happens 28 times, on average...
- ...and so the number of events per week (Y) follows $Y \sim Po(28)$.

Tip: If X follows a
Poisson distribution,
then you know
the events happen
randomly, singly and at
a constant rate.

But Y is just describing
the same events, so
Y must also follow a
Poisson distribution —
only with the parameter
$\lambda = 28$.

Example 1

**Sunflowers grow singly and randomly in a field with an average of
10 sunflowers per square metre. What is the probability that a
randomly chosen area of 0.25 m² contains no sunflowers?**

- The number of sunflowers in 1 m² follows the distribution Po(10).
- So the number of sunflowers in 0.25 m² must follow the
distribution Po(2.5).
- This means P(no sunflowers) $= \dfrac{e^{-2.5} \times 2.5^0}{0!}$

$$= 0.08208... = \boxed{0.0821 \text{ (to 3 sig. fig.)}}.$$

Tip: Here $t = 0.25$, as
0.25 m² = 1 m² × 0.25.

So the number of
sunflowers in 0.25 m²
will follow
Po(10 × 0.25) = Po(2.5)

Example 2

The number of radioactive atoms that decay per second follows the Poisson distribution Po(5). If the probability of no atoms decaying in t seconds is 0.5, verify that $t \approx 0.1386$.

- If the random variable X represents the number of radioactive atoms that decay in t seconds, then $X \sim \text{Po}(5t)$.

- This means $P(X = 0) = \dfrac{e^{-5t}(5t)^0}{0!} = e^{-5t} = 0.5$.

- This equation is satisfied by $t = 0.1386$, since $e^{-5 \times 0.1386} = e^{-0.693} = 0.500$ (to 3 d.p.).

This is the **second** thing you need to know about the Poisson parameter being additive:

If $X \sim \text{Po}(\lambda)$ and $Y \sim \text{Po}(\kappa)$, then $X + Y \sim \text{Po}(\lambda + \kappa)$.

Tip: If X represents the number of events in 1 unit of time or space, and $X \sim \text{Po}(\lambda)$...

...then the number of events in 2 units of time or space is $X + X$, which (from the formula on the right) follows $\text{Po}(\lambda + \lambda) = \text{Po}(2\lambda)$.

This is exactly the same as the formula from p33 with $t = 2$.

Example

The random variables D and C both follow Poisson distributions, and represent the number of claims per week to one insurance company against policies for dogs and cats respectively. The average numbers of claims per week are 5 for dogs and 8 for cats.

a) **State the distribution for the total number (T) of claims against 'dog policies' and 'cat policies'.**

- You know the average numbers of claims per week for dogs and cats are 5 and 8 respectively.

  $D \sim \text{Po}(5)$ and $C \sim \text{Po}(8)$.

- The total number of claims equals the number of 'dog claims' added to the number of 'cat claims'.

  $T = D + C \sim \text{Po}(5 + 8)$

  i.e. $T \sim \text{Po}(13)$

b) **Find the probability that the total number of claims for dogs and cats in a randomly chosen week is between 10 and 12 (inclusive).**

- Use the Poisson probability function:

$$P(10 \le T \le 12) = P(T = 10) + P(T = 11) + P(T = 12)$$
$$= \frac{e^{-13} \times 13^{10}}{10!} + \frac{e^{-13} \times 13^{11}}{11!} + \frac{e^{-13} \times 13^{12}}{12!}$$
$$= 0.08587... + 0.10148... + 0.10993...$$
$$= 0.297 \text{ (to 3 sig. fig.)}$$

Q1 At a particular time, bacteria occur randomly and singly on a piece of glass at an average rate of 600 bacteria per square centimetre.

    a) State the distribution followed by the random variable X, where X is the number of bacteria on 1 cm² of the glass.

    b) State the distribution followed by the random variable Y, where Y is the number of bacteria on 1 mm² of the glass.

    c) Find the probability that there are exactly 3 bacteria on a random 1 mm² of the glass.

Q2 Potholes occur randomly and singly on a stretch of road at an average rate of 3 per kilometre. Find the probability that in a randomly chosen 8 km stretch of this road, there are between 20 and 22 potholes (inclusive).

Q3 Louise and Hannah each receive text messages randomly and singly throughout the day. Louise receives an average of 4 texts per day and Hannah receives an average of 2 per day.

    a) Find the probability that the total number of text messages the two girls receive on a randomly chosen day is equal to 5.

    b) Find the probability that the total number of text messages the two girls receive in a randomly chosen week is equal to 44.

Q4 A bookshop sells wizard books at an average rate of 20 per day and celebrity biographies at an average rate of 15 per day.
If sales of both types of books occur randomly and singly, find the probability that the shop sells a total of 40 of these books in a day.

2. Using Poisson Tables

Just like for the binomial distribution, there are tables for the Poisson distribution that make it relatively easy to find probabilities. You use them in a similar way to the binomial tables, so some of this section might seem familiar.

Using tables to find probabilities

Suppose weeds grow singly and randomly in a garden with an average of 8 weeds per square metre, and you need to find the probability that a randomly chosen square metre contains **no more than 6 weeds**.

You *could* do this using the Poisson probability function. If the random variable X represents the number of weeds in one square metre, then you'd need to work out $P(X = 0) + P(X = 1) + ... + P(X = 5) + P(X = 6)$ using Po(8).

But it's quicker to use a table of the **Poisson cumulative distribution function**. The Poisson cumulative distribution function for Po(λ) shows the probabilities $P(X \leq x)$, for different values of λ and x.

- In the weeds example, $X \sim$ Po(8), so you need to find $\lambda = 8$ across the top of the table — any probabilities you need will be in this column.
- Then you need to look up a value of x. Here, you need to find $P(X \leq 6)$, so find $x = 6$ down the left-hand side of the table, and read across to the column for $\lambda = 8$.

Poisson Cumulative Distribution Function
Values show $P(X \leqslant x)$, where $X \sim$ Po(λ)

①$\lambda = 8$

$\lambda =$	5.5	6.0	6.5	7.0	7.5	8.0	8.5	9.0	9.5	10.0
$x =$ 0	0.0041	0.0025	0.0015	0.0009	0.0006	0.0003	0.0002	0.0001	0.0001	0.0000
1	0.0266	0.0174	0.0113	0.0073	0.0047	0.0030	0.0019	0.0012	0.0008	0.0005
2	0.0884	0.0620	0.0430	0.0296	0.0203	0.0138	0.0093	0.0062	0.0042	0.0028
3	0.2017	0.1512	0.1118	0.0818	0.0591	0.0424	0.0301	0.0212	0.0149	0.0103
4	0.3575	0.2851	0.2237	0.1730	0.1321	0.0996	0.0744	0.0550	0.0403	0.0293
5	0.5289	0.4457	0.3690	0.3007	0.2414	0.1912	0.1496	0.1157	0.0885	0.0671
6	0.6860	0.6063	0.5265	0.4497	0.3782	0.3134	0.2562	0.2068	0.1649	0.1301
7	0.8095	0.7440	0.6728	0.5987	0.5246	0.4530	0.3856	0.3239	0.2687	0.2202
8	0.8944	0.8472	0.7916	0.7291	0.6620	0.5925	0.5231	0.4557	0.3918	0.3328
9	0.9462	0.9161	0.8774	0.8305	0.7764	0.7166	0.6530	0.5874	0.5218	0.4579
10	0.9747	0.9574	0.9332	0.9015	0.8622	0.8159	0.7634	0.7060	0.6453	0.5830
11	0.9890	0.9799	0.9661	0.9467	0.9208	0.8881	0.8487	0.8030	0.7520	0.6968

② $x = 6$

- So if $X \sim$ Po(8), then $P(X \leq 6) = 0.3134$.

The next few examples will look fairly familiar — because they're showing the same ideas as you've already seen for binomial tables.

Examples

When cloth is manufactured, faults occur randomly in the cloth at a rate of 8 faults per square metre. Use the Poisson tables to find:

a) The probability of 7 or fewer faults in a square metre of cloth.

- Use the column for $\lambda = 8$. $P(X \leq 7) = \boxed{0.4530}$
- Then read across from $x = 7$.

b) The probability of more than 4 faults in a square metre of cloth.

- Remember... $P(X > 4) = 1 - P(X \leq 4)$
  $P(X > 4) = 1 - P(X \leq 4)$ $= 1 - 0.0996$
  $= \boxed{0.9004}$

Tip: The faults occur randomly, singly and at a constant rate (= 8 faults per square metre).

So if X represents the number of faults in a square metre, then $X \sim$ Po(8).

c) The probability of exactly 10 faults in a square metre of cloth.

- Remember...
  $P(X = 10) = P(X \leq 10) - P(X \leq 9)$

$P(X = 10) = P(X \leq 10) - P(X \leq 9)$
$= 0.8159 - 0.7166$
$= \boxed{0.0993}$

d) The probability of at least 9 faults in a square metre of cloth.

- Remember...
  $P(X \geq 9) = 1 - P(X < 9)$
  $= 1 - P(X \leq 8)$

$P(X \geq 9) = 1 - P(X \leq 8)$
$= 1 - 0.5925$
$= \boxed{0.4075}$

e) The probability of exactly 4 faults in 0.75 m² of cloth.

- For this one, you need to use the additive property of the Poisson distribution.

Let the random variable Y represent the number of faults in 0.75 m² of cloth.

Since the number of faults in 1 m² of cloth $\sim \text{Po}(8)$, then $Y \sim \text{Po}(0.75 \times 8) = \text{Po}(6)$.

- $P(Y = 4)$ equals P(exactly 4 faults in 0.75 m² of cloth).

$P(Y = 4) = P(Y \leq 4) - P(Y \leq 3)$
$= 0.2851 - 0.1512$
$= \boxed{0.1339}$

Tip: This time you need to use the column for $\lambda = 6$.

Just like with binomial tables, you can find $P(a < X \leq b)$ by **subtracting** one value from the table from another:

- Use the table to find **$P(X \leq b)$** — the probability that X is less than or equal to the **largest** value satisfying the inequality '$a < X \leq b$'...

- ...and subtract **$P(X \leq a)$** to 'remove' the probability that X takes one of the smaller values not satisfying the inequality '$a < X \leq b$'.

Tip: This is the same method as is described on page 14.

Examples

If $W \sim \text{Po}(5.5)$, then find:

a) $P(3 < W \leq 8)$

- $W = 8$ is the largest value satisfying $3 < W \leq 8$, so find $P(W \leq 8)$...

- ...and subtract $P(W \leq 3)$, since $W = 3$ **doesn't** satisfy the inequality $3 < W \leq 8$, and neither does any value smaller than 3.

$P(3 < W \leq 8) = P(W \leq 8) - P(W \leq 3)$
$= 0.8944 - 0.2017$
$= \boxed{0.6927}$

Tip: The table on the previous page contains $\lambda = 5.5$ (or you can use the full Poisson tables on p164).

b) $P(2 \leq W < 7)$

- Find $P(W \leq 6)$, since $W = 6$ is the largest value satisfying $2 \leq W < 7$...

- ...and subtract $P(W \leq 1)$, since $W = 1$ **doesn't** satisfy the inequality $2 \leq W < 7$, and neither does any value smaller than 1.

$P(2 \leq W < 7) = P(W \leq 6) - P(W \leq 1)$
$= 0.6860 - 0.0266$
$= \boxed{0.6594}$

Q1 If $X \sim$ Po(2), use the Poisson tables to find:

  a) $P(X \leq 3)$ b) $P(X \leq 7)$ c) $P(X < 5)$

Q2 If $X \sim$ Po(7.5), use the Poisson tables to find:

  a) $P(X > 6)$ b) $P(X = 9)$ c) $P(2 \leq X \leq 8)$

Q3 The random variable X follows a Poisson distribution
  with mean 6. Use the Poisson tables to find:

  a) $P(X > 4)$ b) $P(2 < X \leq 5)$ c) $P(4 \leq X < 9)$

Q4 The random variable X follows a Poisson distribution with mean 5.5.
  Use the Poisson tables to find:

  a) $P(X > 2)$ b) $P(X = 4)$ c) $P(2 \leq X \leq 7)$

Q5 Telephone calls arrive at a switchboard at an average rate of
  8 per minute. Find the probability that, in a randomly chosen
  minute, the switchboard receives:

  a) exactly 6 phone calls   b) at least 3 phone calls

Q6 The number of tadpoles in a 10 cm^3 sample of water from a stream
  follows a Poisson distribution with mean 0.1. Use tables to find the
  probability that a randomly selected litre of water contains:

  a) fewer than 7 tadpoles   b) more than 15 tadpoles

Using tables 'backwards'

Just like with the binomial tables, sometimes you'll need to use the Poisson
tables 'the other way round'. So you might be given a probability, and asked
to find a corresponding value of x.

Examples

a) **If $X \sim$ Po(4), then find x such that $P(X \leq x) = 0.8893$.**

▪ Use the column in the Poisson tables for $\lambda = 4$.

▪ Go down the column until you find 0.8893, then read off the
  corresponding value of x. This is $x = 6$.

b) **If $X \sim$ Po(5.5), then find x such that $P(X > x) = 0.1905$.**

▪ If $P(X > x) = 0.1905$, then $P(X \leq x) = 1 - 0.1905 = 0.8095$.

▪ So go down the column for $\lambda = 5.5$ till you reach 0.8095, and
  read off the corresponding value of x. This is $x = 7$.

c) **If $X \sim$ Po(8.5), then find the maximum value of a with $P(X \leq a) < 0.1$.**

▪ Use the Poisson table with $\lambda = 8.5$.

▪ You can see that $P(X \leq 4) = 0.0744$ and $P(X \leq 5) = 0.1496$.

▪ So the maximum value of a with $P(X \leq a) < 0.1$ is $a = 4$.

Tip: Remember... a
cumulative frequency
function can only
increase (or stay the
same) as x increases.
So there can't be any
values of a greater than
4 with $P(X \leq a) < 0.1$.

These questions can also involve real-life situations.

> **Example**
>
> **Celebrity Gossip magazine is published weekly. On average, 9 people want to buy the magazine from a particular newsagent each week. What is the minimum number of copies the newsagent should order at the start of the week if she wants the probability of not having enough copies to sell to all the potential customers to be less than 0.05?**
>
> - Let the random variable X represent the number of people wanting to buy a copy of Celebrity Gossip from this newsagent in a particular week. Then $X \sim \text{Po}(9)$.
>
> - The newsagent needs to order at least k copies of Celebrity Gossip, where $P(X > k) < 0.05$.
>
> - From the column of the Poisson table for $\lambda = 9$:
> $P(X \leq 13) = 0.9261$, and so $P(X > 13) = 1 - 0.9261 = 0.0739$.
>   And $P(X \leq 14) = 0.9585$, and so $P(X > 14) = 1 - 0.9585 = 0.0415$.
>
> - So the minimum number of copies the newsagent needs to order is $\boxed{14}$.

Exercise 2.2

Q1 The random variable X follows a Poisson distribution with mean 5.5. Find the values of x such that:

a) $P(X \leq x) = 0.5289$ b) $P(X < x) = 0.9983$

Q2 The random variable Y follows a Poisson distribution with mean 3.5. Find the values of y such that:

a) $P(Y > y) = 0.8641$ b) $P(Y \geq y) = 0.1424$

Q3 If $X \sim \text{Po}(1.5)$, find the largest value of x where the probability of X taking a value less than x is at most 0.25.

Q4 The random variable X follows a Poisson distribution with mean 8. Find the smallest possible value of x where the probability of X taking a value of at least x is less than 0.05.

Q5 A company rents out equipment on a large beach in Spain. On average it rents out 6 inflatables per hour. At the end of each hour the inflatables must be returned. Find the minimum number of inflatables the company should have if it is to be at least 90% certain of meeting demand each hour.

Q6 A photocopier supplier offers a support service to a business. The supplier knows that a particular type of photocopier breaks down at an average rate of 0.5 times per month. The company offers the business a deal: if there are more than y breakdowns in a four-month period, they will pay a penalty. Find the minimum value of y for which the supplier has a probability of less than 0.1 of paying the penalty.

3. The Poisson Approximation of a Binomial Distribution

Learning Objective:

- Be able to find probabilities for a binomial distribution using a Poisson approximation.

Working out probabilities for B(n, p) where n is quite large can be tricky, so using an approximation can save a lot of effort. This is the first of several approximations you'll need to learn in S2.

Approximating the binomial distribution with a Poisson distribution

Sometimes a Poisson distribution can be used as an **approximation** to a binomial distribution.

> If $X \sim$ B(n, p), and:
> 1) n is **large**,   2) p is **small**,
> then X can be approximated by Po(np).

Tip: The **mean** (expected value) of the **binomial distribution** B(n, p) is np — so you need to use that as the **mean** of your **Poisson approximation** too.

- To use this Poisson approximation to B(n, p), you ideally want n to be as **large** as possible and p to be as **small** as possible. (But to use your Poisson tables, you need $np \leq 10$.)

- The bigger the value of n and the smaller the value of p, the better the approximation will be. You can see how the approximation improves for bigger n and smaller p if you look at the graphs below.

Tip: In your exam, you'll usually be told when to use an approximation.

Tip: The mean (expected value) of B(5, 0.2) is $5 \times 0.2 = 1$.

So Po(1) is used to approximate B(5, 0.2).

- This graph shows the probabilities for **B(5, 0.2)** plotted next to those for Po(1).

- The approximation is okay... but there are some fairly big differences in the heights of the bars.

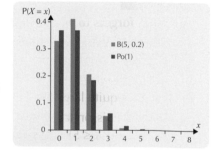

Tip: The mean (expected value) of B(10, 0.1) is $10 \times 0.1 = 1$.

So Po(1) is also used to approximate B(10, 0.1).

- This time the probabilities for **B(10, 0.1)** are plotted next to those for Po(1).

- The approximation is better this time.

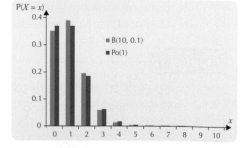

Tip: The mean (expected value) of B(40, 0.025) is $40 \times 0.025 = 1$.

So Po(1) is used once more — this time to approximate B(40, 0.025).

- And these are the probabilities for **B(40, 0.025)** plotted next to those for Po(1).

- The two distributions match pretty well now — the approximation is very good.

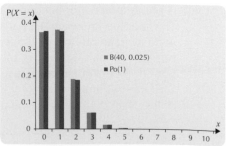

The reason you need a small value for p is because then the **mean** and the **variance** of $B(n, p)$ are **approximately equal**. This is important if $Po(np)$ is going to be a good approximation (remember... the mean and variance of a Poisson distribution are always equal — see page 31).

- If $X \sim B(n, p)$, then $E(X) = np$.
- And if p is small, $(1 - p) \approx 1$.
- This means $Var(X) = np(1 - p) \approx np \times 1 = np$.

Tip: Remember...
if $X \sim B(n, p)$, then
$Var(X) = np(1 - p)$.

Example 1

In a school of 1825 students, what is the probability that at least 6 were born on June 21st? Use a suitable approximation to find your answer. (You may assume that all birthdays are independent and are distributed evenly throughout a 365-day year.)

- If X represents the number of children in the school born on June 21st, then $X \sim B(1825, \frac{1}{365})$.

- You need to find $P(X \geq 6)$.

- Since n is large and p is small, $B(1825, \frac{1}{365})$ can be approximated by $Po(1825 \times \frac{1}{365}) = Po(5)$.

- Now you can use Poisson tables with $\lambda = 5$.
  $P(X \geq 6) = 1 - P(X < 6) = 1 - P(X \leq 5) = 1 - 0.6160 = \boxed{0.3840}$

Tip: You *don't have to* use a Poisson approximation here, but your binomial tables don't go past $n = 50$, and working out $P(X \geq 6)$ 'by hand' isn't easy.

Tip: Poisson tables are on p164.

Tip: If you work this out using $B(1825, \frac{1}{365})$, you also get an answer of 0.3840 — so this is a **very** good approximation.

Example 2

Factory A forgets to add icing to its chocolate cakes with a uniform probability of 0.02. Use a suitable approximation to find the probability that fewer than 6 of the next 100 cakes made will not be iced.

- If X represents the number of 'un-iced' cakes, then $X \sim B(100, 0.02)$.
- Since n is quite large and p is quite small, $X \sim Po(100 \times 0.02) = Po(2)$.
- Now use Poisson tables (with $\lambda = 2$) to find $P(X < 6)$.
  $P(X < 6) = P(X \leq 5) = \boxed{0.9834}$

Tip: If you work this out using $B(100, 0.02)$, you get a probability of 0.9845.

Sometimes you can still use the approximation if p is very close to 1.

Example 3

Factory B adds icing to its chocolate cakes with a uniform probability of 0.99. Use a suitable approximation to find the probability that more than 95 of the next 100 cakes made will be iced.

- If Y represents the number of iced cakes produced by Factory B, then $Y \sim B(100, 0.99)$. Here, n is quite large, but p is not small.

- However, if you let W represent the number of 'un-iced' cakes made, then $W \sim B(100, 0.01)$.

- Now you can use a Poisson approximation: $W \sim Po(100 \times 0.01) = Po(1)$

- So $P(Y > 95) = P(W < 5) = P(W \leq 4)$ — and you can find this from Poisson tables (with $\lambda = 1$).

- $P(W \leq 4) = \boxed{0.9963}$

Tip: This is a similar idea to that used with binomial distributions on p15. There, instead of using tables to find the number of 'successes' where $P(\text{success}) = p > 0.5$, you found the number of 'failures' where $P(\text{failure}) = q < 0.5$.

Tip: If you work this out using $B(100, 0.99)$, you get a probability of 0.9966.

Q1 In each of the following cases, explain whether you would expect the Poisson distribution to be a suitable approximation.
    a) B(20, 0.5)   b) B(5, 0.2)   c) B(200, 0.04)   d) B(250, 0.1)

Q2 State the Poisson distribution that could be used as an approximation to the following binomial distributions.
    a) B(30, 0.1)   b) B(50, 0.05)
    c) B(200, 0.01)   d) B(500, 0.003)

Q3 The random variable $X \sim$ B(90, 0.05).
Using a suitable approximation, find:
    a) $P(X \le 2)$ b) $P(X > 5)$ c) $P(X < 4)$ d) $P(X \ge 5)$

Q4 The random variable $X \sim$ B(150, 0.01).
Using a suitable approximation, find:
    a) $P(X = 3)$ b) $P(3 < X \le 5)$
    c) $P(2 \le X < 7)$ d) $P(1 < X < 4)$

Q5 a) The random variable $X \sim$ B(40, 0.1).
       Without using an approximation, find $P(X \le 2)$.
   b) The random variable $Y \sim$ B(10, 0.4).
       Without using an approximation, find $P(Y \le 2)$.
   c) Use a suitable Poisson approximation to find $P(X \le 2)$ and $P(Y \le 2)$.
   d) Compare your answer to c) with your answers to a) and b).

Q6 A doctor screens patients for a particular disease. From previous experience, he knows that there is a probability of 2% that each person will have contracted the disease. Use a suitable approximation to find the probability that, after screening 300 patients, more than 10 people are found to have the disease.

Q7 A magician claims to be able to work out whether a person is left-handed or right-handed just by looking at their shoes. For each person, he has a probability of 0.9 of being correct. Use a suitable approximation to find the probability that he is correct on more than 85 occasions out of 90.

Q8 Records from a market research company indicate that each time they dial a telephone number, there is a probability of 0.005 that they will dial incorrectly. Use a suitable approximation to find the probability that, out of the 600 phone calls made for one campaign, more than 7 were dialled incorrectly.

4. Modelling Real Problems

This is the part where you get to use what you've learnt to tackle some
real-world problems. Remember... statistics is very much a 'real-life'
subject — you can apply it in all sorts of areas.

Modelling real problems with a Poisson distribution

Make sure you understand what's going on in the next few examples.

Example 1

A car randomly breaks down twice a week on average.
The random variable X represents the number of times the car
will break down next week.

a) **What probability distribution could be used to model X?
   Explain your answer.**

▪ The breakdowns occur randomly, singly and (on average) at a
  constant rate. Since X is the total number of breakdowns in one week,
  X follows a Poisson distribution with an expected value of 2: $X \sim \text{Po}(2)$

b) **Find the probability that the car breaks down
   fewer than 3 times next week.**

▪ Using tables with $\lambda = 2$: $P(X < 3) = P(X \leq 2) = \boxed{0.6767}$

c) **Find the probability that the car breaks down
   more than 4 times next week.**

▪ Again, using tables with $\lambda = 2$: $P(X > 4) = 1 - P(X \leq 4)$
  $$= 1 - 0.9473 = \boxed{0.0527}$$

d) **Find the probability that the car breaks down exactly 6 times in the
   next fortnight.**

▪ If the random variable Y represents the number of breakdowns in the
  next fortnight, then $Y \sim \text{Po}(2 \times 2) = \text{Po}(4)$.

▪ So using Poisson tables with $\lambda = 4$: $P(Y = 6) = P(Y \leq 6) - P(Y \leq 5)$
  $$= 0.8893 - 0.7851$$
  $$= \boxed{0.1042}$$

e) **Find the probability that the car doesn't break down tomorrow.**

▪ This time, let the random variable T represent the number of
  breakdowns tomorrow. This is a single day, so $T \sim \text{Po}(2 \div 7) = \text{Po}(\frac{2}{7})$.

▪ $\lambda = \frac{2}{7}$ isn't in your tables, so you'll have to work this out using the
  probability function.

▪ The probability that the car doesn't break down tomorrow is $P(T = 0)$.

$$P(T = 0) = \frac{e^{-\frac{2}{7}} \times \left(\frac{2}{7}\right)^0}{0!} = 0.751477... = \boxed{0.751} \text{ (to 3 sig. fig.)}$$

Example 2

A restaurant owner needs to buy several crates of apples, so she visits a farm that sells apples by the crate, where each crate contains 150 apples. 1.5% of all the apples sold by the farm are bad, and these bad apples are randomly distributed between the crates. The restaurant owner opens a random crate and inspects each apple.

- If there are <u>no</u> bad apples in this crate, then the restaurant owner will <u>buy</u> the apples she needs from this farm.
- If <u>more than 2 apples</u> in this first crate are bad, then the restaurant owner will <u>not buy</u> from this farm.
- If <u>only 1 or 2 apples</u> in the first crate are bad, then a <u>second crate</u> is opened. The restaurant owner will then only buy from this farm if the second crate contains <u>at most 1 bad apple</u>.

a) Using a suitable approximation, find the probability that none of the apples in the first crate are bad.

- The number of bad apples in each crate follows the binomial distribution B(150, 0.015). Since n is large, and p is small, the number of bad apples in each crate can be modelled by the random variable $X \sim \text{Po}(150 \times 0.015) = \text{Po}(2.25)$.

- So $P(X = 0) = \dfrac{e^{-2.25} \times 2.25^0}{0!} = e^{-2.25} = 0.10539... = \boxed{0.1054 \text{ (to 4 d.p.)}}$

b) Find the probability that more than 2 apples in the first crate are bad.

- You need to find $P(X > 2) = 1 - P(X \le 2)$.

- $P(X = 1) = \dfrac{e^{-2.25} \times 2.25^1}{1!} = e^{-2.25} \times 2.25 = 0.23714...$

- $P(X = 2) = \dfrac{e^{-2.25} \times 2.25^2}{2!} = \dfrac{e^{-2.25} \times 2.25^2}{2} = 0.26679...$

- So $P(X > 2) = 1 - P(X = 0) - P(X = 1) - P(X = 2)$
  $= 1 - 0.10539... - 0.23714... - 0.26679... = \boxed{0.3907 \text{ (to 4 d.p.)}}$

c) Find the probability that a second crate is opened.

- A second crate is opened if $X = 1$ or $X = 2$.

- $P(X = 1 \text{ or } X = 2) = 0.23714... + 0.26679...$
  $= 0.50394... = \boxed{0.5039 \text{ (to 4 d.p.)}}$

d) What is the probability of the restaurant owner buying the apples she needs from this farm?

- There are two ways the owner will buy apples from this farm:
  - **Either:** the first crate will contain no bad apples (probability = 0.10539...)
  - **Or:** the first crate will contain 1 or 2 bad apples **and** the second crate will contain 0 or 1 bad apples.

- Thinking about that second possibility...
  P(1st crate has 1 or 2 bad **and** 2nd crate has 0 or 1 bad)
  = P(1st crate has 1 or 2 bad) × P(2nd crate has 0 or 1 bad)
  = 0.50394... × (0.10539... + 0.23714...)
  = 0.17262...

- So putting all that together...
  P(restaurant owner buys from this farm) = 0.10539... + 0.17262...
  $= \boxed{0.2780 \text{ (to 4 d.p.)}}$

Tip: Since the bad apples are randomly distributed, the number of bad apples in the first crate does not affect the number in the second crate — so you can multiply the probabilities in the second step of d).

Example 3

Carol runs an online shop selling honeymoon getaways. She makes an average of 2 sales per day.

a) Assuming sales occur at random, find the probability that she sells at least 3 honeymoon getaways on any particular day.

- Sales of honeymoon getaways should occur singly. So if the random variable X is the number of honeymoon getaways sold in a day, you have all the conditions for a Poisson distribution.
- In fact, since the average number of sales per day is 2, $X \sim Po(2)$.
- $P(X \geq 3) = 1 - P(X < 3) = 1 - P(X \leq 2)$.
- From tables, $P(X \leq 2) = 0.6767$.
  So $P(X \geq 3) = 1 - 0.6767 = \boxed{0.3233}$

b) Find the probability that she sells at least 3 honeymoon getaways on at least 2 of the 7 days next week.

- This time, you have a fixed number (7) of trials, so this will **not** follow a Poisson distribution.
- In fact, all the conditions for a **binomial** distribution are satisfied. There is a **fixed number** of **independent** trials where there are only **two possible outcomes** ('sell at least 3 honeymoon getaways' or 'don't sell at least 3 honeymoon getaways'), and a **constant probability** of success (0.3233).
- So if the random variable Y represents the total number of 'successes' next week, then $Y \sim B(7, 0.3233)$.
- Now then... $P(Y \geq 2) = 1 - P(Y < 2) = 1 - P(Y = 0) - P(Y = 1)$.
- $P(Y = 0) = \binom{7}{0} \times 0.3233^0 \times (1 - 0.3233)^7$
  $= 0.6767^7 = 0.064979...$

- $P(Y = 1) = \binom{7}{1} \times 0.3233^1 \times (1 - 0.3233)^6$
  $= 7 \times 0.3233 \times 0.6767^6$
  $= 0.217310...$
- So $P(Y \geq 2) = 1 - 0.064979... - 0.217310... = \boxed{0.718 \text{ (to 3 sig. fig.)}}$

Tip: With a Poisson distribution, you're not counting the number of successes in a **fixed number of trials**, but the number of successes in a **fixed period**.

Tip: Here, a 'success' means a day on which Carol sells at least 3 honeymoon getaways.

Review Exercise — Chapter 2

Q1 If $X \sim \text{Po}(3.1)$, find (correct to 4 decimal places):
   a) $P(X = 2)$ b) $P(X = 1)$ c) $P(X = 0)$ d) $P(X < 3)$ e) $P(X \geq 3)$

Q2 If $X \sim \text{Po}(8.7)$, find (correct to 4 decimal places):
   a) $P(X = 2)$ b) $P(X = 1)$ c) $P(X = 0)$ d) $P(X < 3)$ e) $P(X \geq 3)$

Q3 For the following distributions, find: (i) $E(X)$, (ii) $\text{Var}(X)$, and (iii) the standard deviation of X.
   a) $\text{Po}(8)$ b) $\text{Po}(12.11)$ c) $\text{Po}(84.2227)$

Q4 For the following distributions, find: (i) $P(X \leq \mu)$ (ii) $P(X \leq \mu - \sigma)$
   a) $\text{Po}(9)$ b) $\text{Po}(4)$

Q5 Which of the following would follow a Poisson distribution? Explain your answers.
   a) The number of defective products coming off a factory's production line in one day if defective products occur at random at an average of 25 per week.
   b) The number of heads thrown using a coin in 25 tosses if the probability of getting a head is always 0.5.
   c) The number of people joining a post-office queue each minute during lunchtime if people arrive at an average rate of 3 every five minutes.
   d) The total number of spelling mistakes in a document if mistakes are randomly made at an average rate of 3 per page.

Q6 In a radioactive sample, atoms decay at an average rate of 2000 per hour.
   State how the following quantities are distributed, giving as much detail as possible.
   a) The number of atoms decaying per minute.
   b) The number of atoms decaying per day.

Q7 Atoms in one radioactive sample decay at an average rate of 60 per minute, while in another they decay at an average rate of 90 per minute.
   a) How would the total number of atoms decaying each minute be distributed?
   b) How would the total number of atoms decaying each hour be distributed?

Q8 If $X \sim \text{Po}(8)$, use Poisson tables to find:
   a) $P(X \leq 2)$ b) $P(X \leq 7)$ c) $P(X \leq 5)$ d) $P(X < 9)$ e) $P(X \geq 8)$
   f) $P(X > 1)$ g) $P(X > 7)$ h) $P(X = 6)$ i) $P(X = 4)$ j) $P(X = 3)$

Q9 Which of the following random variables could be approximated by a Poisson distribution? Where it is possible, state the Poisson distribution that could be used.
   a) $X \sim \text{B}(4, 0.4)$ b) $Y \sim \text{B}(700, 0.01)$ c) $W \sim \text{B}(850, 0.34)$
   d) $X \sim \text{B}(8, 0.1)$ e) $W \sim \text{B}(10\,000, 0.00001)$ f) $Y \sim \text{B}(80, 0.9)$

Q10 A gaggle of 100 geese is randomly scattered throughout a field measuring 10 m × 10 m.
   What is the probability that in a randomly selected square metre of field, I find:
   a) no geese?   b) 1 goose?   c) 2 geese?   d) more than 2 geese?

1 a) State two conditions needed for a Poisson distribution to be a suitable model for a quantity.

(2 marks)

   b) A birdwatcher knows that the number of chaffinches visiting a particular observation spot per hour follows a Poisson distribution with mean 7.

Find the probability that in a randomly chosen hour during the day:

   (i) fewer than 4 chaffinches visit the observation spot,

(2 marks)

   (ii) at least 7 chaffinches visit the observation spot,

(2 marks)

   (iii) exactly 9 chaffinches visit the observation spot.

(2 marks)

   c) The number of birds <u>other than</u> chaffinches visiting the same observation spot per hour can be modelled by the Poisson distribution Po(22).

Find the probability that exactly 3 birds (of any species) visit the observation spot in a random 15-minute period.

(4 marks)

2 The number of calls received at a call centre each hour can be modelled by a Poisson distribution with mean 20.

   a) Find the probability that in a random 30-minute period:

   (i) exactly 8 calls are received,

(3 marks)

   (ii) more than 8 calls are received.

(2 marks)

   b) For a Poisson distribution to be a suitable model, events have to occur independently. What is meant by "independently" in this context?

(1 mark)

3 A researcher has determined that ancient works of literature copied out in monasteries contain wrong letters scattered randomly throughout the text at a rate of 1 error in every 5 lines of text.

   a) In a document with 20 lines of text, find the probability that:

   (i) no errors were made,

(2 marks)

   (ii) more than 10 errors were made.

(2 marks)

   b) The number of errors in a document of 180 lines is represented by the random variable Y.

   (i) State the distribution of Y.

(1 mark)

   (ii) State the standard deviation of Y.

(1 mark)

4   When a particular engineer is called out to fix a fault, the probability of him being unable to fix the fault is always 0.02.

a)   The engineer's work is assessed after every 400 call-outs. The random variable X represents the number of faults the engineer is unable to fix over those 400 call-outs. Specify the statistical distribution that X will follow, stating the values of any parameters.

(2 marks)

b)   (i)   Under what conditions can a binomial distribution be approximated by a Poisson distribution?

(2 marks)

(ii)   Write down a Poisson distribution that could be used to approximate X.

(1 mark)

(iii)   Write down the mean and variance of your Poisson distribution.

(1 mark)

(iv)   Using your Poisson approximation, calculate the probability that the engineer will be unable to fix fewer than 10 faults over a period of 400 call-outs.

(2 marks)

5   The number of people per hour mistyping their passwords while trying to log in to a particular website is thought to follow a Poisson distribution. On average, it is assumed that 30 people per hour mistype their password while trying to log in.

a)   Find the probability that in a randomly chosen 10-minute period:
(i)   more than 10 people mistype their password,

(2 marks)

(ii)   at least 10 but no more than 15 people mistype their password.

(2 marks)

The number of people per hour (x) mistyping their passwords was counted during 24 consecutive hours. The results are summarised below.

$$\sum x = 752 \qquad \sum x^2 = 24\,338$$

b)   (i)   Calculate the mean and the variance of the x-values.

(3 marks)

(ii)   Explain why these results support the use of a Poisson distribution.

(1 mark)

(iii)   Using the mean you obtained in part b) (i) above, find the probability that exactly 30 people mistype their password in a randomly chosen hour.

(3 marks)

1. Probability Density Functions

You learnt all about probability functions for discrete random variables in S1. Probability density functions are the same sort of thing, but for continuous random variables — they give you the probability of a continuous random variable taking a value in a certain range.

Learning Objectives:

- Understand what is meant by a continuous random variable.
- Know the properties of probability density functions.
- Be able to find probabilities using probability density functions.

Probability density functions

Discrete random variables

Remember that with **discrete** random variables, like the ones you've seen in Chapters 1 and 2, there are **gaps** between the possible **values** that the random variable can take:

For example, if $X \sim$ **B(3, 0.4)**, then you know that X can only take the values **0**, **1**, **2** or **3**, and you could work out the probability of each value using the **probability function** (see page 8). You could even draw a graph of what this probability function looks like.

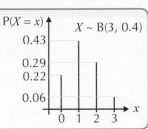

Continuous random variables

- Continuous random variables are similar to discrete random variables — but there is one important **difference**:

> A **continuous random variable** is a random variable which can take **any value** in a certain range.

- They represent things like length, height, weight, rainfall etc. — things that are measured on a **continuous** scale.

Tip: Remember... a continuous scale doesn't have 'gaps' between its possible values.

You can still draw a **graph** showing how likely a continuous random variable is to take values within its possible range. But instead of a series of bars, it will be a **continuous line**.

- These graphs are called **probability density functions** (or **p.d.f.s**). Here, **f(x)** is a p.d.f.
- The **area under** a p.d.f. between two points shows the **probability** that the random variable will take a value in that **range**. For example, the **shaded area** shows the probability that this continuous random variable will take a value between **1** and **2**.

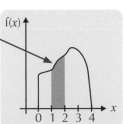

Tip: Remember from C2 that the area under the graph of a function is found by integrating the function.

Tip: The p.d.f. for the normal distribution $X \sim N(\mu, \sigma^2)$ is:

$$f(x) = \frac{1}{\sigma\sqrt{2\pi}} e^{-\frac{1}{2}\left(\frac{x-\mu}{\sigma}\right)^2}$$

Unfortunately, it's really awkward to integrate, which is why you used tables in S1 to find probabilities for the normal distribution.

Tip: See below for more about the properties of a p.d.f.

You saw the graphs of some p.d.f.s back in S1 when you did **normal distributions**. The formula for the p.d.f. of the normal distribution $N(\mu, \sigma^2)$ is given in your exam formula book. In theory, you could integrate it to work out the **probability** of a **normally distributed** random variable taking a value in a certain range (but see the tip in the margin).

For example, the numbers of octaves that cast members in a musical can reach with their voices are **normally distributed** with a mean of 2.2 octaves and a standard deviation of 0.3 octaves.

This normal distribution has a probability density function f(x) which looks like this:

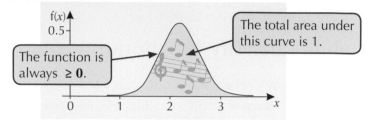

The total area under this curve is 1.

The function is always ≥ 0.

The **most likely** number of octaves is around the **mean** at 2.2 — because that's where the **p.d.f.** is **greatest**.
Values **further** from the mean are **less likely** since the p.d.f. drops away.

The probability that a cast member can reach between 2 and 3 octaves is given by the **area under** the p.d.f. **between** 2 and 3.

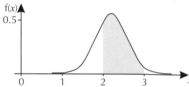

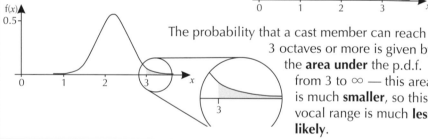

The probability that a cast member can reach 3 octaves or more is given by the **area under** the p.d.f. from 3 to ∞ — this area is much **smaller**, so this vocal range is much **less likely**.

Properties of a p.d.f.

Tip: Where a formula relating to a discrete random variable involves a summation (Σ), the equivalent formula relating to a continuous random variable involves an integral.

For example, $\int_{-\infty}^{\infty} f(x)\,dx = 1$ is the 'continuous equivalent' of $\sum p_i = 1$.

Because (i) **probabilities** can **never** take **negative** values,

and (ii) the **total probability** of a random variable taking a value is **1**,

a p.d.f. **always** has the following **properties**:

For a **continuous random variable** X, with **probability density function** f(x):

- **f(x) ≥ 0 for all $x \in \mathbb{R}$**

  — probabilities can never be negative.

- $\int_{-\infty}^{\infty} \mathbf{f(x)\,dx = 1}$

  — the total probability (the area under the whole curve) must be 1.

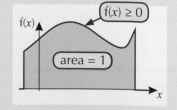

$f(x) \geq 0$

area = 1

You need to be able to decide whether a function is a p.d.f. or not by using the **properties** of p.d.f.s on p50.

Examples

Decide whether the following are p.d.f.s:

a) $f(x) = \begin{cases} x^4 & -1 \le x \le 1 \\ 0 & \textbf{otherwise} \end{cases}$

- First check that $f(x) \ge 0$ for all $x \in \mathbb{R}$ — a sketch of the p.d.f. will help:

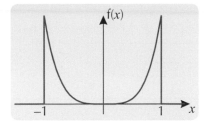

So you can see from the sketch that this function is **non-negative** for all x.

- Now you only need to check that the total probability is 1:

> Split up the integral into the different ranges given by the piecewise function.

$$\int_{-\infty}^{\infty} f(x)\,dx = \int_{-\infty}^{-1} f(x)\,dx + \int_{-1}^{1} f(x)\,dx + \int_{1}^{\infty} f(x)\,dx$$

> The integrals where the p.d.f. is zero will 'disappear'.

$$= \int_{-\infty}^{-1} 0\,dx + \int_{-1}^{1} x^4\,dx + \int_{1}^{\infty} 0\,dx = \int_{-1}^{1} x^4\,dx$$

$$= \left[\frac{x^5}{5}\right]_{-1}^{1} = \left(\frac{1^5}{5}\right) - \left(\frac{(-1)^5}{5}\right) = \frac{1}{5} + \frac{1}{5} = \frac{2}{5}$$

The total probability is **not 1**, so this function is **not a p.d.f.**

b) $f(x) = \begin{cases} \frac{1}{12}(3 - x) & -2 \le x \le 2 \\ 0 & \textbf{otherwise} \end{cases}$

- First check that $f(x) \ge 0$ for all $x \in \mathbb{R}$:

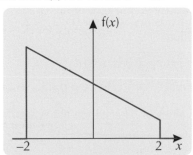

So this function is **non-negative** for all x.

Tip: P.d.f.s are often defined 'piecewise' (bit by bit). You might have come across probability functions like this for discrete random variables in S1 — it just means you have to use a different formula for different values of x.

Tip: If you're struggling to work out whether the curve stays positive, try sketching it in the given range.

Tip: When the p.d.f. is equal to zero, the area under the p.d.f. will also be zero — so you only need to integrate the non-zero bits of the function.

- Now you only need to check that the total probability is 1:

$$\int_{-\infty}^{\infty} f(x)\,dx = \int_{-\infty}^{-2} f(x)\,dx + \int_{-2}^{2} f(x)\,dx + \int_{2}^{\infty} f(x)\,dx$$

$$= \int_{-2}^{2} \tfrac{1}{12}(3 - x)\,dx$$

$$= \tfrac{1}{12}\Big[3x - \tfrac{x^2}{2}\Big]_{-2}^{2}$$

$$= \tfrac{1}{12}[(6 - 2) - (-6 - 2)] = \tfrac{1}{12}[12] = 1$$

> Again, you can ignore the integrals where the p.d.f. is zero.

The p.d.f. is non-negative for all x and the total probability **is 1**, so this function **is a p.d.f.**

Examples

Decide whether the following are p.d.f.s:

a) $f(x) = \begin{cases} \dfrac{1}{24}(x - 2) & 1 \le x \le 9 \\ 0 & \text{otherwise} \end{cases}$

- First check that $f(x) \ge 0$ for all $x \in \mathbb{R}$ — again, draw a sketch:

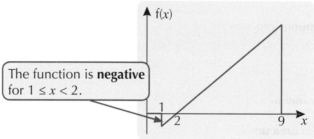

> The function is **negative** for $1 \le x < 2$.

So $f(x)$ is **not a p.d.f.**, as it is **negative** for some values of x.

b) $f(x) = \begin{cases} kx & \text{for } -2 \le x \le 2 \\ 0 & \text{otherwise} \end{cases}$

- If k is positive, then $f(x)$ is negative for $-2 \le x < 0$, so k cannot be positive.

- If k is negative, then $f(x)$ is negative for $0 < x \le 2$, so k cannot be negative.

- If $k = 0$, then $\displaystyle\int_{-\infty}^{\infty} f(x)\,dx = \int_{-\infty}^{\infty} 0\,dx = 0$.
  This integral must equal 1 for $f(x)$ to be a p.d.f., so k cannot be 0.

There are no possible values of k for which $f(x)$ is a p.d.f.

So $f(x)$ is not a p.d.f.

You can use the property $\int_{-\infty}^{\infty} f(x)\,dx = 1$ to find **unknown values** in a p.d.f.

Examples

a) **The continuous random variable X has the probability density function:**
$$f(x) = \begin{cases} kx & 0 < x < 4 \\ 0 & \text{otherwise} \end{cases}$$
Find the value of k.

Tip: You've been told that this function **is** a p.d.f. so you don't need to check that $f(x) \geq 0$.

- The total **area under** the p.d.f. must equal **1**.
  So just integrate the function to find the area in terms of k.

$$\int_0^4 kx\,dx = \left[\frac{kx^2}{2}\right]_0^4 = \left(\frac{k \times 4^2}{2}\right) - \left(\frac{k \times 0^2}{2}\right) = 8k$$

- You could also just use a sketch of $f(x)$ and work out the **area of the triangle**, but integrating will be easier when the functions get more complicated.

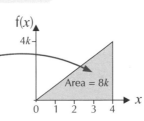

- Use the fact that the area **equals 1** to find k.

  So $8k = 1$, which gives $\boxed{k = \dfrac{1}{8} = 0.125}$

b) **The continuous random variable X has the probability density function:**
$$f(x) = \begin{cases} 2k & 0 < x < 4 \\ k(4x - 6) & 4 \leq x < 6 \\ 0 & \text{otherwise} \end{cases}$$
Find the value of k.

Tip: This continuous random variable is defined by more than one 'non-zero piece'. It just means there are different formulas for different ranges. You'll need to integrate each piece separately.

- The total **area under** the p.d.f. must equal **1**.
  So just integrate the function to find the area.

Total area $= \int_{-\infty}^{\infty} f(x)\,dx$

You need to integrate **both** non-zero bits of the 'piecewise' p.d.f. separately between their limits and **add them together**.

$$= \int_0^4 2k\,dx + \int_4^6 k(4x - 6)\,dx$$

$$= [2kx]_0^4 + [k(2x^2 - 6x)]_4^6$$
$$= [(2k \times 4) - (2k \times 0)]$$
$$\quad + [k(2 \times 6^2 - 6 \times 6) - k(2 \times 4^2 - 6 \times 4)]$$
$$= 8k + 36k - 8k = 36k$$

- Let this expression for the area **equal 1** to find k.

  So $36k = 1$, which means $\boxed{k = \dfrac{1}{36}}$

Q1 Hint: When the p.d.f. has several 'pieces', you just need to sketch each separate piece for the relevant range and then join the pieces up.

Q1   (i)   For each function f(x) below decide whether or not it is a valid p.d.f. Explain your answer.

      (ii)   If it is a valid p.d.f. then sketch its graph.

a) $f(x) = \begin{cases} \frac{1}{2}x^2 & 0 < x < 2 \\ 0 & \text{otherwise} \end{cases}$

b) $f(x) = \begin{cases} \frac{3}{4}x^2 & 1 < x < 2 \\ 0 & \text{otherwise} \end{cases}$

c) $f(x) = \begin{cases} 1 - \frac{1}{2}x & 0 < x < 2 \\ 0 & \text{otherwise} \end{cases}$

d) $f(x) = \begin{cases} \frac{1}{4}x^3 & 0 < x < 2 \\ 1 & \text{otherwise} \end{cases}$

e) $f(x) = \begin{cases} x^2 + 5 & 1 < x < 2 \\ 0 & \text{otherwise} \end{cases}$

f) $f(x) = \begin{cases} \frac{2}{9}(3x - x^2) & 0 < x < 3 \\ 0 & \text{otherwise} \end{cases}$

g) $f(x) = \begin{cases} \frac{1}{3} & 0 < x < 1 \\ x^2 - \frac{5}{3} & 1 \leq x < 2 \\ 0 & \text{otherwise} \end{cases}$

h) $f(x) = \begin{cases} 0.2 & 0 < x < 1 \\ 0.5x^2 & 1 \leq x < 3 \\ 0 & \text{otherwise} \end{cases}$

Q2   The continuous random variable X has the probability density function f(x). Find the value of k for each definition of f(x) below.

a) $f(x) = \begin{cases} kx^2 & 1 < x < 2 \\ 0 & \text{otherwise} \end{cases}$

b) $f(x) = \begin{cases} kx^3 & 0 < x < 2 \\ 0 & \text{otherwise} \end{cases}$

c) $f(x) = \begin{cases} k & 0 < x < 1 \\ kx & 1 \leq x < 2 \\ 0 & \text{otherwise} \end{cases}$

d) $f(x) = \begin{cases} \frac{1}{3} & 0 < x < 1 \\ k(1 - x^2) & 1 \leq x < 2 \\ 0 & \text{otherwise} \end{cases}$

Finding probabilities from probability density functions

Remember from p49 that probabilities are represented by **areas under** p.d.f.s.
Now then... areas under curves can be found by **integrating**, so if X has p.d.f. $f(x)$:

$$P(a < X < b) = \int_a^b f(x)\, dx$$

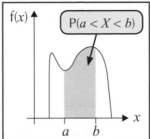

Notice a couple of things...

- The **probability** of a continuous random variable, X, equalling any **single value**, $P(X = x)$, is always **zero** because the area under a graph at a single point always equals zero.

  So it only makes sense to find the probability of X taking a value **within a particular range**.

- This also means that for any continuous random variable, X, and any k:

$$P(X < k) = P(X \leq k)$$

Tip: Remember that
$$\int_a^a f(x)\, dx = 0$$
for any value of a.

Tip: Remember that:
$P(X \leq k)$
$= P(X < k) + P(X = k)$
(since the events $X < k$ and $X = k$ are mutually exclusive).
So, since $P(X = k) = 0$:
$P(X \leq k) = P(X < k) + 0$
$= P(X < k)$

Example 1

The continuous random variable X has the probability density function:

$$f(x) = \begin{cases} \dfrac{3 - x}{4} & 0 < x < 2 \\ 0 & \text{otherwise} \end{cases}$$

a) **Sketch $f(x)$.**

The function $\dfrac{3 - x}{4}$ can be written as $\dfrac{3}{4} - \dfrac{1}{4}x$ — so the graph looks like this:

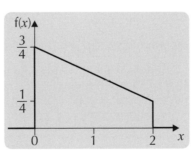

b) **Find $P(0 < x < 1)$.**

You just need to find the area under the p.d.f. between 0 and 1.

Integrate:

$$P(0 < x < 1) = \int_0^1 \frac{3 - x}{4}\, dx = \frac{1}{4}\int_0^1 (3 - x)\, dx = \frac{1}{4}\left[3x - \frac{x^2}{2}\right]_0^1$$
$$= \frac{1}{4}\left[\left(3(1) - \frac{(1)^2}{2}\right) - \left(3(0) - \frac{(0)^2}{2}\right)\right]$$
$$= \frac{1}{4}\left[\frac{5}{2} - 0\right] = \frac{5}{8}$$

Tip: You could also work out the area using the formula for the area of a trapezium.

Example 2

The continuous random variable X has the probability density function:

$$f(x) = \begin{cases} x^2 + a & 0 \leq x \leq 1 \\ 0 & \text{otherwise} \end{cases}$$

a) Sketch f(x), and find the value of a.

- The non-zero bit of the p.d.f. is a quadratic function, and so f(x) looks like this:

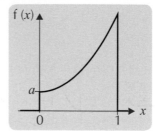

- The area under the graph must equal **1**, so integrate:

$$\int_{-\infty}^{\infty} f(x)\,dx = \int_{-\infty}^{0} f(x)\,dx + \int_{0}^{1} f(x)\,dx + \int_{1}^{\infty} f(x)\,dx$$
$$= \int_{0}^{1}(x^2 + a)\,dx$$
$$= \left[\frac{x^3}{3} + ax\right]_0^1 = \left(\frac{1}{3} + a\right)$$

So $\frac{1}{3} + a = 1 \Rightarrow \boxed{a = \frac{2}{3}}$

b) Find $P(X > \frac{1}{2})$.

Integrate again — this time between $x = \frac{1}{2}$ and $x = 1$.

$$P\left(X > \frac{1}{2}\right) = \int_{\frac{1}{2}}^{1}\left(x^2 + \frac{2}{3}\right)dx$$
$$= \left[\frac{x^3}{3} + \frac{2}{3}x\right]_{\frac{1}{2}}^{1}$$
$$= \left(\frac{1}{3} + \frac{2}{3}\right) - \left(\frac{1}{24} + \frac{1}{3}\right)$$
$$= \frac{15}{24} = \boxed{\frac{5}{8}}$$

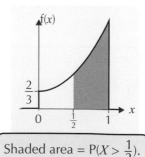

Shaded area = $P(X > \frac{1}{2})$.

Tip: You don't need to bother with the integral $\int_{1}^{\infty} f(x)\,dx$ because you can see from the definition and from the graph that the p.d.f. is zero, so the integral will also be zero.

Example 3

The continuous random variable X has the probability density function:

$$f(x) = \begin{cases} 3x^2 + 1 & 0 < x \leq \frac{1}{2} \\ \frac{3}{4} & \frac{1}{2} < x < 1 \\ 0 & \text{otherwise} \end{cases}$$

a) Sketch f(x).

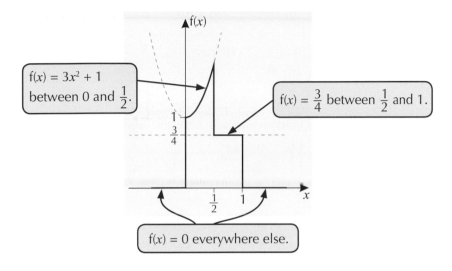

f(x) = $3x^2$ + 1 between 0 and $\frac{1}{2}$.

f(x) = $\frac{3}{4}$ between $\frac{1}{2}$ and 1.

f(x) = 0 everywhere else.

b) Find $P\left(\frac{1}{4} < x < \frac{3}{4}\right)$.

- You need to find the area under the p.d.f. between $\frac{1}{4}$ and $\frac{3}{4}$ — but the formula used to define the p.d.f. changes between these two values, so you'll need to **split** the area up into two bits, find the area of these bits separately, and **add** the results together.

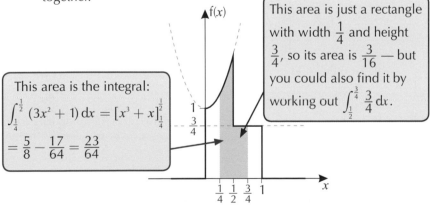

This area is the integral:
$$\int_{\frac{1}{4}}^{\frac{1}{2}} (3x^2 + 1)\,dx = [x^3 + x]_{\frac{1}{4}}^{\frac{1}{2}}$$
$$= \frac{5}{8} - \frac{17}{64} = \frac{23}{64}$$

This area is just a rectangle with width $\frac{1}{4}$ and height $\frac{3}{4}$, so its area is $\frac{3}{16}$ — but you could also find it by working out $\int_{\frac{1}{2}}^{\frac{3}{4}} \frac{3}{4}\,dx$.

- **Add** the areas together to get the total probability:

$$P\left(\frac{1}{4} < x < \frac{3}{4}\right) = \frac{23}{64} + \frac{3}{16} = \frac{35}{64}$$

Tip: Remember that
$$P\left(\frac{1}{4} < X < \frac{3}{4}\right)$$
$$= P\left(\frac{1}{4} < X < \frac{1}{2}\right)$$
$$+ P\left(\frac{1}{2} < X < \frac{3}{4}\right)$$

Q1   The continuous random variable X has the probability density function:

$$f(x) = \begin{cases} 1 - \frac{1}{2}x & 0 < x < 2 \\ 0 & \text{otherwise} \end{cases}$$

a) Find $P(0 < X < 1)$.   b) Find $P(\frac{1}{2} < X < 1)$.

Q2   The continuous random variable X has the probability density function:

$$f(x) = \begin{cases} 2(1 - x) & 0 < x < 1 \\ 0 & \text{otherwise} \end{cases}$$

Find $P(0.25 < X < 0.75)$.

Q3   The continuous random variable X has the probability density function:

$$f(x) = \begin{cases} \frac{1}{4}x^3 & 0 < x < 2 \\ 0 & \text{otherwise} \end{cases}$$

a) Find $P(X < 1)$.   b) Find $P(1 < X < 2)$.

Q4   The continuous random variable X has the probability density function:

$$f(x) = \begin{cases} \frac{2}{9}(3x - x^2) & 0 < x < 3 \\ 0 & \text{otherwise} \end{cases}$$

Find $P(1 < X < 2)$.

Q5   The continuous random variable X has the probability density function:

$$f(x) = \begin{cases} \frac{2}{5} & 0 < x < 1 \\ \frac{2}{5}x & 1 \leq x < 2 \\ 0 & \text{otherwise} \end{cases}$$

a) Find $P(X < 1)$.   b) Find $P(\frac{1}{2} < X < \frac{3}{2})$.

Q6   The continuous random variable X has the probability density function:

$$f(x) = \begin{cases} \frac{1}{3} & 0 < x < 1 \\ \frac{1}{3}(2x - 1) & 1 \leq x < 2 \\ 0 & \text{otherwise} \end{cases}$$

a) Find $P(0 < X < 1.5)$.   b) Find $P(X = 1)$.

2. Cumulative Distribution Functions

The cumulative distribution function of a continuous random variable gives the probability that it will take a value less than or equal to a particular value. Just like it did with discrete random variables.

Cumulative distribution functions

You met cumulative distribution functions (c.d.f.s) for discrete random variables in S1. A c.d.f. for a **continuous** random variable is the same kind of thing — a '**running total**' of probability.

> If X is a continuous random variable with **p.d.f.** f(x),
> then its **cumulative distribution function**, **F(x)**, is given by:
>
> $$F(x_0) = P(X \le x_0) = \int_{-\infty}^{x_0} f(x)\,dx$$

C.d.f.s are usually labelled with capital letters, e.g. **F(x)** — unlike p.d.f.s, which are usually labelled with lower case letters, e.g. **f(x)**.

There are **2 properties** of c.d.f.s which will help you to recognise them:

- **$0 \le F(x) \le 1$**
  — all probabilities are ≥ 0 and the total probability is 1.

- F(x) is **non-decreasing** and **continuous**
  — all probabilities are ≥ 0 so F(x) cannot decrease as x increases.

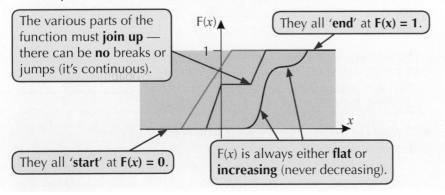

The various parts of the function must **join up** — there can be **no** breaks or jumps (it's continuous).

They all 'start' at **F(x) = 0**.

They all 'end' at **F(x) = 1**.

F(x) is always either **flat** or **increasing** (never decreasing).

Learning Objectives:

- Be able to use the p.d.f. of a continuous random variable to find its c.d.f., and vice versa.

- Be able to find probabilities using a c.d.f.

Tip: Remember that a discrete random variable, X, has a c.d.f. F(x) where $F(x) = P(X \le x)$.

Tip: In the definition of a c.d.f. of a continuous random variable, the limit of the integral is x_0. This is so there's no confusion between the limit and the variable inside the integral, x.

You might sometimes see $F(x) = \int_{-\infty}^{x} f(t)\,dt$ instead, for the same reason.

Tip: You can think about the properties of a c.d.f. another way...

$F(x_0)$ shows the area under a p.d.f. to the left of x_0.

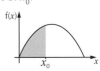

- This area will always be between 0 and 1.

- As x_0 increases, the area under the p.d.f. to the left of x_0 cannot decrease.

- So F(x) is a non-decreasing function between 0 and 1.

Examples

A continuous random variable X has p.d.f. $f(x) = \begin{cases} 3x^2 & \text{for } 0 \le x \le 1 \\ 0 & \text{otherwise} \end{cases}$

a) Find F(0.5).

The graph of the p.d.f. is shown on the right. To find F(0.5), integrate between $-\infty$ and 0.5:

$$F(0.5) = \int_{-\infty}^{0.5} f(x)\,dx = \int_{-\infty}^{0} f(x)\,dx + \int_{0}^{0.5} f(x)\,dx$$

$$= \int_{-\infty}^{0} 0\,dx + \int_{0}^{0.5} 3x^2\,dx = 0 + [x^3]_0^{0.5} = (0.5)^3 = \boxed{0.125}$$

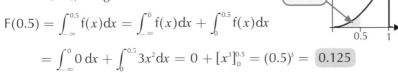

b) Find $F(x_0)$ for some number x_0, where $0 \leq x_0 \leq 1$.

To find $F(x_0)$, integrate between $-\infty$ and x_0:

$$F(x_0) = \int_{-\infty}^{x_0} f(x)dx = \int_{-\infty}^{0} f(x)dx + \int_{0}^{x_0} f(x)dx$$

$$= \int_{-\infty}^{0} 0\,dx + \int_{0}^{x_0} 3x^2\,dx = 0 + [x^3]_0^{x_0} = x_0^3$$

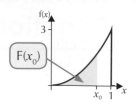

$F(x_0)$

Tip: Notice that $F(0) = 0$ and $F(1) = 1$ — so your c.d.f. has the correct minimum and maximum values (see p59).

The example above found $F(x)$ at a **particular point** — but exam questions will often give you the p.d.f. and ask you to define the c.d.f. **fully**.

You'll need to make sure that:

- You define $F(x)$ for **all** values of x — even when $f(x)$ is 0.
- There are no '**jumps**' (i.e. $F(x)$ is continuous) — if you've got a p.d.f. that's defined piecewise then the value of $F(x)$ at the **end** of one interval should be the same as its value at the **start** of the next.

When the p.d.f. is only defined by one 'piece' (and 0 otherwise) it's easy:

Example 1

A continuous random variable X has probability density function $f(x)$, where:

$$f(x) = \begin{cases} 2x - 2 & \text{for } 1 \leq x \leq 2 \\ 0 & \text{otherwise} \end{cases}$$

Find the cumulative distribution function of X.

- All c.d.f.s must 'start' at $F(x) = 0$ and 'end' at $F(x) = 1$ (see p59).

  Here, $f(x) = 0$ for all $x < 1$, and so $F(x) = 0$ for all $x < 1$.
  Similarly, $f(x) = 0$ for all $x > 2$, and so $F(x) = 1$ for all $x > 2$.

Tip: It sometimes helps to draw the p.d.f. Here, it looks like this:

  So the c.d.f. looks like this either side of $1 \leq x \leq 2$ and you just need to find out what happens in the **middle** (remember it can do anything **except** decrease and jump or break.)

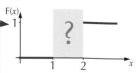

- To find $F(x)$ in the range $1 \leq x \leq 2$, you need to integrate between $-\infty$ and x.
  To avoid having x as the both limit of the integral and the variable you're integrating with respect to, it helps to use t in the integral instead of x.

Tip: The variable t will disappear when you put the limits in.

  For $1 \leq x \leq 2$:

  $$F(x) = \int_{-\infty}^{1} f(t)\,dt + \int_{1}^{x} f(t)\,dt = \int_{-\infty}^{1} 0\,dt + \int_{1}^{x} (2t - 2)\,dt$$
  $$= [t^2 - 2t]_1^x = x^2 - 2x - (1 - 2) = x^2 - 2x + 1$$

Tip: Notice that all the 'pieces' of the c.d.f. join up. This is one of the properties of a c.d.f. and it'll always happen as long as you remember to integrate from $-\infty$.

But you **don't** always need to **write down** the terms like

$$\int_{-\infty}^{1} 0\,dt$$

(because you know they're going to disappear).

- So putting all this together:

  $$F(x) = \begin{cases} 0 & \text{for } x < 1 \\ x^2 - 2x + 1 & \text{for } 1 \leq x \leq 2 \\ 1 & \text{for } x > 2 \end{cases}$$

  $F(x)$ is defined for all values of x and the 'pieces' join together with 'no jumps' — i.e. $F(1) = 0$ using both the first and second 'pieces', and $F(2) = 1$ using both the second and third.

If the p.d.f. is defined by **more than one** 'piece', you need to be careful with the c.d.f. where the 'pieces' **join**. There are two methods for working out the c.d.f. correctly.

Tip: For a different way of making sure the 'pieces' join up, involving constants of integration, see p62.

Example 2

Find the cumulative distribution function of X, whose probability density function is

$$f(x) = \begin{cases} 0.5 & \text{for } 3 \leq x < 4 \\ 1.5 - 0.25x & \text{for } 4 \leq x \leq 6 \\ 0 & \text{otherwise} \end{cases}$$

The graph of this **p.d.f.** is on the right. There'll be **4 pieces** to your c.d.f.

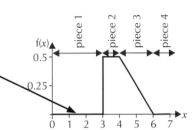

- For $x < 3$, $P(X \leq x) = 0$ — i.e. $F(x) = 0$.

- To join on from this smoothly, $F(3)$ must be equal to 0.

- Then there are **two ways** to make sure the middle pieces join on smoothly:

Tip: Don't forget about 'piece 1' of the p.d.f., where $F(x) = 0$ for all values of x less than 3.

(1) **Always start your integral at $-\infty$:**

For **piece 2**, when $3 \leq x < 4$:   = F(3)

$$F(x) = \int_{-\infty}^{x} f(t)\,dt = \int_{-\infty}^{3} f(t)\,dt + \int_{3}^{x} f(t)\,dt$$

$$= F(3) + \int_{3}^{x} 0.5\,dt$$

$$= 0 + [0.5t]_{3}^{x}$$

$$= \mathbf{0.5x - 1.5}$$

So for the next piece to join on smoothly, you must have $F(4) = 0.5 \times 4 - 1.5 = 2 - 1.5 = 0.5$.

For **piece 3**, when $4 \leq x \leq 6$:

= F(4)

$$F(x) = \int_{-\infty}^{4} f(t)\,dt + \int_{4}^{x} f(t)\,dt = F(4) + \int_{4}^{x} f(t)\,dt$$

$$= 0.5 + \int_{4}^{x} (1.5 - 0.25t)\,dt$$

Because F(4) = 0.5

$$= 0.5 + [1.5t - 0.125t^2]_{4}^{x}$$

$$= 0.5 + (1.5x - 0.125x^2) - (6 - 2)$$

$$= \mathbf{1.5x - 0.125x^2 - 3.5}$$

② **Use an indefinite integral** and choose the **constant of integration** so that the join is 'smooth'.

For **piece 2**, when $3 \leq x < 4$:

$$F(x) = \int f(x)\,dx = \int 0.5\,dx = 0.5x + k_1$$

But $F(3) = 1.5 + k_1 = 0$ (to join the first piece of c.d.f. smoothly). So $k_1 = -1.5$, which gives $\mathbf{F(x) = 0.5x - 1.5}$.

For **piece 3**, when $4 \leq x \leq 6$:

$$\begin{aligned} F(x) = \int f(x)\,dx &= \int (1.5 - 0.25x)\,dx \\ &= 1.5x - 0.125x^2 + k_2 \end{aligned}$$

Now find k_2 so that these two pieces join **smoothly** at $x = 4$.
$F(4) = 0.5 \times 4 - 1.5 = 0.5$ (using 'piece 2')
$ = 1.5 \times 4 - 0.125 \times 4^2 + k_2 = 4 + k_2$ (using 'piece 3')
This means $0.5 = 4 + k_2$, or $k_2 = -3.5$.
So $\mathbf{F(x) = 1.5x - 0.125x^2 - 3.5}$.

Notice that both of these methods give you the same answer.

Now, all that's left is '**piece 4**' where $x > 6$:
A c.d.f. always ends up at 1, so for $x > 6$, $F(x) = F(6) = 1$ — but check that this makes a smooth join with the previous part of the c.d.f.
Using $F(x) = 1.5x - 0.125x^2 - 3.5$ gives $F(6) = 9 - 4.5 - 3.5 = \mathbf{1}$, so it's fine.

Put the bits together to get:

$$F(x) = \begin{cases} 0 & \text{for } x < 3 \\ 0.5x - 1.5 & \text{for } 3 \leq x < 4 \\ 1.5x - 0.125x^2 - 3.5 & \text{for } 4 \leq x \leq 6 \\ 1 & \text{for } x > 6 \end{cases}$$

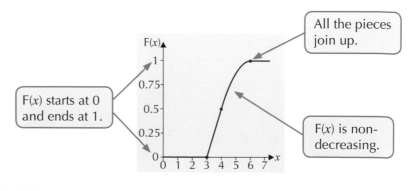

All the pieces join up.

$F(x)$ starts at 0 and ends at 1.

$F(x)$ is non-decreasing.

Exercise 2.1

Q1 Decide whether each of the following functions is a valid c.d.f., giving a reason for your answer.

a) $F(x) = \begin{cases} 0 & x < 0 \\ \frac{1}{2}(2 - x^2) & 0 \le x \le 2 \\ 1 & x > 2 \end{cases}$

b) $F(x) = \begin{cases} 0 & x < -\frac{1}{3} \\ 1 + 3x & -\frac{1}{3} \le x \le 0 \\ 1 & x > 0 \end{cases}$

c) $F(x) = \begin{cases} 0 & x < 0 \\ 2x - 2x^2 & 0 \le x \le 1 \\ 1 & x > 1 \end{cases}$

Q2 For the following p.d.f.s, f(x), find the corresponding c.d.f., F(x):

a) $f(x) = \begin{cases} 1 - \frac{1}{2}x & 0 \le x \le 2 \\ 0 & \text{otherwise} \end{cases}$

b) $f(x) = \begin{cases} 2(1 - x) & 0 \le x \le 1 \\ 0 & \text{otherwise} \end{cases}$

c) $f(x) = \begin{cases} \frac{3}{7}x^2 & 1 \le x \le 2 \\ 0 & \text{otherwise} \end{cases}$

d) $f(x) = \begin{cases} \frac{1}{4}(6x^2 - 3x^3) & 0 \le x \le 2 \\ 0 & \text{otherwise} \end{cases}$

e) $f(x) = \begin{cases} \frac{2}{9}(3x - x^2) & 0 \le x \le 3 \\ 0 & \text{otherwise} \end{cases}$

Q3 For the following p.d.f.s, f(x), find the corresponding c.d.f., F(x):

a) $f(x) = \begin{cases} \frac{2}{5} & 0 \le x < 1 \\ \frac{2}{5}x & 1 \le x \le 2 \\ 0 & \text{otherwise} \end{cases}$

b) $f(x) = \begin{cases} \frac{1}{3} & 0 < x < 1 \\ \frac{1}{3}(2x - 1) & 1 \le x < 2 \\ 0 & \text{otherwise} \end{cases}$

c) $f(x) = \begin{cases} \frac{1}{3} & 0 \le x < 1 \\ -\frac{1}{2}(1 - x^2) & 1 \le x \le 2 \\ 0 & \text{otherwise} \end{cases}$

Finding probability density functions by differentiating

To find a c.d.f. from a p.d.f., you **integrate**, so it makes sense that if you already know the c.d.f., you can **differentiate** to find the p.d.f.

$$f(x) = \frac{d}{dx}(F(x))$$

Examples

Find the p.d.f. of the continuous random variable X with c.d.f. $F(x)$, where

$$F(x) = \begin{cases} 0 & \text{for } x < 0 \\ \frac{1}{2}(3x - x^3) & \text{for } 0 \le x \le 1 \\ 1 & \text{for } x > 1 \end{cases}$$

Differentiate each 'piece' of the c.d.f. separately to find the p.d.f.:

$$\frac{d}{dx}\left(\frac{1}{2}(3x - x^3)\right) = \frac{d}{dx}\left(\frac{3}{2}x - \frac{x^3}{2}\right) = \frac{3}{2} - \frac{3}{2}x^2$$

$$f(x) = \frac{dF(x)}{dx} = \begin{cases} 0 & x < 0 \\ \frac{3}{2} - \frac{3}{2}x^2 & 0 \le x \le 1 \\ 0 & x > 1 \end{cases} = \begin{cases} \frac{3}{2} - \frac{3}{2}x^2 & \text{for } 0 \le x \le 1 \\ 0 & \text{otherwise} \end{cases}$$

$$\frac{d}{dx}(0) = \frac{d}{dx}(1) = 0$$

Exercise 2.2

Q1 For each c.d.f. $F(x)$ below, find the p.d.f. $f(x)$.

a) $F(x) = \begin{cases} 0 & x < 0 \\ 3x^2 - 2x^3 & 0 \le x \le 1 \\ 1 & x > 1 \end{cases}$

b) $F(x) = \begin{cases} 0 & x < 0 \\ \frac{1}{4}(x^3 + 3x^2) & 0 \le x \le 1 \\ 1 & x > 1 \end{cases}$

c) $F(x) = \begin{cases} 0 & x < 0 \\ \frac{1}{4}x & 0 \le x < 1 \\ \frac{1}{20}x^4 + \frac{1}{5} & 1 \le x \le 2 \\ 1 & x > 2 \end{cases}$

Q2 For each c.d.f. $F(x)$ below, find the p.d.f. $f(x)$ and sketch its graph.

a) $F(x) = \begin{cases} 0 & x < 1 \\ \frac{1}{3}x^2 - \frac{1}{3} & 1 \le x \le 2 \\ 1 & x > 2 \end{cases}$

b) $F(x) = \begin{cases} 0 & x < 0 \\ \frac{1}{3}x & 0 \le x < 2 \\ \frac{2x}{3} - \frac{x^2}{12} - \frac{1}{3} & 2 \le x \le 4 \\ 1 & x > 4 \end{cases}$

Finding probabilities using a cumulative distribution function

Tip: The ideas covered in this topic are the same ones you've already used when finding probabilities with the binomial and Poisson tables. (Remember — binomial and Poisson tables show c.d.f.s.)

It's really easy to work out a probability of the form $P(X \leq x_0)$ with a c.d.f. — you just put the value of x_0 into F(x). But you can easily work out the **probability** of a continuous random variable falling within other **ranges** too.

Example 1

The cumulative distribution function F(x) of the continuous random variable X is given below.

$$F(x) = \begin{cases} 0 & x < 0 \\ 0.5(3x - x^3) & 0 \leq x \leq 1 \\ 1 & x > 1 \end{cases}$$

Find:

a) $P(X \leq 0.5)$

This one's easy — just put 0.5 into F(x).
0.5 is between 0 and 1 so use the middle 'piece' of the c.d.f.

$P(X \leq 0.5) = F(0.5) = 0.5 \times (3 \times 0.5 - 0.5^3) = \boxed{0.6875}$

b) $P(X > 0.25)$

The c.d.f. only tells you the probability of X being less than or equal to a value, but you can use the fact that the total probability is 1:

$P(X > 0.25) = 1 - P(X \leq 0.25)$ ◄— $\boxed{P(X > x) = 1 - P(X \leq x)}$
$= 1 - F(0.25)$
$= 1 - 0.5 \times (3 \times 0.25 - 0.25^3)$ ◄— $\boxed{\text{Use the formula for F(x)}}$
$= 1 - 0.3671... = \boxed{0.633 \text{ (to 3 d.p.)}}$

c) $P(0.1 \leq X \leq 0.2)$

This is the probability that X is less than or equal to 0.2 but **not** less than 0.1.

It's given by the probability that X is less than 0.2 **minus** the probability that X is less than 0.1.

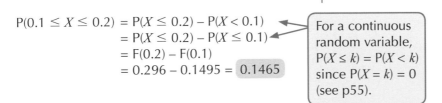

$P(0.1 \leq X \leq 0.2) = P(X \leq 0.2) - P(X < 0.1)$ ◄—
$= P(X \leq 0.2) - P(X \leq 0.1)$ ◄—
$= F(0.2) - F(0.1)$
$= 0.296 - 0.1495 = \boxed{0.1465}$

$\boxed{\text{For a continuous random variable, } P(X \leq k) = P(X < k) \text{ since } P(X = k) = 0 \text{ (see p55).}}$

Tip: It's easy to see why
$P(0.1 \leq X \leq 0.2)$
$= P(X \leq 0.2) - P(X \leq 0.1)$
on this graph.

The green area
$(= P(0.1 \leq X \leq 0.2))$
is equal to:

the area under the graph to the left of $x = 0.2$
$(= P(X \leq 0.2))$

...minus...

the area under the graph to the left of $x = 0.1$
$(= P(X \leq 0.1))$.

d) $P(X < 0.5)$

This one's easy too because $P(X \leq k) = P(X < k)$ since $P(X = k) = 0$.

So $P(X < 0.5) = P(X \leq 0.5) = \boxed{0.6875}$ from part a).

If you have a p.d.f. and you need to find **a few** different probabilities, then it can be easier to:

(i)   use the p.d.f. to work out the c.d.f. first,
(ii) then use the c.d.f. to find the probabilities.

This way you only need to do a single integration.

Example 2

The continuous random variable X has p.d.f. f(x), where

$$f(x) = \begin{cases} \dfrac{x^3}{4} & 0 \leq x \leq 2 \\ 0 & \text{otherwise} \end{cases}$$

a) Find F(x)

- For $x < 0$, $P(X \leq x) = 0$ so F(x) = 0.
  To join on from this smoothly, F(0) must be equal to 0.

- For $0 \leq x \leq 2$:

$$F(x) = \int_{-\infty}^{x} f(t)\,dt = \int_{-\infty}^{0} f(t)\,dt + \int_{0}^{x} f(t)\,dt$$

$$= F(0) + \int_{0}^{x} \left(\frac{t^3}{4}\right) dt$$

$$= 0 + \left[\frac{t^4}{4 \times 4}\right]_{0}^{x} = \left[\frac{t^4}{16}\right]_{0}^{x} = \frac{x^4}{16}$$

- For $x > 2$, F(x) = 1.
  You can check the previous piece joins up with this by putting $x = 2$ into the above expression for F(x):

$$F(2) = \frac{2^4}{16} = \frac{16}{16} = 1$$

- So putting all this together:

$$F(x) = \begin{cases} 0 & x < 0 \\ \dfrac{x^4}{16} & 0 \leq x \leq 2 \\ 1 & x > 2 \end{cases}$$

b) Find $P(X \leq 1.5)$

$$P(X \leq 1.5) = F(1.5) = \frac{(1.5)^4}{16} = 0.31640\ldots = \boxed{0.316 \text{ (3 d.p.)}}$$

c) Find $P(X > 0.5)$

$$P(X > 0.5) = 1 - P(X \leq 0.5) = 1 - F(0.5)$$

$$= 1 - \frac{(0.5)^4}{16} = 1 - 0.00390\ldots = \boxed{0.996 \text{ (3 d.p.)}}$$

d) Find $P(0.5 \leq X \leq 1.5)$

$$P(0.5 \leq X \leq 1.5) = P(X \leq 1.5) - P(X \leq 0.5) = F(1.5) - F(0.5)$$

$$= 0.31640\ldots - 0.00390\ldots = \boxed{0.313 \text{ (3 d.p.)}}$$

Exercise 2.3

Q1 $F(x) = \begin{cases} 0 & x < 0 \\ \frac{1}{4}(x^3 + 3x^2) & 0 \le x \le 1 \\ 1 & x > 1 \end{cases}$

Use the c.d.f. F(x) above to find:

a) $P(X \le 0.2)$ b) $P(X < 0.5)$ c) $P(0.3 \le X \le 0.8)$

Q2 $F(x) = \begin{cases} 0 & x < 0 \\ \frac{1}{3}x & 0 \le x < 2 \\ \frac{2}{3}x - \frac{1}{12}x^2 - \frac{1}{3} & 2 \le x \le 4 \\ 1 & x > 4 \end{cases}$

Use the c.d.f. F(x) above to find:

a) $P(X \le 1)$ b) $P(X > 3)$ c) $P(1 \le X \le 2)$

Q3 $f(x) = \begin{cases} \frac{1}{8}x & 0 \le x \le 4 \\ 0 & \text{otherwise} \end{cases}$

a) For the p.d.f. f(x) above, find the c.d.f. F(x).
b) Use the c.d.f. F(x) to find:

  i) $P(X < 1)$ ii) $P(2 < X < 3)$

Q4 The function f(x) below is the p.d.f. for the continuous random variable X.

$$f(x) = \begin{cases} \frac{1}{12} & 0 \le x \le 1 \\ -\frac{1}{3}(1 - x^3) & 1 < x \le 2 \\ 0 & \text{otherwise} \end{cases}$$

a) Find the indefinite integral $\int \frac{1}{12}dx$.
b) The c.d.f. of X, F(x), equals 0 at x = 0.
   Use this fact to find the constant of integration in part a).
c) Find the indefinite integral $\int -\frac{1}{3}(1 - x^3)dx$.
d) Use the fact that F(2) = 1 to find the constant of integration in c).
e) Hence state the cumulative distribution function of X for all values of x.
f) Use F(x) to find:

  (i) $P(X < 0.5)$ (ii) $P(X > 1.5)$

Q5 $f(x) = \begin{cases} \frac{1}{4} & 0 \le x < 3 \\ \frac{1}{8}(5 - x) & 3 \le x \le 5 \\ 0 & \text{otherwise} \end{cases}$

a) For the p.d.f. f(x) above, find the c.d.f. F(x).
b) Use the c.d.f. F(x) to find:

  (i) $P(X < 2)$ (ii) $P(X > 4)$ (iii) $P(1 \le X \le 3)$ (iv) $P(X = 4.5)$

3. Mean and Variance

Learning Objectives:

- Be able to calculate the mean (expected value) of a continuous random variable.
- Be able to calculate the variance of a continuous random variable.
- Be able to calculate the mean and variance of transformations of continuous random variables of the form $aX + b$.

In S1 you learnt how to find the mean (expected value) and variance of a discrete random variable. And surprise, surprise... you can find them for continuous random variables too by using the probability density function.

Mean of a continuous random variable

The expected value (mean) of X: $E(X)$ or μ

For every continuous random variable you can work out the **mean** (or **expected value**) from the probability density function.

To find $E(X)$ for a **continuous** random variable, you use **integration**.

Tip: Remember that $E(X)$ for a discrete random variable is given by the summation:
$$E(X) = \sum x_i p_i$$
In the formula for the expected value of a continuous random variable you need to replace p_i with $f(x)\,dx$ and integrate.

> If X is a continuous random variable with p.d.f. $f(x)$, then its mean (μ) or expected value ($E(X)$) is given by:
>
> $$\mu = E(X) = \int_{-\infty}^{\infty} x f(x)\,dx$$

You'll have to **split** the integral up into the different **ranges** that $f(x)$ is **defined** for and work out each integral separately.

Example 1

Find the expected value of the continuous random variable X with p.d.f. f (x) given below:

$$f(x) = \begin{cases} \frac{3}{32}(4 - x^2) & \text{for } -2 \leq x \leq 2 \\ 0 & \text{otherwise} \end{cases}$$

> Split the integral up into the **three** different ranges:
> $-\infty < x < -2, \qquad -2 \leq x \leq 2, \qquad 2 < x < \infty$

$$E(X) = \int_{-\infty}^{\infty} x f(x)\,dx = \int_{-\infty}^{-2} x f(x)\,dx + \int_{-2}^{2} x f(x)\,dx + \int_{2}^{\infty} x f(x)\,dx$$

Two of the integrals are 0.

$$= \int_{-\infty}^{-2} 0\,dx + \int_{-2}^{2} x \times \frac{3}{32}(4 - x^2)\,dx + \int_{2}^{\infty} 0\,dx$$

$$= \int_{-2}^{2} \left(\frac{3}{8}x - \frac{3x^3}{32}\right)dx = \left[\frac{3x^2}{16} - \frac{3x^4}{128}\right]_{-2}^{2}$$

$$= \left(\frac{3 \times 2^2}{16} - \frac{3 \times 2^4}{128}\right) - \left(\frac{3 \times (-2)^2}{16} - \frac{3 \times (-2)^4}{128}\right)$$

$$= 0$$

Tip: From now on you can ignore the bits of the p.d.f. defined as 0 and just integrate the non-zero bits.

You'd expect a mean of **0** here, since $f(x)$ is **symmetrical** about the **y-axis**.

Example 2

Find the expected value of the continuous random variable X with p.d.f. f (x) given below:

$$f(x) = \begin{cases} \frac{1}{3} & 0 < x < 1 \\ \frac{1}{3}(2x - 1) & 1 \leq x < 2 \\ 0 & \text{otherwise} \end{cases}$$

> Split the integral up into the two different ranges where f(x) is non-zero:
> $$0 < x < 1, \quad 1 \leq x < 2$$

$$E(X) = \int_{-\infty}^{\infty} x f(x) dx = \int_{0}^{1} x f(x) dx + \int_{1}^{2} x f(x) dx$$

$$= \int_{0}^{1} x \times \frac{1}{3} dx + \int_{1}^{2} x \times \left(\frac{1}{3}(2x - 1)\right) dx$$

$$= \int_{0}^{1} \frac{x}{3} dx + \int_{1}^{2} \left(\frac{2}{3}x^2 - \frac{1}{3}x\right) dx$$

$$= \left[\frac{x^2}{6}\right]_{0}^{1} + \left[\frac{2x^3}{9} - \frac{x^2}{6}\right]_{1}^{2}$$

$$= \frac{1}{6} + \left[\left(\frac{2(2)^3}{9} - \frac{(2)^2}{6}\right) - \left(\frac{2(1)^3}{9} - \frac{(1)^2}{6}\right)\right]$$

$$= \frac{11}{9}$$

E($aX + b$)

You can also find the mean of **$aX + b$** where a and b are **constants**.

For a continuous random variable X:

$$\boxed{E(aX + b) = aE(X) + b}$$

Tip: $aX + b$ is called a linear transformation of X.

Tip: This formula is exactly the same as the one for discrete random variables in S1.

Examples

The continuous random variable X has p.d.f. f (x), where
$$f(x) = \begin{cases} \frac{3}{37}x^2 & \text{for } 3 \leq x \leq 4 \\ 0 & \text{otherwise} \end{cases}$$

a) Find the expected value, μ.

Use the formula from p68.

$$\mu = E(X) = \int_{-\infty}^{\infty} x f(x) dx = \int_{3}^{4} x \times \frac{3}{37}x^2 dx$$

$$= \int_{3}^{4} \frac{3}{37}x^3 dx = \frac{3}{37}\left[\frac{x^4}{4}\right]_{3}^{4} = \frac{3}{37 \times 4}(4^4 - 3^4) = \frac{3 \times (256 - 81)}{148} = \frac{525}{148}$$

Tip: Always check your mean looks sensible. Here, you'd expect the mean to be somewhere between 3 and 4 (so $525 \div 148 = 3.547...$ seems 'about right').

b) Find E(3X + 2).

$$\boxed{E(aX + b) = aE(X) + b}$$

$$E(3X + 2) = 3E(X) + 2 = 3 \times \frac{525}{148} + 2 = \frac{1575 + 296}{148} = \boxed{\frac{1871}{148}}$$

You already know E(X) from part a)

Tip: Remember
$$P(X < x_0) = \int_{-\infty}^{x_0} f(x)\,dx.$$

c) Find P(X < μ).

Now that you've found the mean you can just plug it in to find the probability that X will be less than it.

$$P(X < \mu) = \int_{-\infty}^{\mu} f(x)dx = \int_{3}^{\frac{525}{148}} \frac{3}{37}x^2 dx$$

$$= \frac{3}{37}\left[\frac{x^3}{3}\right]_{3}^{\frac{525}{148}} = \frac{3}{37 \times 3}\left(\left(\frac{525}{148}\right)^3 - 3^3\right) = \boxed{0.477 \text{ (to 3 d.p.)}}.$$

Exercise 3.1

Q1 Find E(X) for the continuous random variable X with p.d.f. f(x):

a) $f(x) = \begin{cases} 1 - \frac{1}{2}x & 0 \le x \le 2 \\ 0 & \text{otherwise} \end{cases}$

b) $f(x) = \begin{cases} \frac{1}{4}x^3 & 0 \le x \le 2 \\ 0 & \text{otherwise} \end{cases}$

c) $f(x) = \begin{cases} \frac{2}{9}(3x - x^2) & 0 \le x \le 3 \\ 0 & \text{otherwise} \end{cases}$

Q2 A continuous random variable X has p.d.f. f(x), where:

$$f(x) = \begin{cases} \frac{3}{7}x^2 & 1 \le x \le 2 \\ 0 & \text{otherwise} \end{cases}$$

Find: a) μ b) E(2X − 1) c) P(X < μ)

Q3 A continuous random variable X has p.d.f. f(x), where:

$$f(x) = \begin{cases} \frac{2}{5} & 0 \le x < 1 \\ \frac{2}{5}x & 1 \le x \le 2 \\ 0 & \text{otherwise} \end{cases}$$

Find: a) μ b) E(4X + 2)

Q4 A continuous random variable X has p.d.f. f(x), where:

$$f(x) = \begin{cases} \frac{1}{3} & 0 \le x \le 1 \\ -\frac{1}{2}(1 - x^2) & 1 < x \le 2 \\ 0 & \text{otherwise} \end{cases}$$

Find: a) μ b) E(3X − 2)

Q5 a) Find $\int_0^4 \frac{1}{4}x^2\,dx$.

b) Hence find E(X) for the continuous random variable X with p.d.f.:

$$f(x) = \begin{cases} \frac{1}{8}x & 0 \le x \le 4 \\ 0 & \text{otherwise} \end{cases}$$

Variance of a continuous random variable

The variance of X: Var(X) or σ^2

Tip: You should have learnt about dispersion in S1.

The **variance** of a continuous random variable, X, is a measure of **dispersion** — basically how **spread out** the probability density function is from the **mean**.

For example, consider two continuous random variables which can be modelled by **normal distributions** with mean **0** but different **variances**.

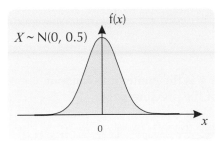
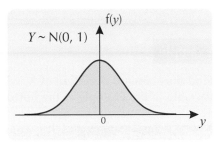

Y has a greater **variance** than X, and you can see by the graph that the p.d.f. of Y is more **spread out** about the mean than that of X.

You can find the variance of a continuous random variable using the same formula that you learnt for discrete random variables in S1. But to work it out, you need to **integrate** rather than use a summation.

If X is a continuous random variable with **p.d.f.** f(x), then its variance, Var(X), is:

$$\text{Var}(X) = \text{E}(X^2) - [\text{E}(X)]^2 \qquad \boxed{\text{This formula is from S1.}}$$

$$= \text{E}(X^2) - \mu^2 \qquad \boxed{\text{E}(X) = \mu}$$

$$= \int_{-\infty}^{\infty} x^2\, \text{f}(x)\,\text{d}x - \mu^2 \qquad \boxed{\begin{array}{l}\text{See the tip in the margin} \\ \text{for more about E}(X^2).\end{array}}$$

Tip: For a discrete random variable X:
$\text{E}(X^2) = \sum x_i^2 p_i$.

If X is a continuous random variable then:
$\text{E}(X^2) = \int x^2 \text{f}(x)\,\text{d}x$.

Again, the only differences are that p_i is replaced with f(x) dx and there's an integration instead of a summation.

Example

The continuous random variable X has p.d.f. f(x) given below, and a mean of 0. Find the variance of X.

$$\text{f}(x) = \begin{cases} \dfrac{3}{32}(4 - x^2) & \text{for } -2 \le x \le 2 \\ 0 & \text{otherwise} \end{cases}$$

Just use the **formula** and **integrate**:

$\boxed{\begin{array}{l}\text{You saw on page 68 that} \\ \text{the mean of this p.d.f. is 0.}\end{array}}$

$$\text{Var}(X) = \text{E}(X^2) - \mu^2 = \int_{-\infty}^{\infty} x^2 \text{f}(x)\,\text{d}x - \mu^2 = \int_{-2}^{2} x^2 \times \frac{3}{32}(4 - x^2)\,\text{d}x - 0^2$$

$$= \int_{-2}^{2} \left(\frac{3x^2}{8} - \frac{3x^4}{32} \right)\text{d}x = \left[\frac{x^3}{8} - \frac{3x^5}{160} \right]_{-2}^{2}$$

$$= \left(\frac{2^3}{8} - \frac{3 \times 2^5}{160} \right) - \left(\frac{(-2)^3}{8} - \frac{3 \times (-2)^5}{160} \right) = \boxed{0.8}$$

The standard derivation of X: σ

The **standard deviation** is just another measure of a random variable's **dispersion** — sometimes used **instead** of the variance.

It's found by taking the **square root** of the **variance**, and it's written σ.

If X is a continuous random variable with **p.d.f.** $f(x)$, then:

$$\text{Standard deviation} = \sigma = \sqrt{\text{Var}(X)}$$

Example

Find the standard deviation of X, where X is the continuous random variable in the Example at the bottom of the previous page.

Just take the square root of the variance:

$$\sigma = \sqrt{\text{Var}(X)} = \sqrt{0.8} = \boxed{0.894 \,(3\,\text{d.p.})}$$

Var($aX + b$)

You can easily find the variance of $aX + b$ where a and b are constants. You've seen this formula before in S1:

> For a continuous random variable X with p.d.f. $f(x)$:
> $$\text{Var}(aX + b) = a^2\text{Var}(X)$$

Tip: You can find the mean and variance of any function of X. But when the function is a linear transformation (i.e. of the form $aX + b$), the formulas for the mean and variance are nice and easy.

Just square the a and get rid of the b altogether.

Example

The continuous random variable X has p.d.f. $f(x)$, where

$$f(x) = \begin{cases} \frac{3}{37}x^2 & \text{for } 3 \leq x \leq 4 \\ 0 & \text{otherwise} \end{cases}$$

Tip: See page 69 for the calculation of the mean of this p.d.f.

If $E(X) = \frac{525}{148}$, find:

a) Var(X)

$$\text{Var}(X) = E(X^2) - \mu^2 = \int_{-\infty}^{\infty} x^2 f(x)dx - \left(\frac{525}{148}\right)^2 = \int_{3}^{4} x^2 \times \frac{3}{37}x^2 dx - \left(\frac{525}{148}\right)^2$$

$$= \frac{3}{37}\left[\frac{x^5}{5}\right]_{3}^{4} - \left(\frac{525}{148}\right)^2 = \frac{3}{185}(4^5 - 3^5) - \left(\frac{525}{148}\right)^2 = 0.0815467...$$

$$= \boxed{0.0815 \,(\text{to 4 d.p.})}$$

b) Var($3X + 2$)

$$\text{Var}(3X + 2) = 3^2 \times \text{Var}(X) = 9 \times 0.0815467... = \boxed{0.734 \,(\text{to 3 d.p.})}.$$

> $\text{Var}(aX + b) = a^2\text{Var}(X)$

Exercise 3.2

Q1 Find the variance of each of the following p.d.f.s, f(x):

a) $f(x) = \begin{cases} 1 - \frac{1}{2}x & 0 \leq x \leq 2 \\ 0 & \text{otherwise} \end{cases}$

b) $f(x) = \begin{cases} \frac{1}{4}x^3 & 0 \leq x \leq 2 \\ 0 & \text{otherwise} \end{cases}$

c) $f(x) = \begin{cases} \frac{2}{9}(3x - x^2) & 0 \leq x \leq 3 \\ 0 & \text{otherwise} \end{cases}$

Q1-4 Hint: You worked out the values of E(X) for these p.d.f.s in Exercise 3.1, Questions 1-4 — see page 70.

Q2 A random variable X has p.d.f. $f(x) = \begin{cases} \frac{3}{7}x^2 & 1 \leq x \leq 2 \\ 0 & \text{otherwise} \end{cases}$

Find:

a) the variance, σ^2.

b) Var(2X).

c) Var(2X + 1).

d) the standard deviation, σ.

Q3 A random variable X has p.d.f. $f(x) = \begin{cases} \frac{2}{5} & 0 \leq x \leq 1 \\ \frac{2}{5}x & 1 < x \leq 2 \\ 0 & \text{otherwise} \end{cases}$

Find:

a) the variance of X.

b) the variance of $4X + 2$.

Q4 A random variable X has p.d.f. $f(x) = \begin{cases} \frac{1}{3} & 0 \leq x \leq 1 \\ -\frac{1}{2}(1 - x^2) & 1 < x \leq 2 \\ 0 & \text{otherwise} \end{cases}$

Find:

a) Var(X).

b) Var(–X).

c) Var(3X + 2).

d) the standard deviation.

4. Mode, Median and Quartiles

Learning Objective:

- Be able to calculate the mode, median, upper and lower quartiles and the interquartile range of a continuous random variable.

There are a few more measures that you need to know how to calculate for continuous random variables. You should have come across the basic ideas in S1 when you were looking at data sets, though.

Finding the mode

In statistics, the **mode** usually means the most likely value — so it's the value with the **highest probability**.

Even though for a continuous random variable each individual value has a probability of zero, you can still define the mode as follows:

> If X is a continuous random variable with p.d.f. f(x), then its **mode** is the value of x where f(x) reaches its **maximum**.

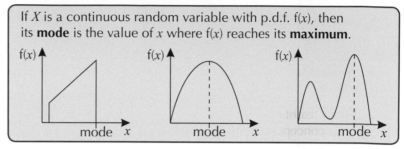

There are **two** ways you can find the **mode**:

- You might be able to find the mode by simply drawing a **graph** of the p.d.f. — this would work with the first example above.

- Sometimes you'll need to **differentiate** the p.d.f. and set the derivative equal to zero to find the maximum — you might need to do this in the second and third examples above.

Tip: Remember, to find the maxima and minima of a function, you need to find the points where the gradient is zero — this means differentiating the function and setting it equal to 0. Make sure you get a maximum and not a minimum and that it is within the range relevant to that part of the p.d.f.

Examples

Find the mode of the continuous random variables below:

a) X with p.d.f. $f(x) = \begin{cases} \frac{3}{16}(x^3 - 7x^2 + 10x) & \text{for } 0 \leq x \leq 2 \\ 0 & \text{otherwise} \end{cases}$

- It's best to start with a sketch of the p.d.f.

  Since $x^3 - 7x^2 + 10x = x(x^2 - 7x + 10)$
  $= x(x - 5)(x - 2)$,
  f(x) looks like the graph to the right.

  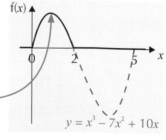

  The maximum is here, but you'll need to differentiate to find it.

- **Differentiate** to find the maximum of f(x) in the range $0 \leq x \leq 2$.
  $$\frac{d}{dx}\left(\frac{3}{16}(x^3 - 7x^2 + 10x)\right) = \frac{3}{16}(3x^2 - 14x + 10)$$

  Tip: You can ignore the fraction $\frac{3}{16}$ when you find where this derivative equals zero. You just need to solve $3x^2 - 14x + 10 = 0$.

  This equals **zero** when $x = \dfrac{14 \pm \sqrt{14^2 - 4 \times 3 \times 10}}{6} = \dfrac{14 \pm \sqrt{76}}{6}$.

  $\dfrac{14 + \sqrt{76}}{6} > 2$, so it's too big (the maximum must be within $0 \leq x \leq 2$).

  So the **mode** of X is $x = \dfrac{14 - \sqrt{76}}{6} = \boxed{0.880 \text{ (to 3 d.p.)}}$.

b) Y with p.d.f. $g(y) = \begin{cases} 2y - 2 & \text{for } 1 \leq y \leq 2 \\ 0 & \text{otherwise} \end{cases}$

- Sketch the p.d.f. first:

- There's no need to differentiate here. You can see from the graph that the **maximum** value of $g(y)$ in the range $1 \leq y \leq 2$ is at $y = 2$.

- So the **mode** of Y is 2.

Finding the median and quartiles

The **median** and the **quartiles** just represent an ***x*-value** for which $P(X \leq x)$ is equal to a certain percentage.

You should have learnt about the median and quartiles for **data sets** in S1 — it's the same concept here really:

- The probability of X taking a value less than the **median** is **0.5**.
- The probability of X taking a value less than the **lower quartile** is **0.25**.
- The probability of X taking a value less than the **upper quartile** is **0.75**.

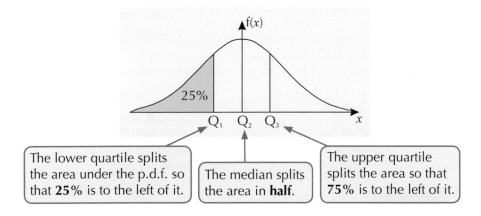

The lower quartile splits the area under the p.d.f. so that **25%** is to the left of it.

The median splits the area in **half**.

The upper quartile splits the area so that **75%** is to the left of it.

You can use the **cumulative distribution function** to work out the median and quartiles.

> If X is a **continuous random variable** with **cumulative distribution function** F(x) then:
>
> - The **median** (Q_2) of X is given by $F(Q_2) = 0.5$.
> - The **lower quartile** (Q_1) of X is given by $F(Q_1) = 0.25$.
> - The **upper quartile** (Q_3) of X is given by $F(Q_3) = 0.75$.

Example 1

The continuous random variable X has c.d.f. $F(x)$, where

$$F(x) = \begin{cases} 0 & x < 0 \\ \frac{1}{4}x^2 & 0 \leq x \leq 2 \\ 1 & x > 2 \end{cases}$$

Find the lower quartile (Q_1) and the upper quartile (Q_3).

- $F(0) = 0$ and $F(2) = 1$, so both Q_1 and Q_3 must lie in the range $0 \leq x \leq 2$. This means you'll need to use $F(x) = \frac{1}{4}x^2$.

- To find the **lower quartile**, let $F(Q_1) = \mathbf{0.25}$

$$\Rightarrow \frac{1}{4}Q_1^{\ 2} = 0.25$$

$$\Rightarrow Q_1^{\ 2} = 4 \times 0.25 = 1$$

$$\Rightarrow Q_1 = \boxed{1}$$

- To find the **upper quartile**, let $F(Q_3) = \mathbf{0.75}$

$$\Rightarrow \frac{1}{4}Q_3^{\ 2} = 0.75$$

$$\Rightarrow Q_3^{\ 2} = 4 \times 0.75 = 3$$

$$\Rightarrow Q_3 = \sqrt{3} = \boxed{1.732 \,(3\,\text{d.p.})}$$

Interquartile range

Once you've worked out the quartiles, you can work out another measure of **dispersion** of a p.d.f. The **interquartile range** is just the **difference** between the upper and lower quartiles, $\mathbf{Q_3 - Q_1}$.

Example 2

Find the interquartile range of the random variable with c.d.f. $F(x)$, where:

$$F(x) = \begin{cases} 0 & x < 0 \\ \frac{1}{4}x^2 & 0 \leq x \leq 2 \\ 1 & x > 2 \end{cases}$$

The previous example showed that $Q_1 = 1$ and $Q_3 = 1.732...$

So the **interquartile range** is:

$$Q_3 - Q_1 = 1.732... - 1 = \boxed{0.732 \,(\text{to 3 d.p.})}$$

Watch out for when F(x) is defined **piecewise** — you'll have to work out F(x) at the point where the pieces join to see which 'piece' Q_1, Q_2 and Q_3 lie in.

Example 3

The continuous random variable X has p.d.f. f(x), where

$$f(x) = \begin{cases} 0.4 & \text{for } 1 \leq x < 2 \\ 0.4(x-1) & \text{for } 2 \leq x \leq 3 \\ 0 & \text{otherwise} \end{cases}$$

Find the interquartile range, $Q_3 - Q_1$.

- You've not been given the c.d.f., so you'll need to work it out from the p.d.f. Integrate to find the c.d.f., making sure the 'joins are smooth'.

  - For $x < 1$, F(x) = 0
  - For $1 \leq x < 2$:

    $$F(x) = \int_{-\infty}^{x} f(t)\,dt = \int_{-\infty}^{1} f(t)\,dt + \int_{1}^{x} f(t)\,dt$$

    $$= F(1) + \int_{1}^{x} 0.4\,dt = 0 + [0.4t]_1^x = 0.4x - 0.4$$

  - For $2 \leq x \leq 3$:

    $$F(x) = \int_{-\infty}^{x} f(t)\,dt = \int_{-\infty}^{2} f(t)\,dt + \int_{2}^{x} f(t)\,dt$$

    $$= F(2) + \int_{2}^{x} 0.4(t-1)\,dt = 0.4 + \left[0.4\left(\tfrac{t^2}{2} - t\right)\right]_2^x$$

    $$= 0.4 + [0.2t^2 - 0.4t]_2^x$$

    $$= 0.4 + [(0.2x^2 - 0.4x) - (0.2 \times 2^2 - 0.4 \times 2)]$$

    $$= 0.2x^2 - 0.4x + 0.4$$

  So $F(x) = \begin{cases} 0 & \text{for } x < 1 \\ 0.4x - 0.4 & \text{for } 1 \leq x < 2 \\ 0.2x^2 - 0.4x + 0.4 & \text{for } 2 \leq x \leq 3 \\ 1 & \text{for } x > 3 \end{cases}$

- Find the values of F(x) where the pieces join to work out which piece contains each quartile.

  $$F(1) = 0, \qquad F(2) = 0.4, \qquad F(3) = 1$$

  | $F(Q_1) = 0.25$ so $1 < Q_1 < 2$ | $F(Q_3) = 0.75$ so $2 < Q_3 < 3$ |

- Solve $F(Q_1) = 0.25$ to find the lower quartile.
  You know $1 < Q_1 < 2$, so solve: $0.4Q_1 - 0.4 = 0.25$

  $$\Rightarrow 0.4Q_1 = 0.65$$

  $$\Rightarrow Q_1 = \frac{0.65}{0.4} = 1.625.$$

- Solve $F(Q_3) = 0.75$ to find the upper quartile.
  You know $2 < Q_3 < 3$, so solve: $0.2Q_3^2 - 0.4Q_3 + 0.4 = 0.75$

  $$\Rightarrow 0.2Q_3^2 - 0.4Q_3 - 0.35 = 0$$

  $$\Rightarrow Q_3 = \frac{0.4 + \sqrt{0.44}}{0.4} = 1 + \frac{\sqrt{0.44}}{0.4} = 2.658 \text{ (3 d.p.)}$$

- So **interquartile range** $= Q_3 - Q_1 = 1 + \frac{\sqrt{0.44}}{0.4} - 1.625 = \boxed{1.033 \text{ (3 d.p.)}}$

Tip: This means F(1) = 0.

Tip: This means
$F(2) = 0.4 \times 2 - 0.4$
$= 0.4$

Tip: This means
$F(3) = 0.2(3)^2 - 0.4(3) + 0.4$
$= 1$
So the pieces join together smoothly.

Tip: The other solution to the quadratic is not in the correct range.

Example 4

The continuous random variable X has p.d.f. $f(x)$, where

$$f(x) = \begin{cases} \frac{1}{3} & 0 < x < 2 \\ (x-2)^2 & 2 \le x < 3 \\ 0 & \text{otherwise} \end{cases}$$

a) Find the lower quartile.

- Start by working out the c.d.f.

For $x \le 0$, $F(x) = 0$

For $0 < x < 2$, $F(x) = \int_{-\infty}^{x} f(t)\, dt = F(0) + \int_{0}^{x} \frac{1}{3}\, dt = \left[\frac{1}{3}t\right]_{0}^{x} = \frac{1}{3}x$

For $2 \le x < 3$, $F(x) = \int_{-\infty}^{x} f(t)\, dt = F(2) + \int_{2}^{x} (t-2)^2\, dt$

$$= \frac{2}{3} + \int_{2}^{x}(t^2 - 4t + 4)\, dt = \frac{2}{3} + \left[\frac{t^3}{3} - 2t^2 + 4t\right]_{2}^{x}$$

$$= \frac{2}{3} + \left[\left(\frac{x^3}{3} - 2x^2 + 4x\right) - \left(\frac{8}{3} - 8 + 8\right)\right]$$

$$= \frac{x^3}{3} - 2x^2 + 4x - 2$$

So $F(x) = \begin{cases} 0 & x \le 0 \\ \frac{1}{3}x & 0 < x < 2 \\ \frac{x^3}{3} - 2x^2 + 4x - 2 & 2 \le x < 3 \\ 1 & x \ge 3 \end{cases}$

Tip: So F(0) = 0.

Tip: So $F(2) = \frac{2}{3}$.

Tip: So $F(3) = 9 - 18 + 12 - 2 = 1$

- $F(2) = \frac{2}{3}$ and so since $F(Q_1) = 0.25$, Q_1 must be less than 2:

So $F(Q_1) = 0.25$

$\Rightarrow \frac{1}{3}Q_1 = 0.25$

$\Rightarrow Q_1 = 0.25 \times 3 = \boxed{0.75}$

b) Find the median.

Again, since $F(2) = \frac{2}{3}$, Q_2 must be less than 2.

So $F(Q_2) = 0.5$

$\Rightarrow \frac{1}{3}Q_2 = 0.5 \Rightarrow Q_2 = 0.5 \times 3 = \boxed{1.5}$

c) Show that the upper quartile lies between 2.6 and 2.7.

- The upper quartile is Q_3 where $F(Q_3) = 0.75$.
  $F(x)$ is a c.d.f., which means it is an increasing function and so if Q_3 lies between 2.6 and 2.7, then $F(2.6) \le F(Q_3) \le F(2.7)$.

So you only need to show:

$$F(2.6) = \frac{(2.6)^3}{3} - 2(2.6)^2 + 4(2.6) - 2 = 0.739 \text{ (3 d.p.)}$$

$$F(2.7) = \frac{(2.7)^3}{3} - 2(2.7)^2 + 4(2.7) - 2 = 0.781$$

These are either side of 0.75, so Q_3 lies between 2.6 and 2.7.

Tip: The formula for F(x) is quite complicated for $2 \le x < 3$ (where Q_3 lies), so it would be difficult to find Q_3. But showing it lies between two values is easy.

Exercise 4.1

Q1 For each of the following p.d.f.s, $f(x)$, find the mode:

    a) $f(x) = \begin{cases} 1 - \frac{1}{2}x & 0 \leq x \leq 2 \\ 0 & \text{otherwise} \end{cases}$
    b) $f(x) = \begin{cases} \frac{1}{4}x^3 & 0 \leq x \leq 2 \\ 0 & \text{otherwise} \end{cases}$

Q2 A random variable has the c.d.f. $F(x) = \begin{cases} 0 & x < -\frac{1}{3} \\ 1 + 3x & -\frac{1}{3} \leq x \leq 0 \\ 1 & x > 0 \end{cases}$

Find:
a) the median   b) the lower quartile   c) the interquartile range

Q3 A random variable has the c.d.f. $F(x) = \begin{cases} 0 & x < 0 \\ \frac{2}{5}x & 0 \leq x < 1 \\ \frac{1}{5}(x^2 + 1) & 1 \leq x \leq 2 \\ 1 & x > 2 \end{cases}$

Find:
a) the median   b) the upper quartile   c) the interquartile range

Q4 Show that the median of X lies between 1.56 and 1.57, where X has the c.d.f. $F(x)$ given by:

$$F(x) = \begin{cases} 0 & x < 0 \\ \frac{1}{4}x & 0 \leq x < 1 \\ \frac{1}{20}x^4 + \frac{1}{5} & 1 \leq x \leq 2 \\ 1 & x > 2 \end{cases}$$

Q5 A random variable X has p.d.f. $f(x) = \begin{cases} \frac{3}{34}(x^3 - x^2) & 1 \leq x \leq 3 \\ 0 & \text{otherwise} \end{cases}$

a) Find the c.d.f. $F(x)$.
b) Show that the median lies between 2.6 and 2.7.
c) By evaluating $F(x)$ for one more value of x, give the median to one decimal place.

Q6 A random variable X has the p.d.f. $f(x) = \begin{cases} \frac{1}{2}(3 - x) & 1 \leq x \leq 3 \\ 0 & \text{otherwise} \end{cases}$

Find:
a) the c.d.f. $F(x)$ b) the median
c) the interquartile range   d) the mode
e) the mean and variance   f) the mean and variance of $3X - 2$

Review Exercise — Chapter 3

Q1 Find the value of k for each of the probability density functions below.

a) $f(x) = \begin{cases} kx & \text{for } 1 \leq x \leq 10 \\ 0 & \text{otherwise} \end{cases}$

b) $g(x) = \begin{cases} 0.2x + k & \text{for } 0 \leq x \leq 1 \\ 0 & \text{otherwise} \end{cases}$

Q2 For each of the probability density functions below, find:

    (i) $P(X < 1)$,   (ii) $P(2 \leq X \leq 5)$,   (iii) $P(X = 4)$.

a) $f(x) = \begin{cases} 0.08x & \text{for } 0 \leq x \leq 5 \\ 0 & \text{otherwise} \end{cases}$

b) $g(x) = \begin{cases} 0.02(10 - x) & \text{for } 0 \leq x \leq 10 \\ 0 & \text{otherwise} \end{cases}$

Q3 Find the exact value of k for each of the probability density functions below. Then for each p.d.f., find $P(X < 1)$.

a) $f(x) = \begin{cases} kx^2 & \text{for } 0 \leq x \leq 5 \\ 0 & \text{otherwise} \end{cases}$

b) $g(x) = \begin{cases} 0.1x^2 + kx & \text{for } 0 \leq x \leq 2 \\ 0 & \text{otherwise} \end{cases}$

Q4 Say whether the following are probability density functions. Explain your answers.

a) $f(x) = \begin{cases} 0.1x^2 + 0.2 & \text{for } 0 \leq x \leq 2 \\ 0 & \text{otherwise} \end{cases}$

b) $g(x) = \begin{cases} x & \text{for } -1 \leq x \leq 1 \\ 0 & \text{otherwise} \end{cases}$

Q5 Find the cumulative distribution function (c.d.f.) for each of the following p.d.f.s.

a) $f(x) = \begin{cases} 0.08x & \text{for } 0 \leq x \leq 5 \\ 0 & \text{otherwise} \end{cases}$

b) $g(x) = \begin{cases} 0.02(10 - x) & \text{for } 0 \leq x \leq 10 \\ 0 & \text{otherwise} \end{cases}$

c) $h(x) = \begin{cases} 2x & \text{for } 0 \leq x \leq 0.5 \\ 1 & \text{for } 0.5 \leq x \leq 1 \\ 3 - 2x & \text{for } 1 \leq x \leq 1.5 \\ 0 & \text{otherwise} \end{cases}$

d) $m(x) = \begin{cases} 0.5 - 0.1x & \text{for } 2 \leq x \leq 4 \\ 0.1 & \text{for } 4 \leq x \leq 10 \\ 0 & \text{otherwise} \end{cases}$

Q6 Find the probability density function (p.d.f.) for each of the following c.d.f.s.

a) $F(x) = \begin{cases} 0 & \text{for } x < 0 \\ x^4 & \text{for } 0 \le x \le 1 \\ 1 & \text{for } x > 1 \end{cases}$

b) $G(x) = \begin{cases} 0 & \text{for } x < 1 \\ \frac{1}{100}(x-1)^2 & \text{for } 1 \le x < 6 \\ \frac{3}{8}x - 2 & \text{for } 6 \le x \le 8 \\ 1 & \text{for } x > 8 \end{cases}$

Q7 The continuous random variable X has p.d.f. f(x), where

$$f(x) = \begin{cases} \frac{2}{3}(x-1) & 1 \le x \le 2 \\ \frac{2}{3} & 2 \le x \le 3 \\ 0 & \text{otherwise} \end{cases}$$

Find E(X).

Q8 The random variables X and Y have p.d.f.s. f(x) and g(y) respectively, where

$f(x) = \begin{cases} 0.08x & \text{for } 0 \le x \le 5 \\ 0 & \text{otherwise} \end{cases}$ and $g(y) = \begin{cases} 0.02(10 - y) & \text{for } 0 \le y \le 10 \\ 0 & \text{otherwise} \end{cases}$

a) Find the mean and variance of X and Y.
b) Find the mean and variance of $4X + 2$ and $3Y - 4$.
c) Find the mode and median of X.
d) Find the interquartile range of X.

Q9 The continuous random variable X has p.d.f. f(x), where

$$f(x) = \begin{cases} k(x^2 - 3x) & 1 \le x \le 2 \\ 0 & \text{otherwise} \end{cases}$$

a) Find the value of k such that f(x) is a valid p.d.f.
b) Find the c.d.f. F(x).
c) Show that the median equals 1.5.
d) Show that $1.2 \le Q_1 \le 1.3$ and $1.7 \le Q_3 \le 1.8$.
e) Find Q_1 and Q_3 to one decimal place.

1   The continuous random variable X has probability density function f(x),
     as defined below.

$$f(x) = \begin{cases} \frac{1}{k}(x+4) & \text{for } 0 \leq x \leq 2 \\ 0 & \text{otherwise} \end{cases}$$

a)   Find the value of k.

(3 marks)

b)   Find the cumulative distribution function of X, F(x).

(5 marks)

c)   Calculate E(X).

(3 marks)

d)   Calculate the variance of:
      (i) X

(3 marks)

      (ii) $4X - 2$

(2 marks)

e)   Find the median of X.

(4 marks)

f)   Write down the mode of X.

(1 mark)

2   The continuous random variable X has probability density function f(x),
     as defined below:

$$f(x) = \begin{cases} \frac{x}{2} & 0 \leq x < 1 \\ 3\left(1 - \frac{x}{2}\right) & 1 \leq x \leq 2 \\ 0 & \text{otherwise} \end{cases}$$

a)   Sketch the graph of f(x).

(1 mark)

b)   Hence, or otherwise, find the mode of X.

(1 mark)

c)   Find the cumulative distribution function of X, F(x).

(6 marks)

d)   Hence find the interquartile range of X.

(5 marks)

3   The continuous random variable X has cumulative distribution function $F(x)$, as defined below.

$$F(x) = \begin{cases} 0 & \text{for } x < 1 \\ k(x - 1) & \text{for } 1 \leq x < 3 \\ 0.5(x - 2) & \text{for } 3 \leq x \leq 4 \\ 1 & \text{for } x > 4 \end{cases}$$

a)   Calculate the value of k.

(2 marks)

b)   Calculate the interquartile range of X.

(5 marks)

c)   (i)   Specify the probability density function of X, $f(x)$.

(3 marks)

  (ii)   Sketch the graph of $f(x)$.

(1 mark)

d)   (i)   Find the mean (μ) of X.

(3 marks)

  (ii)   Find the variance (σ^2) of X.

(3 marks)

  (iii)   Find $P(X < \mu - \sigma)$.

(2 marks)

4   The continuous random variable X has cumulative distribution function:

$$F(x) = \begin{cases} 0 & x < 0 \\ 3x^2 - 2x^3 & 0 \leq x \leq 1 \\ 1 & x > 1 \end{cases}$$

a)   Find $P(0.25 \leq X \leq 0.75)$.

(2 marks)

b)   Show that the upper quartile of X lies between 0.67 and 0.68.

(3 marks)

c)   Show that the median of X is 0.5.

(2 marks)

d)   (i)   Specify the probability density function of X, $f(x)$.

(2 marks)

  (ii)   Sketch the graph of $f(x)$.

(1 mark)

e)   Find the mean (μ) of X.

(3 marks)

1. The Continuous Uniform Distribution

Chapter 3 was all about continuous random variables, in general. Here you're introduced to the continuous uniform distribution, which is a particular type of distribution that a continuous random variable can follow.

Learning Objectives:

- Be able to recognise when the continuous uniform distribution is a suitable model for a distribution.
- Be able to use the continuous uniform distribution to find probabilities.
- Be able to derive and use formulas for the mean and variance of a continuous uniform distribution.
- Be able to derive and use the cumulative distribution function of a continuous uniform distribution.

Tip: See p49-50 for more about the area under a p.d.f.

Tip: The p.d.f. of a continuous uniform distribution is always rectangular. You might also see this distribution called the **rectangular** distribution.

Tip: The interval [*a*, *b*] means that *a* is the lower limit for *X* and *b* is the upper limit for *X*. In other words, $a \leq X \leq b$.

Continuous uniform distributions

A random variable with a **continuous uniform distribution** can take any value in a particular range, and its value is **equally likely** to be **anywhere** in the range.

This means that its **probability density function** (p.d.f.) is **constant** — i.e. it takes the **same value** over the whole range of the distribution.

For example, suppose that the continuous random variable *X* has a **uniform distribution** and can take any value from 1 to 5. And we want to sketch the graph of the probability density function of *X*, f(*x*).

- We know that the **range** of possible values is **1 to 5**.
- And we know that **f(*x*) is constant** over this range — i.e. it's shown by a **horizontal line**.
- So using the fact that the **total area** under the p.d.f. must equal **1**, the graph will be a rectangle with **width** (5 − 1) = **4**, and **height** (1 ÷ 4) = **0.25**.

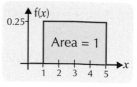

Using the graph, we can define the **probability density function f(*x*)** as:

$$f(x) = \begin{cases} 0.25 & \text{for } 1 \leq x \leq 5 \\ 0 & \text{otherwise} \end{cases}$$

You can go through the above process for **any** continuous uniform distribution, but there's a **general formula** that makes things much easier.

If *X* is a random variable with a **continuous uniform distribution** over the interval [*a*, *b*]:

- This is written as **X ~ U[*a*, *b*]**.
- And the **probability density function** of *X* is:

$$f(x) = \begin{cases} \dfrac{1}{b-a} & \text{for } a \leq x \leq b \\ 0 & \text{otherwise} \end{cases}$$

where *a* and *b* are constants

Example 1

The continuous random variable $X \sim U[-5, 5]$.

a) Write down the probability density function of X, f(x).

- First, work out $\dfrac{1}{b-a}$ for your values of a and b:

  a is the lower limit for X — so $a = -5$.
  b is the upper limit for X — so $b = 5$.

  So $\dfrac{1}{b-a} = \dfrac{1}{5-(-5)} = \dfrac{1}{10} = 0.1$

- Now you can define **f(x):** $f(x) = \begin{cases} 0.1 \text{ for } -5 \le x \le 5 \\ 0 \text{ otherwise} \end{cases}$

Tip: Always make sure you define f(x) for all x-values — i.e. **outside** the range [a, b] as well.

b) Sketch the graph of f(x).

The graph will be a rectangle with
width = $5 - (-5) = 10$ and
height = $f(x) = 0.1$.

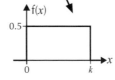

Continue the line a short distance along the x-axis
to show that $f(x) = 0$ for x outside the range [-5, 5].

One of the **key things** to remember about a **probability density function** is that the **area underneath** it $= 1$. You can use this fact to find missing values.

Example 2

The continuous random variable X has the probability density function:
$$f(x) = \begin{cases} 0.5 \text{ for } 0 \le x \le k \\ 0 \text{ otherwise} \end{cases}$$

Find the value of k.

- The easiest way to see what's going on here is to **sketch** f(x).

- You know that the area under $f(x) = 1$, so:

  Area of rectangle $= (k - 0) \times 0.5 = 1$

  $\Rightarrow 0.5k = 1$

  $\Rightarrow \boxed{k = 2}$

Tip: If you're happy doing this without a sketch, you can just use the definition of f(x) to find k:

You know that:
$\dfrac{1}{b-a} = 0.5,$

$\Rightarrow \dfrac{1}{k-0} = 0.5$

$\Rightarrow k - 0 = 2$

$\Rightarrow k = 2$

Continuous uniform distributions describe things that are **equally likely** to take **any** value within an interval. This means that they're good for modelling quantities that take different values within an interval **completely at random**.

You need to be able to **recognise** when a continuous uniform distribution is a **suitable model** for a distribution.

Example

A runner's time over 100 m is measured as 12.3 seconds, to the nearest 0.1 second. Let the random variable X represent the error (in seconds) in the recorded time.

a) Suggest a suitable model for the distribution of X and explain why your suggestion is suitable.

- The time is measured to the nearest 0.1 second, so the **actual time** could be anywhere between 12.25 and 12.35 seconds.

- This means that the **error**, **X**, could be anything up to 0.05 seconds above or below the recorded time. This error is **random** within the interval −0.05 to 0.05 seconds — there's no reason for it to be high, low or in the middle. So a suitable model for X is the **continuous uniform distribution over the interval [−0.05, 0.05]**.

b) Write down the probability density function of X.

$X \sim U[-0.05, 0.05]$, so $f(x) = \begin{cases} 10 & \text{for } -0.05 \leq x \leq 0.05 \\ 0 & \text{otherwise} \end{cases}$

Tip: Here:

$\dfrac{1}{b-a} = \dfrac{1}{0.1} = 10$

Exercise 1.1

Q1 For each of a)–d), write down the probability density function of X. Then sketch the graph of this probability density function.

a) $X \sim U[2, 7]$ b) $X \sim U[-0.5, 1.5]$ c) $X \sim U[\frac{1}{3}, 1]$ d) $X \sim U[1, 100]$

Q2 In each of a) and b), the continuous random variable X has a uniform distribution with probability density function $f(x)$. Find k in each case.

a) $f(x) = \begin{cases} 0.25 & \text{for } -3 \leq x \leq k \\ 0 & \text{otherwise} \end{cases}$ b) $f(x) = \begin{cases} \frac{5}{8} & \text{for } k \leq x \leq 7 \\ 0 & \text{otherwise} \end{cases}$

Q3 Each of the graphs below shows the probability density function of a uniformly distributed continuous random variable X. In each case, find k and write down the distribution of X.

Q4 Hint: Notice that Y represents the weight of the **heavier** piece.

Q4 A loaf of bread weighs 800 g. The loaf is sliced into two at a random point. The random variable Y represents the weight (in grams) of the heavier piece. Write down the probability distribution of Y.

Q5 Fred gets the train to work each day. There's a train he can catch every 15 minutes. If Fred leaves his house at a random time and T is the time (in minutes) that he waits for a train, describe the distribution of T.

Q6 A machine makes circular biscuits with diameters, D, which are randomly distributed between 5.9 cm and 6.3 cm.

a) Describe the distribution of D.

b) Define the probability density function of D and sketch its graph.

Finding probabilities

Remember that for a continuous random variable, **probability** is shown by the **area under** the **probability density function**. So to find the probability that a random variable takes a value in a certain range, you need to calculate the area under the p.d.f. for the given range.

Luckily, for **continuous uniform distributions** this is nice and easy because the area is always a **rectangle**.

Tip: Often you have to integrate to find areas (see p55). But here it's just a matter of finding areas of rectangles.

Example

If $X \sim U[8, 18]$, find:

a) P(10 < X < 14.1)

- It's best to start by drawing a sketch of the p.d.f.

- You know that it's a **rectangle** with an **area** of **1** and a **width** of $18 - 8 = $ **10**, so the **height** must be $1 \div 10 = $ **0.1**.

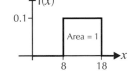

- $P(10 < X < 14.1) = $ the area under the p.d.f. between $x = 10$ and $x = 14.1$. Again, it's a good idea to draw yourself a quick sketch, marking on the area you want to find.

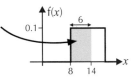

- This area $= (14.1 - 10) \times 0.1 = 4.1 \times 0.1 = 0.41$.
  So $P(10 < X < 14.1) = $ 0.41

b) P(X ≤ 14)

- $P(X \leq 14) = $ the area under the p.d.f. for $x \leq 14$.
- This area $= (14 - 8) \times 0.1 = 6 \times 0.1 = 0.6$.
  So $P(X \leq 14) = $ 0.6

c) P(X < 14)

- For a continuous distribution, $P(X < x) = P(X \leq x)$.
- So $P(X < 14) = P(X \leq 14) = $ 0.6

d) P(X ≥ 10.5)

- $P(X \geq 10.5) = $ the area under the p.d.f. for $x \geq 10.5$.
- This area $= (18 - 10.5) \times 0.1 = 7.5 \times 0.1 = 0.75$.
  So $P(X \geq 10.5) = $ 0.75

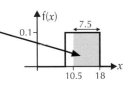

Tip: Remember, for continuous distributions $P(X = x) = 0$, so the signs < and ≤ mean the same thing, as do the signs > and ≥.

Now, suppose that the continuous random variable X is uniformly distributed over the range $[a, b]$ and let Y be a **linear function** of X. Then Y will also follow a **continuous uniform distribution** and you can find the **limits for Y** simply by **substituting the limits for X** into the expression for Y.

In other words...

If $X \sim U[a, b]$ and $Y = cX + d$, then $Y \sim U[(c \times a + d), (c \times b + d)]$

Tip: A linear function is a function of the form $Y = cX + d$.

Example

If $X \sim U[4, 7]$ and $Y = 8X - 3$, write down the distribution of Y. Then find $P(Y > 50)$.

- **Substituting** the limits **4** and **7** into $Y = 8X - 3$, gives:

  $Y \sim U[(8 \times 4 - 3), (8 \times 7 - 3)] \Rightarrow \boxed{Y \sim U[29, 53]}$

- Now you can sketch the p.d.f. of Y.
  The **width** of the rectangle is $(53 - 29) = \mathbf{24}$,
  so the **height** must be $\frac{1}{24}$.

- The area under the p.d.f. for $y > 50 = 3 \times \frac{1}{24} = \frac{1}{8}$.
  So $P(Y > 50) = \boxed{\frac{1}{8}}$

Tip: You need to be able to apply the usual probability rules to random variable problems.

Here's one more example. This time we have **two random variables**, and we need to find the probability that they **both** take values in a certain range.

Example

X and Y are independent random variables, with $X \sim U[1, 3]$ and $Y \sim U[0, 5]$. Find the probability that both X and Y take values greater than 1.2.

Tip: Remember, in S1 you learnt that for independent events A and B: P(A and B) = P(A) × P(B).

- Since X and Y are **independent**:
  $P(X > 1.2 \text{ and } Y > 1.2) = P(X > 1.2) \times P(Y > 1.2)$
- As usual, draw a sketch to help you find the areas.

- **$P(X > 1.2)$** is the area under the p.d.f. for X between 1.2 and 3. That's $0.5 \times 1.8 = \mathbf{0.9}$.

- **$P(Y > 1.2)$** is the area under the p.d.f. for Y between 1.2 and 5. That's $0.2 \times 3.8 = \mathbf{0.76}$.

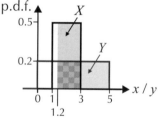

- So $P(X > 1.2 \text{ and } Y > 1.2)$
  $= P(X > 1.2) \times P(Y > 1.2) = 0.9 \times 0.76 = \boxed{0.684}$

Exercise 1.2

Q1 The continuous random variable $X \sim U[1, 9]$. Find:
   a) $P(X > 5)$ b) $P(2 < X < 7)$ c) $P(X \leq 2.4)$

Q2 The continuous random variable $X \sim U[-5, 0]$. Find:
   a) $P(X \geq -3)$ b) $P(-2.4 \leq X \leq -1.2)$ c) $P(X > -6)$

Q3 The continuous random variable X has a uniform distribution with probability density function:

$$f(x) = \begin{cases} 0.1 \text{ for } 3 \leq x \leq 13 \\ 0 \text{ otherwise} \end{cases}$$

Find:

a) $P(X > 7)$ b) $P(4 < X < 11)$ c) $P(X \geq 10.1)$

Q4 The random variable $X \sim U[2, k]$ and $P(X \geq 3) = 0.5$. Find k.

Q5 a) The random variable $Y \sim U[k, 7]$ and $P(2.5 < Y < 4) = 0.25$. Find k.

b) If $Z = 2Y + 1$, find $P(Z < 6)$.

Q6 X and Y are independent random variables with $X \sim U[2, 7]$ and $Y \sim U[4, 5]$. Find the probability that both X and Y are greater than 4.5.

Q7 A school nurse measures the heights of children correct to the nearest centimetre. Let the random variable X represent the error (in cm) in one of the nurse's measurements.

a) Write down the distribution of X.

b) Find the probability that a height recorded by the nurse is more than one millimetre higher than the child's exact height.

Q8 The weights of chocolate bars are measured correct to the nearest quarter of a gram. The random variable X represents the error (in grams) in the measurement of the weight of a chocolate bar.

a) Write down the distribution of X.

b) Find the probability that the recorded weight of a randomly selected chocolate bar will be inaccurate by at least 0.1 g.

c) Stating any assumptions you make, find the probability that two randomly selected chocolate bars will both have recorded weights that are inaccurate by at least 0.1 g.

> **Q8 a) Hint:** Write the distribution using decimals.

> **Q8 b) Hint:** You need to consider both ends of the distribution.

The mean and variance

Suppose you have a random variable $X \sim U[a, b]$.

You can work out the **expected value** (or **mean**) and the **variance** of X using the formulas below.

$$E(X) = \frac{a + b}{2} \qquad Var(X) = \frac{(b - a)^2}{12}$$

Example 1

Find the expected value and the variance of $X \sim U[4, 10]$.

- Use the formulas.

$$E(X) = \frac{a + b}{2} = \frac{4 + 10}{2} = \boxed{7}$$

$$Var(X) = \frac{(b - a)^2}{12} = \frac{(10 - 4)^2}{12} = \boxed{3}$$

Example 2

Find the expected value and the variance of $Y \sim U[-6, 15]$.

- Again, just use the formulas.

$$E(Y) = \frac{a + b}{2} = \frac{-6 + 15}{2} = \boxed{4.5}$$

$$Var(X) = \frac{(b - a)^2}{12} = \frac{(15 - (-6))^2}{12}$$
$$= \frac{21^2}{12}$$
$$= \frac{147}{4} = \boxed{36.75}$$

Example 3

If $X \sim U[a, b]$, and $E(X) = Var(X) = 1$, find a and b.

- First, use the formula for $E(X)$.

$$E(X) = \frac{a + b}{2} = 1.$$
So $a + b = 2$, or $a = 2 - b$.

- Next, use the formula for $Var(X)$.

$$Var(X) = \frac{(b - a)^2}{12} = 1.$$
So $(b - a)^2 = b^2 - 2ab + a^2 = 12$.

- Substitute in your expression for a ($= 2 - b$).

$$b^2 - 2ab + a^2 = b^2 - 2b(2 - b) + (2 - b)^2$$
$$= b^2 - 4b + 2b^2 + 4 - 4b + b^2$$
$$= 4b^2 - 8b + 4 = 12$$

- Rearrange the last line of this working to get a quadratic equation in b.
$$b^2 - 2b - 2 = 0$$

- Solve using the quadratic formula.

$$b = \frac{2 \pm \sqrt{(-2)^2 - 4 \times 1 \times (-2)}}{2}$$
$$= \frac{2 \pm \sqrt{12}}{2}$$
$$= 1 \pm \sqrt{3}$$

- Pick the correct solution for b.

It looks like there are two possible values here for b, but remember that $a = 2 - b$.
So if $b = 1 - \sqrt{3}$, then $a = 2 - (1 - \sqrt{3}) = 1 + \sqrt{3}$.
But this would mean that $a > b$ — and you know that $b > a$.
So this means $\boxed{b = 1 + \sqrt{3}}$, giving $a = 2 - (1 + \sqrt{3})$, i.e. $\boxed{a = 1 - \sqrt{3}}$

Tip: You know that $b > a$, because $X \sim U[a, b]$.

Using the formulas to find the mean or variance is pretty easy.

But in the exam, you could be asked to **derive** the formulas from first principles — this means working the formulas out for yourself from scratch. The working is shown on the next couple of pages — make sure you can follow every line.

Deriving the formula for the expected value of U[a, b]

You saw on p68 that if X is a continuous random variable with p.d.f. f(x), then its mean (μ) or expected value (E(X)) is given by:

$$E(X) = \mu = \int_{-\infty}^{\infty} xf(x)dx$$

So take this formula as your starting point, substitute in the expression for the p.d.f. of X, and then integrate very carefully.

$$\mathbf{E(X)} = \int_{-\infty}^{\infty} xf(x)dx = \int_{a}^{b} x\left(\frac{1}{b-a}\right)dx \longleftarrow \text{Since } f(x) = \begin{cases} \frac{1}{b-a} & \text{for } a \leq x \leq b \\ 0 & \text{otherwise} \end{cases}$$

$$= \frac{1}{b-a}\int_{a}^{b} xdx \longleftarrow \text{Since } \frac{1}{b-a} \text{ is just a number}$$

$$= \frac{1}{b-a}\left[\frac{x^2}{2}\right]_{a}^{b} \longleftarrow \text{Integrating 'x'}$$

$$= \frac{1}{b-a}\left[\frac{b^2}{2} - \frac{a^2}{2}\right]$$

$$= \frac{b^2 - a^2}{2(b-a)}$$

$$= \frac{(b-a)(b+a)}{2(b-a)} \longleftarrow \text{Since } b^2 - a^2 = (b-a)(b+a)$$

$$= \frac{b+a}{2} = \frac{a+b}{2}$$

You can also see from the **symmetry** of the p.d.f. that the expected value of X must be **halfway between** a and b.

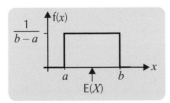

- The p.d.f. of the continuous uniform distribution is symmetrical about the midpoint of a and b, which is at $x = \frac{a+b}{2}$.
- X is equally likely to fall **anywhere** in this range. So every value that X takes **above** the midpoint is likely to be balanced by a value that falls just as far **below** the midpoint.
- Eventually, all these values will 'cancel each other out', meaning the expected value must be at $x = \frac{a+b}{2}$.

Deriving the formula for the variance of U[a, b]

Deriving the formula for the **variance** is slightly trickier...

You saw on p71 that if X is a continuous random variable with p.d.f. f(x), then its variance (Var(X) = σ^2) is given by:

$$\sigma^2 = \int_{-\infty}^{\infty} x^2 f(x)dx - \mu^2$$

Tip: Remember...
Var(X) = E(X^2) − [E(X)]^2
$\quad$ = E(X^2) − μ^2

So E(X^2) = Var(X) + μ^2
$\quad = \int_{-\infty}^{\infty} x^2 f(x)dx$

$$\mathbf{Var}(X) = \int_{-\infty}^{\infty} x^2 f(x)dx - \mu^2$$

$$= \int_{a}^{b} x^2\left(\frac{1}{b-a}\right)dx - \mu^2 \quad \longleftarrow \text{Since } f(x) = \begin{cases} \dfrac{1}{b-a} & \text{for } a \le x \le b \\ 0 & \text{otherwise} \end{cases}$$

$$= \frac{1}{b-a}\int_{a}^{b} x^2 dx - \mu^2 \quad \longleftarrow \text{Since } \frac{1}{b-a} \text{ is just a number}$$

$$= \frac{1}{b-a}\left[\frac{x^3}{3}\right]_{a}^{b} - \mu^2 \quad \longleftarrow \text{Integrating '}x^2\text{'}$$

$$= \frac{1}{b-a}\left[\frac{b^3}{3} - \frac{a^3}{3}\right] - \mu^2$$

$$= \frac{b^3 - a^3}{3(b-a)} - \left(\frac{a+b}{2}\right)^2 \quad \longleftarrow \text{Since } \mu = \frac{a+b}{2}$$

$$= \frac{b^2 + ab + a^2}{3} - \frac{(a+b)(a+b)}{4} \quad \begin{array}{l}\text{Since } b^3 - a^3 \\ = (b-a)(b^2 + ab + a^2)\end{array}$$

$$= \frac{b^2 + ab + a^2}{3} - \frac{a^2 + 2ab + b^2}{4}$$

$$= \frac{4b^2 + 4ab + 4a^2 - 3a^2 - 6ab - 3b^2}{12}$$

$$= \frac{b^2 - 2ab + a^2}{12}$$

$$= \frac{(b-a)^2}{12}$$

Tip: Remember...
$$\frac{b^3 - a^3}{3(b-a)}$$
$$= \frac{(b-a)(b^2 + ab + a^2)}{3(b-a)}$$
$$= \frac{b^2 + ab + a^2}{3}$$

Exercise 1.3

Q1 Find E(X) for these distributions.

$\quad$ a) $X \sim$ U[1, 7] $\qquad$ b) $X \sim$ U[0, $\frac{1}{3}$] $\qquad$ c) $X \sim$ U[−24, −6]

Q2 Find Var(X) for these distributions.

$\quad$ a) $X \sim$ U[2, 5] $\qquad$ b) $X \sim$ U[−0.25, 0.75] $\quad$ c) $X \sim$ U[−30, −18]

Q3 The continuous random variable X is uniformly distributed with this probability density function:

$$f(x) = \begin{cases} 0.4 & 3.9 \le x \le 6.4 \\ 0 & \text{otherwise} \end{cases}$$

$\quad$ Find E(X) and Var(X).

Chapter 4 Continuous Distributions

Q4 The continuous random variable X has a uniform distribution with p.d.f. f(x) shown below.

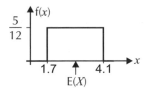

Find E(X) and Var(X).

Q5 The continuous random variable X is such that $X \sim U[13, 17]$.
a) Find E(X) and Var(X).
b) The continuous random variable $Y = 2X - 9$. Find E(Y) and Var(Y).

Q6 The continuous random variable X is such that $X \sim U[3, k]$.
If E(X) = 4.5, find k.

Q7 Babies' weights are measured to the nearest 10 g.
If X represents the errors in the measurements (in grams):
a) State the distribution of X.
b) Find E(X) and Var(X).

The cumulative distribution function

Remember, a **cumulative distribution function** (c.d.f.), F(x), shows $P(X \leq x)$.
If X has a continuous uniform distribution $U[a, b]$, then its c.d.f. is:

$$F(x) = \begin{cases} 0 & \text{for } x < a \\ \dfrac{x-a}{b-a} & \text{for } a \leq x \leq b \\ 1 & \text{for } x > b \end{cases}$$

Tip: There's a lot more information about cumulative distribution functions on pages 59-66.

Example 1

If $X \sim U[1, 11]$, find:

a) F(x)

- Use the formula with $a = 1$ and $b = 11$.

$$\frac{x-a}{b-a} = \frac{x-1}{11-1} = \frac{x-1}{10}$$

- Don't forget to write down all 3 parts.

So $F(x) = \begin{cases} 0 & \text{for } x < 1 \\ \dfrac{x-1}{10} & \text{for } 1 \leq x \leq 11 \\ 1 & \text{for } x > 11 \end{cases}$

b) P($X \leq 4$)

- Put $x = 4$ into your formula.

$$P(X \leq 4) = F(4) = \frac{4-1}{10}$$
$$= \boxed{0.3}$$

As always, watch out if there are minus signs around.

> **Example 2**
>
> If $X \sim U[-7, 22]$, find:
>
> a) $F(x)$
>
> - Here, $a = -7$ and $b = 22$. $\quad \dfrac{x - a}{b - a} = \dfrac{x - (-7)}{22 - (-7)} = \dfrac{x + 7}{29}$
>
> $$\text{So } F(x) = \begin{cases} 0 & \text{for } x < -7 \\ \dfrac{x + 7}{29} & \text{for } -7 \leq x \leq 22 \\ 1 & \text{for } x > 22 \end{cases}$$
>
> b) $P(X \leq -3)$
>
> - Put $x = -3$ into your formula. $\quad P(X \leq -3) = F(-3) = \dfrac{-3 + 7}{29} = \dfrac{4}{29}$

Deriving the formula for the c.d.f. of $U[a, b]$

Tip: Remember...
The p.d.f. of a continuous random variable $X \sim U[a, b]$ is:

$$f(x) = \begin{cases} \dfrac{1}{b - a} & \text{for } a \leq x \leq b \\ 0 & \text{otherwise} \end{cases}$$

You need to be able to derive the general formula for the c.d.f. of a continuous uniform distribution.

You saw on p60 that if X is a continuous random variable with p.d.f. $f(x)$, then to find its c.d.f. $F(x)$ you need to **integrate**.

$$F(x) = \int_{-\infty}^{x} f(t)\,dt$$

There are **three** parts to work out:

- For $x < a$:

$$F(x) = \int_{-\infty}^{x} 0\,dt = 0$$

Tip: So to make the join at $x = a$ 'smooth', you must have
$F(a) = \int_{-\infty}^{a} f(t)\,dt = 0$.

Or you could use the **graph**:

- For $x_0 < a$, the area under the p.d.f. to the left of x_0 is 0.
- So $F(x_0) = P(X \leq x_0) = 0$.

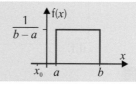

Tip: It's better to use a specific value x_0 when you're working out the c.d.f. using a graph — then it can't be confused with the variable on the horizontal axis.

- For $a \leq x \leq b$:

$$F(x) = \int_{-\infty}^{a} f(t)\,dt + \int_{a}^{x} f(t)\,dt$$
$$= F(a) + \int_{a}^{x} \frac{1}{b - a}\,dt$$
$$= 0 + \left[\frac{t}{b - a} \right]_{a}^{x}$$
$$= \frac{x}{b - a} - \frac{a}{b - a}$$
$$= \frac{x - a}{b - a}$$

Tip: This tells you that
$F(b) = \dfrac{b - a}{b - a} = 1$.

Or you could use the **graph**:

- For $a \leq x_0 \leq b$, the area under the p.d.f. to the left of x_0 is the area of the shaded rectangle.
- So $F(x_0) = P(X \leq x_0) = \dfrac{x_0 - a}{b - a}$.

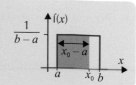

- For $x > b$:

$$F(x) = \int_{-\infty}^{b} f(t)\,dt + \int_{b}^{x} f(t)\,dt$$
$$= F(b) + \int_{b}^{x} 0\,dt$$
$$= 1 + 0 = 1$$

Or you could use the **graph**:
- For $x_0 > b$, the area under the p.d.f. to the left of x_0 is 1.
- So $F(x_0) = P(X \le x_0) = 1$.

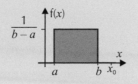

Using a c.d.f. to find a p.d.f.

You can use all the normal properties of a c.d.f. to find probabilities.

And since you **integrate** a p.d.f. of a continuous uniform distribution to find the corresponding c.d.f., you can **differentiate** the c.d.f. to find the corresponding p.d.f.

Example

The continuous random variable X has c.d.f. $F(x)$ as shown below.

$$F(x) = \begin{cases} 0 & \text{for } x < 3 \\ \dfrac{x-3}{15} & \text{for } 3 \le x \le 18 \\ 1 & \text{for } x > 18 \end{cases}$$

a) Use F(x) to find P(4 < X < 12).

- Just use the normal properties of a c.d.f.
$$P(4 < X < 12) = P(X < 12) - P(X \le 4)$$
$$= \frac{9}{15} - \frac{1}{15} = \boxed{\frac{8}{15}}$$

Tip: Remember...
$$P(a < X < b)$$
$$= P(X < b) - P(X \le a)$$

b) Find f(x), the p.d.f. of X.

- Differentiate the different parts of the c.d.f. separately.
  For $x < 3$:
$$f(x) = \frac{d}{dx}(0) = 0$$
  For $3 \le x \le 18$:
$$f(x) = \frac{d}{dx}\left(\frac{x-3}{15}\right) = \frac{1}{15}$$
  For $x > 18$:
$$f(x) = \frac{d}{dx}(1) = 0$$

- So $f(x) = \begin{cases} \dfrac{1}{15} & \text{for } 3 \le x \le 18 \\ 0 & \text{otherwise} \end{cases}$

Exercise 1.4

Q1 The continuous random variable X is such that $X \sim U[15, 19]$.

a) Find the probability density function $f(x)$.

b) Find the cumulative distribution function $F(x)$.

c) Find $F(16)$.

Q2 The graph shows the probability density function $f(x)$ of a continuous random variable X.

a) Find the cumulative distribution function $F(x)$.

b) Use $F(x)$ to find $P(X < 8.4)$.

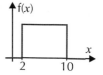

Q3 The cumulative distribution function of a continuous random variable X is given by:

$$F(x) = \begin{cases} 0 & x < 22 \\ \dfrac{x - 22}{7} & 22 \leq x \leq 29 \\ 1 & x > 29 \end{cases}$$

a) Find $P(X < 24)$.

b) Find the probability density function $f(x)$ of X.

Q4 The cumulative distribution function of a continuous random variable X is given by:

$$F(x) = \begin{cases} 0 & x < 1.7 \\ 5(x - 1.7) & 1.7 \leq x \leq 1.9 \\ 1 & x > 1.9 \end{cases}$$

Find $E(X)$ and $Var(X)$.

Q5 Given that X is a uniformly distributed random variable with $E(X) = 11$ and $Var(X) = \dfrac{4}{3}$, find the c.d.f. $F(x)$.

2. Normal Approximations

You met the normal distribution $N(\mu, \sigma^2)$ in S1. There are no gaps between its possible values, so it's a continuous distribution. But with a little care, it can be used to approximate two important discrete distributions.

Learning Objectives:

- Be able to apply a continuity correction when using a normal distribution to approximate a discrete random variable.
- Be able to use a normal approximation to a binomial random variable.
- Be able to use a normal approximation to a Poisson random variable.

Continuity corrections

The normal distribution can be used to approximate both the binomial and Poisson distributions under particular circumstances.

But using the normal distribution (which is continuous) to approximate a discrete distribution is slightly awkward.

- The binomial and Poisson distributions are **discrete**, so if the random variable X follows either of these distributions, you can work out $P(X = 0)$, $P(X = 1)$, etc.
- But a normally-distributed variable is **continuous**, and so if $Y \sim N(\mu, \sigma^2)$, $P(Y = 0) = P(Y = 1) = 0$, etc. (see page 55).

To allow for this, you have to use a **continuity correction**.

- You assume that the discrete value $X = 1$ is 'spread out' over the interval $0.5 < Y < 1.5$.

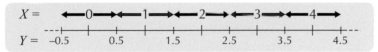

- Then to approximate the discrete probability $P(X = 1)$, you find the continuous probability $P(0.5 < Y < 1.5)$.
- Similarly, the discrete value $X = 2$ is spread out over the interval $1.5 < Y < 2.5$, so $P(X = 2)$ is approximated by $P(1.5 < Y < 2.5)$, and so on.

The interval you need to use with the normal distribution depends on the discrete probability you're trying to find out.

The general idea is always the same, though — each discrete value b covers the continuous interval from $b - \frac{1}{2}$ up to $b + \frac{1}{2}$.

Discrete	Normal	
$P(X = b)$	$P(b - \frac{1}{2} < Y < b + \frac{1}{2})$	
$P(X \leq b)$	$P(Y < b + \frac{1}{2})$	...to include b
$P(X < b)$	$P(Y < b - \frac{1}{2})$	...to exclude b
$P(X \geq b)$	$P(Y > b - \frac{1}{2})$	...to include b
$P(X > b)$	$P(Y > b + \frac{1}{2})$	...to exclude b

Q1 A discrete random variable X has possible values 0, 1, 2, 3...
X is to be approximated by the normal variable Y.
What interval for Y would you find to approximate:

a) $P(X = 5)$?　　b) $P(12 \leq X \leq 15)$?　c) $P(X \leq 10)$?

Q2 The random variable X follows a binomial distribution.
The normal random variable Y is to be used to approximate probabilities for X.
Write down the probability for Y that would approximate:

a) $P(X = 200)$　　b) $P(X < 300)$　　c) $P(X \geq 99)$

Q3 A discrete random variable X following a Poisson distribution is to be approximated by the normal random variable Y. Write down the probability for Y that would approximate:

a) $P(X = 50)$　　b) $P(X > 33)$　　c) $P(X = 48$ or $X = 49)$

Q4 An unfair coin is to be tossed 1000 times and the number of heads (X) recorded. A random variable Y following a normal distribution is to be used to approximate the probabilities below. Write down the probability for Y that would approximate:

a) the probability of getting exactly 200 heads

b) the probability of getting at least 650 heads

c) the probability of getting less than 300 heads

Normal approximation to a binomial distribution

Certain **binomial** distributions can be approximated by a normal distribution (as long as you use a **continuity correction**).

For the normal approximation to a binomial distribution to work well, you need the following conditions to be true:

> Suppose the random variable X follows a
> **binomial distribution**, i.e. $X \sim B(n, p)$.
>
> If　(i)　$p \approx \dfrac{1}{2}$,
>
> and　(ii)　n is large,
>
> then X can be approximated by the normal
> random variable $Y \sim N(np, npq)$, where $q = 1 - p$.

- This means that as long as p isn't too far from $\dfrac{1}{2}$ and n is quite large, then you don't need to use $B(n, p)$ to work out probabilities for X. (And remember... if n is large, $B(n, p)$ can be quite tricky to use.)

- Instead you can get a good approximation to the probabilities for X using a normal distribution.

- In fact, even if p isn't all that close to 0.5, this approximation usually works well as long as *np* and *nq* are **both bigger than 5**.

Tip: Use the mean and variance of the **binomial** distribution as the mean and variance of the **normal** approximation.

So use the approximation $N(\mu, \sigma^2)$, where:

i)　$\mu = np$, and

ii)　$\sigma^2 = npq$

See pages 18-19 for more about the mean and variance of a binomial distribution.

Tip: Remember... the symbol '$\approx$' means 'approximately equal to'.

Example 1

The random variable $X \sim B(80, 0.4)$ is to be approximated using the normally distributed random variable $Y \sim N(\mu, \sigma^2)$.

a) **Verify that a normal approximation is appropriate, and specify the distribution of Y.**

- n is fairly large, and p is not far from $\frac{1}{2}$, so a normal approximation is appropriate.
- $E(X) = np = 80 \times 0.4 = 32$
  $Var(X) = npq = np(1 - p) = 80 \times 0.4 \times 0.6 = 19.2$
- So use the approximation $\boxed{Y \sim N(32, 19.2)}$

Tip: So the standard deviation of Y is $\sigma = \sqrt{19.2}$.

b) **Apply a continuity correction to the probability $P(32 < X \leq 35)$.**

- This means you need to write down the probability for Y that corresponds to this probability for X.
- $P(32 < X \leq 35)$ means the probability that X is either 33, 34 or 35.
- So using a continuity correction, this corresponds to $\boxed{P(32.5 < Y < 35.5)}$.

Tip: Remember... X is a discrete random variable (it follows a binomial distribution). So $P(32 < X \leq 35)$ means $P(X = 33, 34$ or $35)$.

c) **Use Z-tables to find an approximate value for $P(32 < X \leq 35)$.**

- Now you have to transform your normal variable Y to the standard normal variable $Z \sim N(0, 1)$, and use Z-tables to find $P(32.5 < Y < 35.5)$.

$$P(32.5 < Y < 35.5) = P\left(\frac{32.5 - 32}{\sqrt{19.2}} < Z < \frac{35.5 - 32}{\sqrt{19.2}}\right)$$
$$= P(0.11 < Z < 0.80)$$
$$= P(Z < 0.80) - P(Z \leq 0.11)$$
$$= 0.7881 - 0.5438 = \boxed{0.2443}$$

Tip: Remember... transform $Y \sim N(\mu, \sigma^2)$ to the standard normal variable $Z \sim N(0, 1)$ by subtracting the mean of Y ($= \mu$) and then dividing by its standard deviation ($= \sigma$):
$$Z = \frac{Y - \mu}{\sigma}$$

You need to round your z-values to 2 decimal places so that you can look them up in normal distribution tables.

(See pages 157-158 for normal distribution tables.)

If you find it helps to draw a graph while doing this kind of question, then you definitely should. For example:

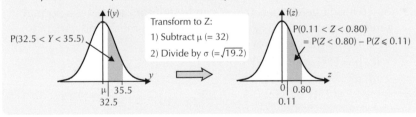

d) **Use Z-tables to find an approximate value for $P(X < 45)$.**
- Go through the same process for this new probability.
- With a continuity correction, you need to find **$P(Y < 44.5)$**.
- So now transform this to a probability for Z, and use Z-tables.

$$P(Y < 44.5) = P\left(Z < \frac{44.5 - 32}{\sqrt{19.2}}\right)$$
$$= P(Z < 2.85)$$
$$= \boxed{0.9978}$$

Tip: Remember...
Z-tables only tell you
probabilities $P(Z \le z)$ for
$z \ge 0$.

If you have to find
$P(Z > z)$, or you have
a value of $z < 0$, then
you need to draw (or
imagine) a picture of
the normal distribution
curve:

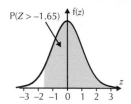

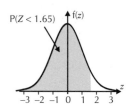

You're going to need to remember how to use Z-tables to find all sorts of probabilities. If in doubt, sketch a graph.

Example 2

The random variable $X \sim B(90, 0.47)$.
Use a normal approximation to find $P(X \ge 35)$.

- Approximate X with $Y \sim N(\mu, \sigma^2)$, where:
  i) $\mu = 90 \times 0.47 = 42.3$
  ii) $\sigma^2 = 90 \times 0.47 \times (1 - 0.47) = 22.419$
- With a continuity correction, you need to find $P(Y > 34.5)$.
- So now transform this to a probability for Z, and use Z-tables.

$$P(Y > 34.5) = P\left(Z > \frac{34.5 - 42.3}{\sqrt{22.419}}\right)$$
$$= P(Z > -1.65)$$
$$= P(Z < 1.65)$$
$$= 0.9505$$

This is one of the reasons why the normal distribution is so amazingly useful — because it can be used to approximate other distributions. It means you can use it in all sorts of real-life situations.

Example 3

Each piglet born on a farm is equally likely to be male or female.

a) **Out of the next 250 piglets born, use a suitable approximation to find the probability that there will be more males born than females.**

- First define the random variable, and state how it is distributed.
  If X represents the number of male piglets born,
  then $X \sim B(250, 0.5)$.

- Since n is large and p is 0.5, X can be approximated by a normal random variable $Y \sim N(\mu, \sigma^2)$. Work out the mean and variance of X to find the values of μ and σ^2.
  i) $\mu = E(X) = np = 250 \times 0.5 = 125$, and
  ii) $\sigma^2 = Var(X) = np(1 - p)$
  $= 250 \times 0.5 \times 0.5 = 62.5$.

  So $Y \sim N(125, 62.5)$.

- Apply a continuity correction to the normal variable Y...
  $P(X > 125) \approx P(Y > 125.5)$

- ...then transform this to Z, and use your Z-tables.
  $$P(Y > 125.5) = P\left(Z > \frac{125.5 - 125}{\sqrt{62.5}}\right)$$
  $$= P(Z > 0.06)$$
  $$= 1 - P(Z \le 0.06)$$
  $$= 1 - 0.5239 = 0.4761$$

Tip: Using
B(250, 0.5) instead
of the normal
approximation, you get
0.4748 (to 4 d.p.) —
so this is a very good
approximation.

b) Use your approximation to find the probability that exactly 110 male piglets will be born.

- Apply a continuity correction to the normal variable Y.
   $P(X = 110) \approx P(109.5 < Y < 110.5)$.

- Transform to Z, and use your Z-tables.

$$P(109.5 < Y < 110.5) = P\left(\frac{109.5 - 125}{\sqrt{62.5}} < Z < \frac{110.5 - 125}{\sqrt{62.5}}\right)$$
$$= P(-1.96 < Z < -1.83)$$
$$= P(1.83 < Z < 1.96)$$
$$= P(Z < 1.96) - P(Z \le 1.83)$$
$$= 0.9750 - 0.9664$$
$$= \boxed{0.0086}$$

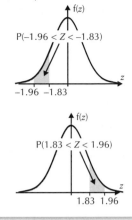

Tip: Remember... if in doubt, draw a sketch:

$P(-1.96 < Z < -1.83)$

$P(1.83 < Z < 1.96)$

The normal approximation can work well even for p slightly further from $\frac{1}{2}$.

Tip: Using B(250, 0.5) instead of the normal approximation, you get 0.0084 (to 4 d.p.). So this is also a very good approximation.

Example 4

a) Only 23% of the young of a particular species of bird survive to adulthood. If 80 chicks of this species are randomly selected, use a suitable approximation to find the probability that at least 30% of them survive.

- Start by defining the random variable, and stating how it is distributed.
   If X represents the number of survivors, then $X \sim \text{B}(80, 0.23)$.

- Here, p **isn't** particularly close to 0.5, but n is quite large, so calculate np and nq:
   $np = 80 \times 0.23 = \mathbf{18.4}$ and $nq = 80 \times (1 - 0.23) = \mathbf{61.6}$.
   Both np and nq are much greater than 5, so X can be approximated by a continuous random variable $Y \sim \text{N}(\mu, \sigma^2)$. Work out the mean and variance of X to find the values of μ and σ^2.
   i) $\mu = np = 18.4$, and
   ii) $\sigma^2 = \text{Var}(X) = np(1-p) = 80 \times 0.23 \times (1 - 0.23)$
   $\qquad\qquad = 14.168$

   So $Y \sim \mathbf{N(18.4, 14.168)}$.

- Apply a continuity correction to the normal variable Y.
   30% of 80 = 24, which means you need to find $P(X \ge 24)$.
   So with a continuity correction, you need to find $P(Y > 23.5)$.

- Transform to Z, and use your Z-tables.

$$P(Y > 23.5) = P\left(Z > \frac{23.5 - 18.4}{\sqrt{14.168}}\right)$$
$$= P(Z > 1.35)$$
$$= 1 - P(Z \le 1.35)$$
$$= 1 - 0.9115 = \boxed{0.0885}$$

Tip: Although p isn't particularly close to $\frac{1}{2}$, the normal approximation should still work reasonably well as long as np and nq are both greater than 5 — see p98.

Tip: Draw a normal curve if you need to:

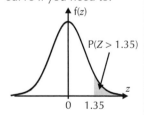

$P(Z > 1.35)$

Tip: Using the original binomial distribution of B(80, 0.23) gives an answer of 0.0904 (to 4 d.p.), so this is a pretty good approximation (it's correct to 2 decimal places).

b) If the survival rate were instead 18%, find the probability that more than three-quarters of the 80 chicks would die.

- The distribution of X has changed, so you should check that a normal approximation is still reasonable.

    This time, if X is the number of survivors, then $X \sim B(80, 0.18)$ — this means $np = 80 \times 0.18 = 14.4$ and $nq = 80 \times (1 - 0.18) = 65.6$. Again, even though p is now quite far from 0.5, these are both much greater than 5, so a normal approximation should be reasonable.

    $np = 14.4$ and $npq = 80 \times 0.18 \times (1 - 0.18) = 11.808$

    So approximate X with the random variable $Y \sim N(14.4, 11.808)$.

- State the probability you need to find, and apply a continuity correction to find the equivalent probability for Y.

    If more than three-quarters of the chicks do **not** survive, that means you need to find $P(X < 20)$.

    With a continuity correction, this means you need $P(Y < 19.5)$.

- Transform to Z, and use your Z-tables.

$$P(Y < 19.5) = P\left(Z < \frac{19.5 - 14.4}{\sqrt{11.808}}\right)$$
$$= P(Z < 1.48)$$
$$= \boxed{0.9306}$$

Tip: Using the original binomial distribution B(80, 0.18) gives an answer of 0.9270 (to 4 d.p.), so this is another pretty good approximation (again, it's correct to 2 decimal places).

Exercise 2.2

Q1 Which of the binomial distributions described below would a normal approximation be suitable for? Give reasons for your answers.

a) $X \sim B(600, 0.51)$ b) $X \sim B(100, 0.98)$

c) $X \sim B(100, 0.85)$ d) $X \sim B(6, 0.5)$

Q2 The normal random variable $Y \sim N(\mu, \sigma^2)$ is to be used to approximate these binomial distributions. Find μ and σ^2 in each case.

a) $X \sim B(350, 0.45)$ b) $X \sim B(250, 0.35)$ c) $X \sim B(70, 0.501)$

Q3 The random variable $X \sim B(200, 0.6)$.
Use the normal approximation to the binomial distribution to find:

a) $P(X < 105)$ b) $P(X = 122)$ c) $P(110 < X < 130)$

Q4 The random variable $X \sim B(1000, 0.48)$.
Use a normal approximation to find:

a) $P(X \geq 500)$ b) $P(X < 472)$ c) $P(492 \leq X \leq 502)$

Q5 The random variable X is such that $X \sim B(80, 0.8)$.

a) Calculate $P(X = 70)$ using the normal approximation to the binomial distribution.

b) Calculate $P(X = 70)$ using the binomial distribution. Give your answer correct to four decimal places.

Q6 A biased dice has a probability of 0.39 of landing on an even number. The dice is rolled 400 times. Use a suitable approximation to estimate the probability that more than 140 even numbers are rolled.

Q7 It is estimated that 5% of people are carriers of a certain disease. A health authority tests a sample of 1000 people to see if they carry the disease. If more than 75 people test positive they will offer a vaccination to the whole population.

    a) Which distribution could be used to model this situation? Include the parameters of the distribution in your answer.

    b) Explain why the normal distribution would be a suitable approximation for this distribution.

    c) Estimate the probability that the whole population will be offered a vaccination.

Q8 The Acme and Buildit companies manufacture light bulbs. 5% of Acme's light bulbs are faulty, whereas only 2% of Buildit's light bulbs are faulty. When carrying out quality control:

- Acme choose 200 bulbs at random and reject all the bulbs manufactured that day if more than 15 of the sample are faulty.
- Buildit select 500 bulbs at random and reject all the bulbs manufactured that day if more than 20 of the sample are faulty.

Use the normal approximation to the binomial distribution to test which company's light bulbs are more likely to be rejected on any given day.

Normal approximation to a Poisson distribution

The normal distribution can also be used to approximate certain **Poisson distributions** (yet another reason why the normal distribution is so important).

Because a Poisson distribution is **discrete**, you still have to use a **continuity correction**.

For the normal approximation to a Poisson distribution to work well, you need the following condition to hold:

> Suppose the random variable X follows a **Poisson distribution**, i.e. $X \sim \text{Po}(\lambda)$.
>
> If λ is large, then X can be approximated by the normal random variable $Y \sim N(\lambda, \lambda)$.

- Ideally, you want λ 'as large as possible'. In practice, as long as $\lambda > 10$, then the approximation should be fine.

Tip: Remember... you need to use a continuity correction because a Poisson distribution is **discrete** (it can only take values 0, 1, 2...), but a normal distribution is **continuous**. See p97 for more information.

Tip: Use the mean and variance of the Poisson distribution (which both equal λ — see p31) as the mean and variance of your normal approximation.

To use the normal approximation to a Poisson distribution, you go through the same steps as when you were approximating a binomial distribution.

Examples

If $X \sim Po(49)$, use a normal approximation to find:

a) $P(X < 50)$

- First find the mean and variance of the normal approximation.

    The mean and variance of X both equal $\lambda = 49$.

    So approximate X using the normal random variable $Y \sim N(49, 49)$.

- Apply a continuity correction to the normal variable Y.

    $P(X < 50) \approx P(Y < 49.5)$

- Transform this to Z, and use your Z-tables.

    $P(Y < 49.5) = P\left(Z < \dfrac{49.5 - 49}{\sqrt{49}}\right)$
    $= P(Z < 0.07)$
    $= \boxed{0.5279}$

Tip: Use a sketch of the normal curve if you need to:

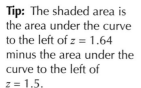

$P(Z > -0.64)$

b) $P(X \geq 45)$

- Apply a continuity correction to the normal variable Y.

    $P(X \geq 45) \approx P(Y > 44.5)$

- Transform this to Z, and use your Z-tables.

    $P(Y > 44.5) = P\left(Z > \dfrac{44.5 - 49}{\sqrt{49}}\right)$
    $= P(Z > -0.64)$
    $= P(Z < 0.64)$
    $= \boxed{0.7389}$

$P(Z < 0.64)$

c) $P(X = 60)$

- Apply a continuity correction to the normal variable Y.

    $P(X = 60) \approx P(59.5 < Y < 60.5)$

- Transform this to Z, and use your Z-tables.

    $$P(59.5 < Y < 60.5) = P\left(\dfrac{59.5 - 49}{\sqrt{49}} < Z < \dfrac{60.5 - 49}{\sqrt{49}}\right)$$
    $$= P(1.5 < Z < 1.64)$$
    $$= P(Z < 1.64) - P(Z \leq 1.50)$$
    $$= 0.9495 - 0.9332 = \boxed{0.0163}$$

Tip: The shaded area is the area under the curve to the left of $z = 1.64$ minus the area under the curve to the left of $z = 1.5$.

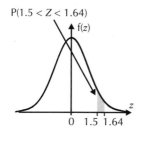

$P(1.5 < Z < 1.64)$

A publishing company produces books containing an average of 2.5 random errors per page.
One particular chapter in a book is 10 pages long.

Use a suitable approximation to find the probability of:
a) fewer than 20 errors in the chapter

- First define the random variable, and state how it is distributed.

    The errors happen randomly, singly and (on average) at a constant rate, and so the number of errors that occur on a single page will follow a Poisson distribution.

    Since there's an average of 2.5 errors per page, the number of errors on one page will follow the distribution Po(2.5). So if X represents the number of errors in 10 pages, then $X \sim \text{Po}(25)$.

- Say why a normal approximation is suitable here...
    ...and state the mean and variance of the normal approximation.

    Since λ is large (greater than 10), you can approximate X using the normal random variable Y, where $Y \sim \text{N}(25, 25)$.

- State the probability you need to find, and apply a continuity correction to find the equivalent probability for the normal variable Y.

    You need to find $P(X < 20)$. With a continuity correction, this is approximately equal to $P(Y < 19.5)$.

- Transform this to Z, and then use your Z-tables.

$$P(Y < 19.5) = P\left(Z < \frac{19.5 - 25}{\sqrt{25}}\right)$$
$$= P(Z < -1.1)$$
$$= P(Z > 1.1)$$
$$= 1 - P(Z \le 1.1)$$
$$= 1 - 0.8643 = \boxed{0.1357}$$

b) exactly 25 errors in the chapter

- Apply a continuity correction to find a probability for Y.
$$P(X = 25) \approx P(24.5 < Y < 25.5)$$

- Transform this to Z, and then use your Z-tables.

$$P(24.5 < Y < 25.5) = P\left(\frac{24.5 - 25}{\sqrt{25}} < Z < \frac{25.5 - 25}{\sqrt{25}}\right)$$
$$= P(-0.1 < Z < 0.1)$$
$$= P(Z < 0.1) - P(Z \le -0.1)$$
$$= P(Z < 0.1) - P(Z \ge 0.1)$$
$$= P(Z < 0.1) - (1 - P(Z < 0.1))$$
$$= 2 \times P(Z < 0.1) - 1$$
$$= 2 \times 0.5398 - 1 = \boxed{0.0796}$$

Tip: Make sure you can follow **all** the rearrangements in b):
(i) $P(-0.1 < Z < 0.1)$
$\quad = P(Z < 0.1)$
$\qquad - P(Z \le -0.1)$

because the shaded area equals:
- the area under the curve to the left of $z = 0.1$ $(= P(Z < 0.1))$...
- ...take away the area to the left of $z = -0.1$ $(= P(Z \le -0.1))$.

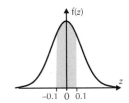

(ii) $P(Z \le -0.1)$
$\quad = P(Z \ge 0.1)$

because of the symmetry of a normal graph.

(iii) $P(Z \ge 0.1)$
$\quad = 1 - P(Z < 0.1)$

because the total area under the curve is 1.

Exercise 2.3

Q1 State whether a normal approximation would be suitable for each of the following Poisson distributions.

a) $X \sim \text{Po}(1)$ b) $X \sim \text{Po}(103)$ c) $X \sim \text{Po}(7)$

Q2 The normal random variable $Y \sim N(\mu, \sigma^2)$ is to be used to approximate these Poisson distributions. Find μ and σ^2 in each case.

a) $X \sim \text{Po}(36)$ b) $X \sim \text{Po}(99)$ c) $X \sim \text{Po}(60)$

Q3 The random variable $X \sim \text{Po}(16)$. Use the normal approximation to the Poisson distribution to estimate:

a) $P(X < 20)$ b) $P(X = 19)$ c) $P(11 < X < 15)$

Q4 The random variable $X \sim \text{Po}(48)$. Use the normal approximation to the Poisson distribution to estimate:

a) $P(X \geq 50)$ b) $P(X < 45)$ c) $P(47 \leq X \leq 51)$

Q5 The random variable $X \sim \text{Po}(50)$.

a) Use the normal approximation to the Poisson distribution to estimate $P(X = 49)$.

b) Calculate $P(X = 49)$ exactly and comment on the accuracy of your answer to part a).

Q6 A website receives on average 156 hits per hour.

a) Which distribution can be used to model X, the number of hits the website receives in an hour?

b) Use the normal variable $Y \sim N(\mu, \sigma^2)$ to approximate the probability that the website will receive:

(i) exactly 160 hits in an hour

(ii) more than 180 hits in an hour

Q7 An average of 20 babies are born every day on a maternity ward.

a) Use a normal approximation to estimate the probability that exactly 22 babies are born on a particular day.

b) Use a normal approximation to estimate the probability that more than 175 babies will be born during a particular week.

Choosing a suitable approximation

You've seen a few different approximations now...

- On pages 40-41 of Chapter 2, you saw how a **Poisson** distribution can be used to approximate the **binomial** distribution.
- Over the last few pages you've seen how a **normal** distribution can be used to approximate **binomial** and **Poisson** distributions.

This can get a bit confusing if you're not careful — so learn all the details in the following two diagrams.

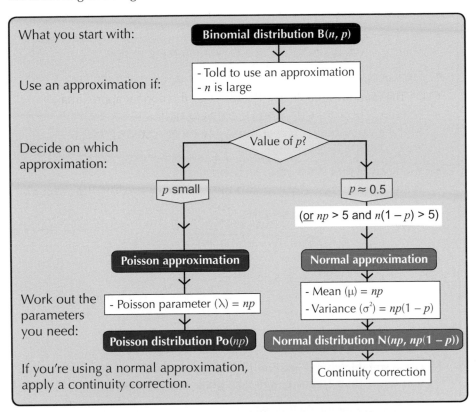

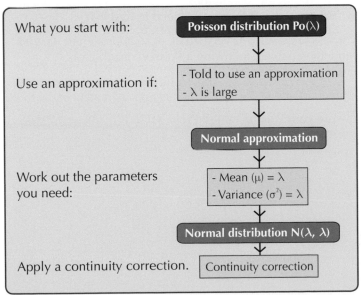

A supermarket gives a customer a free bag when that customer can fit no more items into their existing bags. The number of bags given away was counted. It was found that 62% of customers needed at least one free bag, 2% of customers needed more than 5 free bags, and an average of 8 bags were given away each minute.

If the supermarket has 400 customers one particular morning:

a) Use a suitable approximation to find the probability that more than 250 customers take at least one bag.

Tip: Always go through the same process you've been using so far...

1) First define the random variable, and state how it is distributed.

2) Say which approximation is suitable... and find the necessary parameter(s).

3) Apply a continuity correction if necessary.

- Let X represent the number of customers who take at least one bag. Then $X \sim B(400, 0.62)$, and you need to find $P(X > 250)$.

- Here, n is large and p is not too far from 0.5 — so approximate X with a normal random variable Y.

- The mean of X is $\mu = np = 400 \times 0.62 = 248$.
  And the variance of X is $\sigma^2 = 400 \times 0.62 \times (1 - 0.62) = 94.24$.
  So $Y \sim N(248, 94.24)$.

- You need to find $P(X > 250)$.
  With a continuity correction, this means you have to find $P(Y > 250.5)$.

- Transform to Z, and use Z-tables:

$$P(Y > 250.5) = P\left(Z > \frac{250.5 - 248}{\sqrt{94.24}}\right)$$
$$= P(Z > 0.26)$$
$$= 1 - P(Z \leq 0.26)$$
$$= 1 - 0.6026 = \boxed{0.3974}$$

b) Use a suitable approximation to find the probability that fewer than 10 customers take more than 5 bags.

- Let M represent the total number of customers taking more than 5 bags. Then $M \sim B(400, 0.02)$, and you need to find $P(M < 10)$.

Tip: Both M and L are discrete random variables, so you don't need to use a continuity correction here.

- Here, n is large and p is very small — so approximate M with a random variable L following a Poisson distribution. Here, $L \sim Po(400 \times 0.02) = Po(8)$.

- You need to find $P(M < 10)$, which is approximately equal to $P(L < 10)$.

- Now use your Poisson tables: $P(L < 10) = P(L \leq 9) = \boxed{0.7166}$

c) Use a suitable approximation to find the probability that more than 500 bags are given away in the first hour after the store opens.

- Let R represent the number of bags given away in the first hour. This is not a fixed number of trials, so it's not a binomial distribution. But the period is fixed (1 hour), so it's Poisson.

- Since an average of 8 bags per minute are given away, the number given away per hour will be $60 \times 8 = 480$. So $R \sim \text{Po}(480)$. Here, the Poisson parameter is large, so use a normal approximation.

- Approximate R with the random variable S, where $S \sim \text{N}(480, 480)$.

- You need to find $P(R > 500)$. With a continuity correction, this is approximately equal to $P(S > 500.5)$.

- Now transform this to Z, and use your Z-tables.

$$P(S > 500.5) = P\left(Z > \frac{500.5 - 480}{\sqrt{480}}\right)$$
$$= P(Z > 0.94)$$
$$= 1 - P(Z \leq 0.94)$$
$$= 1 - 0.8264 = \boxed{0.1736}$$

Exercise 2.4

Q1 State the distribution (including any parameters) that is most suitable to approximate each of the following.
   a) B(60, 0.1)   b) Po(20)
   c) B(200, 0.49)   d) B(200, 0.01)

Q2 Each of the situations in this question can be modelled with a binomial or Poisson distribution. For each situation, state:
   (i)   the exact distribution that describes the situation
   (ii) the distribution you could use as an approximation
   a) The number of doughnuts sold in a particular hour if a shop sells an average of 220 doughnuts every hour.
   b) The number of people who buy low-fat doughnuts if 200 people buy doughnuts altogether, and the probability that someone buys a low-fat doughnut is 0.03.

Q3 A school cafeteria sells an average of 27 cheesy oatcakes every breaktime.
   a) State the distribution modelling this situation.
   b) Use a suitable approximation to estimate the probability that the cafeteria sells more than 30 cheesy oatcakes one breaktime.

Q4 An unbiased dice is rolled 1000 times. Use a suitable approximation to estimate the probability that an even number is rolled on fewer than 480 occasions.

Review Exercise — Chapter 4

Q1 Define and sketch the p.d.f.s of the following random variables:

    a) $X \sim U[7, 11]$,   b) $Y \sim U[-4, 18]$.

Q2 The random variable $X \sim U[0, 10]$. Find:

    a) $P(X < 4)$,   b) $P(X \geq 8)$,   c) $P(X = 5)$,   d) $P(3 < X \leq 7)$.

Q3 If $X \sim U[1, 4]$ and $Y = 5X + 2$, define and sketch the probability density function of Y.

Q4 $X \sim U[4, 19]$ and $Y = 6X - 3$.

    a) Calculate E(X), Var(X), and the cumulative distribution function of X, F(x).

    b) Calculate E(Y), Var(Y), and the cumulative distribution function of Y, G(y).

Q5 The distance between two stars is measured to the nearest light year. If the random variable X represents the experimental error (in light years), write down the probability distribution of X.

Q6 X and Y are independent random variables with $X \sim U[4, 8]$ and $Y \sim U[-8, 12]$. Find:

    a) $P(X < 6 \text{ and } Y > 0)$,   b) $P(X < 6 \text{ or } Y > 0)$.

Q7 I travel by train to work five days per week.

My morning train is randomly delayed every morning by anything up to 12 minutes.
If the delay is any greater than 8 minutes, I arrive late for work.

    a) Find the probability that I am late for work on a randomly chosen workday.

    b) Find the probability that I arrive on time every day during a particular working week.

Q8 X is a uniformly distributed random variable with cumulative distribution function given by:

$$F(x) = \begin{cases} 0 & x < 1.75 \\ 4(x - 1.75) & 1.75 \leq x \leq 2 \\ 1 & x > 2 \end{cases}$$

Find:

    a) (i) $P(X < 1.8)$ (ii) $P(X \geq 1.9)$ (iii) $P(1.8 < X < 1.9)$.

    b) The probability density function, f(x).

Q9 The random variable X follows a binomial distribution: $X \sim B(100, 0.45)$.
Using a normal approximation and continuity corrections, find:

    a) $P(X > 50)$,   b) $P(X \leq 45)$,   c) $P(40 < X \leq 47)$.

Q10 The random variable X follows a Poisson distribution: $X \sim Po(25)$.
Using a normal approximation and continuity corrections, find:

    a) $P(X \leq 20)$,   b) $P(X > 15)$,   c) $P(20 \leq X < 30)$.

Q11 I need a new car, because the number of times my current car breaks down per week follows the distribution Po(50). My current record number of breakdowns in a single week is 55. Find the probability that I will set a new record next week.

Exam-Style Questions — Chapter 4

1   The random variable X is binomially distributed with $X \sim B(100, 0.6)$.

    a)   (i)   State the conditions needed for X to be well approximated by
               a normal distribution.

(2 marks)

         (ii) Explain why a continuity correction is necessary in these circumstances.

(2 marks)

    b)   Using a suitable approximation, find:

         (i) $P(X \geq 65)$

(4 marks)

         (ii) $P(50 < X < 62)$

(3 marks)

2   A 40 cm length of ribbon is cut in two at a random point.
The random variable X represents the length of the shorter piece of ribbon in cm.

    a)   Specify the probability distribution of X.

(2 marks)

    b)   Sketch the probability density function of X.

(1 mark)

    c)   Calculate $E(X)$ and $Var(X)$.

(3 marks)

    d)   Find:

         (i) $P(X > 5)$,

(1 mark)

         (ii) $P(X = 2)$.

(1 mark)

3   The random variable X follows a binomial distribution: $X \sim B(n, p)$.
X is approximated by the normally distributed random variable Y.
Using this normal approximation, $P(X \leq 151) = 0.8944$ and $P(X > 127) = 0.9970$.

    a)   Find the mean and standard deviation of the normal approximation.

(8 marks)

    b)   Use your results from a) to find n and p.

(4 marks)

4   A factory has the capacity to increase its output by 50 items per week. A potential new customer has said it could sign a contract to order an average of 40 items per week, although the exact number of items needed each week will vary according to a Poisson distribution.

a)   Specify a distribution that could be used to model the number of extra items that will be ordered per week if the new contract is signed.

(1 mark)

b)   Using a suitable approximation, find the probability that the number of items the potential new customer will order in a given week will exceed the factory's spare capacity.

(3 marks)

c)   The contract says that if the factory does not meet the new customer's order in two consecutive weeks, the factory must pay compensation. The factory's manager decides that he will only sign the contract if the probability of having to pay compensation in a given two-week period is less than 0.01.

Should the factory's manager sign the contract? Explain your answer.

(1 mark)

5   A continuous random variable X is uniformly distributed over the interval $[-2, 7]$.

a)   Fully specify the probability density function of X.

(2 marks)

b)   Sketch the probability density function of X.

(1 mark)

c)   Write down the cumulative distribution function of X.

(2 marks)

A continuous random variable Y is defined by $Y = 3X + 6$.

d)   Calculate:

(i) $E(Y)$,

(2 marks)

(ii) $\text{Var}(Y)$.

(2 marks)

e)   Find:

(i) $P(Y < 20)$,

(1 mark)

(ii) $P(10 < Y < 20)$.

(1 mark)

1. Populations and Samples

For all statistical experiments, you'll need some data. In this section you will learn how to collect information about populations using surveys — and what sort of surveys work best for certain populations.

Populations and censuses

Populations

For any statistical investigation, there will be a **group** of something (it could be people, items, animals... or anything else) that you want to **find out about**.

The **whole group**, consisting of **every single** person/item/animal etc. that you want to investigate, is called the **population**. This could be:

- All the students in a maths class
- All the penguins in Antarctica
- All the chocolate puddings produced by a company in a year

A population can be either **finite** or **infinite**:

- Populations are said to be **finite** if it's possible for someone to **count** how many members there are.
- Populations are said to be **infinite** if it's **impossible** to know exactly how many members there are — there won't literally be infinitely many members... just **too many to count**.

Finite populations	**Infinite populations**
The number of	The number of
...fish in an aquarium.	...fish in the Atlantic Ocean.
...trees in a garden.	...leaves in a forest.
...members in a pop band.	...pop fans in the world.

To collect information about your population, you can carry out a **survey**. This means **questioning** the people or **examining** the items.

Censuses

When you collect information from **every member** of a population, it's called a **census** — it's a **survey** of the **whole population**.

It helps if the population is fairly **small** and **easily accessible** — so that getting information from every member is a straightforward task.

Learning Objectives:

- Know what is meant by a population, and be able to identify whether a population is infinite or finite.
- Know what is meant by a census and a sample, and their advantages and disadvantages.
- Be able to identify the sampling units and the sampling frame of a sample.
- Know what is meant by simple random sampling, and why it should be used.

Tip: This is a bit confusing — a population might have a finite number of members in theory, but if it's impossible to count them all in practice, the population is said to be infinite.

You need to know the **advantages** and **disadvantages** of carrying out a **census**, so here they are:

> ### Advantage
> - It's an **accurate representation** of the population because every member has been surveyed — it's **unbiased**.

> ### Disadvantages
> - For **large** populations, it takes a lot of **time** and **effort** to carry out.
> - This can make it **expensive** to do.
> - It can be difficult to make sure **all** members are surveyed. If some are missed, the survey may be **biased**.
> - If the tested items are **used up** or **damaged** in some way by doing a census, a census is **impractical**.

Sampling

If doing a census is **impossible** or **impractical**, you can find out about a population by questioning or examining just a **selection** of the people or items. This selected group is called a **sample**.

Before selecting your sample, you need to identify the **sampling units** — these are the **individual members** of the population that **can be sampled**.

A **full list** of all the sampling units is called a **sampling frame**. This list must give a **unique name** or **number** to each sampling unit, and is used to represent the population when selecting a random sample (see p116).

Ideally, a sampling frame would be the **whole population** — but this is often **impractical**, especially with **infinite** populations.

Example 1

A company produces 100 chocolate puddings every day, and each pudding is labelled with a unique product number.
Every day, a sample of 5 puddings is eaten as part of a quality control test.

a) **Why is it necessary for the company to take a sample rather than carry out a census?**

   If they did a census of all the puddings, they'd have to eat all the puddings and there would be none left to sell.

b) **Identify the sampling units.**

   The individual puddings.

c) **Suggest a sampling frame.**

   A list of all 100 **unique** product numbers.

Example 2

Mr Simson runs a successful online pet store. He wants to know if his customers are satisfied with the new fish food that he's selling this month. He decides to do a survey by collecting email addresses during the checkout process of each fish-food customer and sending out a questionnaire.

a) **Why might Mr Simson decide to take a sample rather than carry out a census?**

> If he emailed every customer who bought fish food in a month, he'd have a **lot of data** to process. A sample would be much **quicker** and **easier**.

Tip: Often there won't be a reason why a census simply **cannot** be done — it'll just be much quicker or easier to use a sample.

b) **Identify the sampling units.**

> The individual customers who buy the new fish food.

c) **Suggest a sampling frame.**

> A **list** of all the email addresses collected from fish-food customers during the month.

Tip: You'll always be asked to 'suggest' a sampling frame — the list can be in any form (unique numbers, names, letters etc.), as long as every sampling unit can be identified uniquely.

Data collected from a sample is often used to draw **conclusions** about the **whole population** (see p118). So it's important that the sample is as similar to the population as possible — it must be a **representative sample**.

If a sample is not representative, it is **biased**. A biased sample is one which **doesn't fairly represent** the population. A sample could be biased for a **number of reasons** and sometimes it's difficult to get a completely unbiased sample — but there are a few rules you can use to **avoid** introducing bias unnecessarily:

To avoid sampling bias:

- Select from the correct population and make sure none of the population is **excluded** — that means drawing up an accurate **sampling frame**.

  > If you want to find out the views of residents from a particular street, your sample should:
  > - **only include** residents from that street, and
  > - be chosen from a **complete list** of all the residents.

- Select your sample at **random**.

  > **Non-random** sampling methods include, for example, the sampler:
  > - asking friends — who may all give similar answers, or
  > - asking for volunteers — who may all have strong views.

Tip: For more on random sampling, see the next page.

- Make sure all your sample members **respond**.

  > If some of your sampled residents are out when you go to interview them, it's important that you go back and get their views another time.

Taking a random sample is really important for avoiding bias — one way to make sure your sample is completely random is to use **simple random sampling**.

In simple random sampling:

- Every person or item in the population has an **equal chance** of being in the sample.
- Each selection is **independent** of every other selection.

> To get a random sample:
> - Use an accurate **sampling frame**.
> - Give every **sampling unit** a **number**.
> - Generate a list of **random numbers** and **match** them to the sampling units to select your sample.

Here's an example of **simple random sampling** using a **random-number table**.

Tip: Getting a truly random sample may not always be possible — some people in the sample may not respond, may not be possible to contact etc.

Tip: This means every single possible combination of sampling units is equally likely.

Tip: Use a computer, calculator, dice or random number tables to generate random numbers.

Example

A zoo has 80 cottontop tamarins. Describe how the random-number table opposite could be used to select a sample of three of them, for a study on tail lengths.

8330	3992	1840
0330	1290	3237
9165	4815	0766

- First, draw up a **sampling frame** (a list of the 80 cottontop tamarins), giving each cottontop tamarin a **2-digit** number between **01** and **80**.
- Then use the random-number table to choose three numbers — you can use each 4-digit number in the table as two 2-digit numbers next to each other.
- Start at the beginning and find the first three numbers which are between 01 and 80.

  These are too big.

  The first five numbers are: 83, 30, 39, 92, 18

- So choose the numbers 30, 39 and 18.
  Select the cottontop tamarins with the matching numbers.

Tip: You could roll a dice to choose which number to start at in the random-number table. Rolling a four means starting at the fourth 2-digit number in the table.

In most situations, it's **more practical** to survey a **sample** rather than carry out a census, but your results might not be as **reliable** — make sure you can explain **why**.

Advantages

- Sample surveys are **quicker** and **cheaper** than a census, and it's easier to get hold of all the required information.
- It's the only option when surveyed items are **used up** or **damaged**.

Disadvantages

- There'll be **variability** between samples — each possible sample will give **different** results, so you could just happen to select one which doesn't **accurately reflect** the population. E.g. you could randomly pick the 3 tamarins with the longest tails or the 3 with the shortest tails.
- Samples can easily be affected by **sampling bias**.

Tip: One way to reduce the likelihood of large variability is by using a large sample size. The more sampling units that are surveyed, the more reliable the information should be.

Q1   For each population described say whether it is finite or infinite.

   a) The members of the Ulverston Musical Appreciation Society.

   b) The population of Australia.

   c) The stars in the Milky Way galaxy.

   d) The 2008 Olympic gold medallists.

   e) The jalapeño chilli plants on sale at Church Lane Garden Centre.

   f) The cells in a human body.

Q2   Members of a local book club have to be consulted about the next book they'll read.

   a) What is the population?

   b) Suggest a suitable sampling frame.

   c) Explain whether a sample or a census should be used.

Q3   For his GCSE Statistics project, Aiden is investigating whether a student's ability to memorise a random string of letters is related to their ability to spell. He intends to ask students from his school, which has 1200 pupils, to do a standard spelling test and then to memorise a random string of 20 letters. He will then draw a scatter graph and, if appropriate, calculate a correlation coefficient.

   a) What is the population?

   b) Suggest a suitable sampling frame.

   c) Give two reasons why he should use a sample rather than carry out a census.

> **Q3 a) Hint:** The spelling test is standard and the string of numbers is random, so as long as Aiden hasn't seen either of these before, he could do this test on himself.

Q4   All dogs which are admitted to the Graymar Animal Sanctuary are microchipped with a unique identification number.
Between 2010 and 2011, 108 dogs were admitted.
A random sample of dogs which were admitted between 2010 and 2011 is selected for long-term monitoring.

   a) Suggest a suitable sampling frame.

   b) How many sampling units are there?

Q5   The houses on Park Road are numbered from 1 to 173.
Forty households are to be chosen to take part in a council survey.
Describe a method for choosing an unbiased sample.

Q6   Pooja is doing a survey on whether people buy ethically sourced products. She asked her mother to hand out questionnaires to 20 of her friends. Pooja's teacher said this sample was biased. What reasons might he give for saying this?

2. Sampling Distributions

Learning Objectives:

- Understand the concept of a statistic.
- Be able to calculate the sampling distribution of a statistic.

Simple random sampling chooses unbiased samples of a population — now you'll learn what to do with those samples. You can use sample data to estimate characteristics of the population.

The sampling distribution of a statistic

Statistics

Before you learn about sampling distributions you'll need this definition:

> **Parameters** are quantities that **describe** the characteristics of a **population** — e.g. the **mean** (μ), **variance** (σ^2), or **proportion** that satisfy certain criteria. **Greek letters** like μ and σ are often used for parameters.

Parameters can be **estimated** from **sample data** using quantities called **statistics**:

Tip: For more on taking random samples, see p116.

> - Suppose a **random sample** of observations ($X_1, ..., X_n$) is taken from the population.
>
> - A quantity that is calculated only from these **known observations** is called a **statistic**.
>
> - A statistic is a **random variable** — it takes different values for **different samples**.
>
> - **Latin letters** likes m and s are often used for statistics.

Some statistics can be used to **estimate** a population **parameter**.

For example, if a random sample of **size n**, $X_1, ..., X_n$, is taken from a population with an **unknown mean** μ, the **sample mean**, $\overline{X}$, can be used to estimate the population mean, μ.

$\overline{X}$ is a **statistic** given by:

Tip: The values of n and X_i only depend on your sample data.

$$\overline{X} = \frac{\sum X_i}{n}$$

It's important that you can recognise what's a statistic and what's not...

Tip: You could get marks in an exam just for saying whether something is a statistic or not.

Example

A random sample of size 10 ($X_1, ..., X_{10}$) is taken from a population with unknown mean, μ.
State whether or not the following are statistics:

a) $X_{10} - X_1$

Yes. This quantity can be calculated using only the known observations X_{10} and X_1.

---

b) $\sum X_i$

> Yes. This quantity can be calculated using only the known observations $X_1, ..., X_{10}$.

c) $\sum X_i^2 - \mu$

> No. You'd need the unknown mean μ to work out this quantity, so it cannot be calculated using only known observations.

d) $\dfrac{\sum (X_i - \overline{X})^2}{n - 1}$

> Yes. This quantity can be calculated using only the known observations $X_1, ..., X_{10}$, the sample mean $\overline{X}$ (which is itself a statistic and so can be calculated from known observations) and the sample size n (= 10).

Tip: $\dfrac{\sum (X_i - \overline{X})^2}{n - 1}$ is known as the sample variance S^2. You'll learn about this if you do S3.

e) $\dfrac{\sum |X_i - \mu|}{n}$

> No. This quantity depends on the unknown mean μ.

In the previous example, the 10 observations are independent **random variables**, labelled X_1, X_2, etc., and each takes a **value** from the population.

A **statistic** calculated from these observations is also a **random variable**, since its value depends on the values in the sample. If you took a **sample** of observations and calculated a particular **statistic**, then kept taking other samples and calculating the same statistic, you'd end up with **lots of values** of the same statistic.

Now then... if a statistic is a random variable, it must have a **probability distribution**, like all the random variables you've seen so far.

Sampling distributions

The **probability distribution** of a statistic is called its **sampling distribution**:

> For a **random sample** $X_1, ..., X_n$ of a population, the **sampling distribution** of a **statistic**, Y, gives all the **possible values**, y, that the statistic can take, along with their probabilities, $P(Y = y)$.

Tip: Remember that a probability distribution of a discrete random variable can be shown as a table giving all the information.

Example 1

A pirate's treasure chest contains a large number of coins. Unfortunately, the pirate has been diddled and the chest only contains 5p and 10p coins. The ratio of 5p to 10p coins is 4:1. A random sample of 2 coins is taken from the chest.
a) List all the possible samples.

The possible samples are: (5, 5), (5, 10), (10, 5), (10, 10)

You have to include both (5, 10) and (10, 5) — they're different samples.

b) Let X_i represent the value (in pence) of the ith coin in the sample. Find the probability distribution of X_i.

The **ratio** of 5p to 10p coins is 4:1, so $P(X_i = 5) = \frac{4}{5}$ and $P(X_i = 10) = \frac{1}{5}$ — that's 0.8 and 0.2 as decimals.

The probability distribution specifies all the possible values X_i could take, and the probabilities of each value:

x_i	5	10
$P(X_i = x_i)$	0.8	0.2

c) Find the sampling distribution of the sample mean, $\overline{X}$.

The sample mean will be different for **each sample**.

Calculate the mean for **each** different sample and then work out the probability of each:

$(5, 5)$ gives a sample mean of $\overline{X} = \dfrac{(5 + 5)}{2} = 5$.

$P(\overline{X} = 5) = P(\text{sample is } (5, 5)) = 0.8 \times 0.8 = 0.64$

$(5, 10)$ and $(10, 5)$ both give a sample mean of $\overline{X} = \dfrac{(5 + 10)}{2} = 7.5$.

$P(\overline{X} = 7.5) = P(\text{sample is } (5, 10) \text{ or } (10, 5))$
$= (0.8 \times 0.2) + (0.2 \times 0.8) = 0.32$

$(10, 10)$ gives a sample mean of $\overline{X} = \dfrac{(10 + 10)}{2} = 10$.

$P(\overline{X} = 10) = P(\text{sample is } (10, 10)) = 0.2 \times 0.2 = 0.04$

So the sampling distribution of $\overline{X}$ is:

$\bar{x}$	5	7.5	10
$P(\overline{X} = \bar{x})$	0.64	0.32	0.04

Tip: You can use the same general method for other statistics, e.g. the sample median.

Tip: Each observation is an independent random variable — so you can multiply the probabilities.

Tip: If more than one sample gives the same value of the statistic, work out the probability of each sample and add the results together.

Tip: Check that these probabilities add up to 1 — if not, you've made a mistake.

Example 2

Lotte's shoe shop stocks a large number of size 7 and size 8 trainers in the ratio of 3:1. A random sample of 3 trainers is taken from the shop, and their sizes recorded.

a) List the sizes in all the possible samples.

The possible samples are: $(7, 7, 7)$, $(7, 7, 8)$, $(7, 8, 7)$, $(7, 8, 8)$, $(8, 7, 7)$, $(8, 7, 8)$, $(8, 8, 7)$, $(8, 8, 8)$

Tip: Because there are a large number of trainers in Lotte's shop, we can assume that each choice in the sample will be independent of the others.

b) Let X_i represent the size of the ith trainer in the sample. Find the probability distribution of X_i.

The **ratio** of size 7 to 8 is 3:1, so $P(X_i = 7) = \frac{3}{4}$ and $P(X_i = 8) = \frac{1}{4}$ — that's 0.75 and 0.25 as decimals.

So the probability distribution of X_i is:

x_i	7	8
$P(X_i = x_i)$	0.75	0.25

c) **Find the sampling distribution of the median, N.**

Calculate the median for each different sample and then work out the probability of each:

Tip: The median of each sample is just the middle value of the three — it'll either be 7 or 8.

$(7, 7, 7)$, $(7, 7, 8)$, $(7, 8, 7)$, $(8, 7, 7)$ all give a median of 7.

$$P(N = 7) = P(\text{sample is } (7, 7, 7)) + P(\text{sample is } (7, 7, 8))$$
$$+ P(\text{sample is } (7, 8, 7)) + P(\text{sample is } (8, 7, 7))$$
$$= (0.75 \times 0.75 \times 0.75) + (0.75 \times 0.75 \times 0.25)$$
$$+ (0.75 \times 0.25 \times 0.75) + (0.25 \times 0.75 \times 0.75)$$
$$= 0.84375$$

Tip: Remember, X_1, X_2 and X_3 are independent, so you can multiply the probabilities.

$(7, 8, 8)$, $(8, 7, 8)$, $(8, 8, 7)$, $(8, 8, 8)$ all give a median of 8.

$$P(N = 8) = P(\text{sample is } (7, 8, 8)) + P(\text{sample is } (8, 7, 8))$$
$$+ P(\text{sample is } (8, 8, 7)) + P(\text{sample is } (8, 8, 8))$$
$$= (0.75 \times 0.25 \times 0.25) + (0.25 \times 0.75 \times 0.25)$$
$$+ (0.25 \times 0.25 \times 0.75) + (0.25 \times 0.25 \times 0.25)$$
$$= 0.15625$$

So the sampling distribution of N is

n	7	8
$P(N = n)$	0.84375	0.15625

You might be asked to work with statistics which have binomial or Poisson distributions like this...

Example 1

A company makes celebrity-themed coat hangers. A constant proportion of the coat hangers they make are rejected for being not quite realistic enough. A random sample of 20 coat hangers is inspected. The random variable X_i is defined as: $X_i = 0$ if coat hanger i is acceptable, and $X_i = 1$ if it's faulty. Write down the sampling distribution of the statistic $Y = \sum X_i$.

- Each coat hanger is an **independent trial** with constant probability, p, of being faulty. (The probability is unknown so just call it p.)

- Since $X_i = 0$ if the coat hanger is acceptable and $X_i = 1$ if the coat hanger is faulty, then Y is just the number of faulty items.

- So Y can be modelled by a **binomial distribution** (see p5): $Y \sim B(20, p)$.

Example 2

Sina is revising for her S2 exam. She takes her revision breaks randomly and independently of each other, but at a constant average rate. The random variable X_i represents the number of revision breaks Sina takes in an hour. Sina records the number of revision breaks Y in a random sample of 3 hours. Write down the sampling distribution of $Y = \sum X_i$.

- Sina's breaks occur independently, randomly and can only happen one at a time, so they can be modelled by the **Poisson distribution**.

- Let λ be the number of revision breaks Sina has per hour (this quantity is unknown). Each X_i can be modelled by $Po(\lambda)$.

- So Y can be modelled by a **Poisson distribution** (see p27): $Y \sim Po(3\lambda)$.

Tip: You need to multiply λ by 3 to go from 1 unit of time (1 hour) to the sampled period of 3 units of time (3 hours). See p33 for the additive property of the Poisson distribution.

Q1 Heights of South African giraffes are known to follow a normal distribution with unknown mean μ and unknown standard deviation σ. 10 giraffes are measured and their heights are X_1 to X_{10}. Which of the following are statistics?

a) $\dfrac{\sum X_i}{10}$ b) $\dfrac{\sum (X_i - \mu)^2}{10}$ c) $X_1 + X_2$ d) $\sum (X_i - \sigma)$

Q2 A test consists of 40 multiple-choice questions with 4 answers to choose from for each. Correct answers score 1 and wrong answers score 0. A student picks answers randomly for each question and a random sample of 3 of his answers is taken. The random variable X is the total of these 3 scores.
Find the sampling distribution of the sample mean, $\overline{X}$.

Q3 Each sheep in a large herd is tagged with either 0 or 1 (depending on its favourite flavour of grass). The ratio of 0s to 1s is 2:1. A sample of three sheep is taken out. The random variable X is the total of the sampled sheep tags. Find the sampling distribution of X.

Q4 40% of the employees of a large company like carrot cake. Six employees are chosen at random. $X =$ the number of employees who do not like carrot cake in the sample. Find the probability distribution of X.

Q5 Phil plays computer games, scoring 5 if he wins and 0 if he loses. He is equally likely to win or lose. He records the score in a random sample of 3 games and N is the median of his 3 scores.

a) Find the probability distribution of N.

Tom also plays computer games, scoring 2 if he wins and 0 if he loses, but he is three times likelier to win than lose. He also records his scores in a random sample of 3 games.

b) M is the median of his 3 scores.
Find the probability distribution of M.

c) $\overline{X}$ is the mean of his 3 scores.
Find the probability distribution of $\overline{X}$.

Q6 A musical instrument manufacturer makes air guitars. Quality control reject 2% of the air guitars based on their sound quality. A random sample of 35 air guitars have their sound tested. The random variable X_i is defined as: $X_i = 0$ if air guitar i has acceptable sound quality, and $X_i = 1$ if not.
Write down the sampling distribution of $Y = \sum X_i$.

Q7 Chef Matteo burns meals randomly at an average rate of 5 every 2 hours of work. The random variable X_i represents the number of meals Matteo burns in an hour. Matteo's boss records the number of meals he burns, Y, in a random sample of 6 hours of work.
Write down the sampling distribution of $Y = \sum X_i$.

3. Hypothesis Tests

This is what this chapter's been building up to. Hypothesis testing is all about using data from a sample to test whether a statement about a whole population is believable... or really unlikely.

Learning Objectives:

- Be able to formulate null and alternative hypotheses.
- Be able to decide when to use a one- or two-tailed test.
- Understand what is meant by significance levels.
- Understand what is meant by a test statistic, and be able to find a test statistic's sampling distribution.
- Be able to test an observed value of a test statistic for significance.
- Be able to find a critical region and identify the actual significance level of a test.

Null and alternative hypotheses

A **hypothesis** (plural: **hypotheses**) is a claim or a statement that **might** be true, but which might **not** be.

- A **hypothesis test** is a method of testing a hypothesis about a population using **observed data** from a **sample**.
- You'll need **two** hypotheses for every hypothesis test — a **null** hypothesis and an **alternative** hypothesis.

Null hypothesis

- The **null hypothesis** is a statement about the **value** of a population parameter (e.g. a binomial probability p, or a Poisson mean λ). The null hypothesis is always referred to as H_0.
- H_0 needs to give a **specific value** to the parameter, since all the calculations in your hypothesis test will be based on this value.

The example below (which I'll keep coming back to throughout the section) shows how you could use a hypothesis test to check whether a coin is 'fair' (i.e. whether it's equally likely to land on heads or tails).

Aisha wants to test whether a coin is fair.
She decides to carry out a hypothesis test.

- Testing whether a coin is fair is a test about the probability (p) that it lands on heads.
- If the coin is **fair**, then the value of p will be 0.5.
  If the coin is **biased**, then the value of p could be **anything except 0.5**.
- Aisha's null hypothesis needs to assume a **specific** value for p.
  So Aisha's null hypothesis is:

$$H_0: p = 0.5$$

- Now then... the fact that Aisha is carrying out this test at all probably means that she has some doubts about whether the coin really is fair.
- But that's okay... you **don't** have to **believe** your null hypothesis — it's just an assumption you make for the purposes of carrying out the test.
- In fact, as you'll soon see, it's pretty common to choose a null hypothesis that you think is **false**.

There are **two** possible results of a hypothesis test.
Depending on your data, you can:
   a) "**Fail to reject H_0**" — this means that your data provides **no evidence** to think that your null hypothesis is **untrue**.
   b) "**Reject H_0**" — this means that your data provides evidence to think that your null hypothesis is **unlikely to be true**.

In case you need to reject H_0, you need an alternative hypothesis 'standing by'.

Tip: Hypothesis testing is sometimes called significance testing.

Tip: Aisha's using p as the probability that the coin lands on heads, but you could equally use it as the probability the coin lands on tails.

Tip: There's more about the possible outcomes of a hypothesis test on p125.

Two kinds of alternative hypothesis

Tip: You **must** decide what your alternative hypothesis is before you collect any data.

Before you collect any data, you need to think ahead and decide what you're going to conclude if you end up rejecting H_0 — i.e. what you're rejecting H_0 in favour of.

This is your **alternative hypothesis**.
The alternative hypothesis is always referred to as H_1.

There are **two kinds** of alternative hypothesis:

- A **one-tailed** alternative hypothesis.

    A one-tailed alternative hypothesis specifies whether the parameter you're investigating is **greater than** or **less than** the value you used in H_0. Using a one-tailed alternative hypothesis means you're carrying out a **one-tailed hypothesis test**.

Tip: You'll see more about one-tailed tests and two-tailed tests later.

- A **two-tailed** alternative hypothesis.

    A two-tailed alternative hypothesis **doesn't specify** whether the parameter you're investigating is greater than or less than the value you used in H_0 — all it says is that it's **not equal** to the value in H_0. Using a two-tailed alternative hypothesis means you're carrying out a **two-tailed hypothesis test**.

Back to the example with Aisha and her coin...

Aisha has a choice of alternative hypotheses, and she'll need to choose which to use **before** she starts collecting data.

Tip: Remember... p is the probability that the coin lands on heads.

- She could use a **one-tailed** alternative hypothesis — there are two possibilities:

    $H_1: p > 0.5$ — this would mean the coin is biased towards **heads**

    or $H_1: p < 0.5$ — this would mean the coin is biased towards **tails**

Tip: Notice that H_1 does not give a specific value to the population parameter — it gives a range of values.

- She could use a **two-tailed** alternative hypothesis:

    $H_1: p \neq 0.5$ — this would mean the coin is **biased**, but it **doesn't** say whether it's biased in favour of heads or tails

To decide which alternative hypothesis to use, you have to consider:

- **What you want to find out** about the parameter:

    For example, if you were investigating the proportion (q) of items produced in a factory that were faulty, then you might only want to test whether q has **increased** (you might not be so concerned about testing whether it's decreased).

- Any **suspicions** you might already have about the parameter's value:

    For example, if Aisha in the example above thought that the coin was actually biased towards heads, then she'd use $H_1: p > 0.5$. So if her data means she can reject H_0, then she'll have gathered evidence to back up the suspicion she already has.

Possible conclusions after a hypothesis test

Okay... I'm going to assume now that you've written your null and alternative hypotheses, and then **collected some data**. You need to know the **possible conclusions** that you can come to after performing a hypothesis test.

There are **two** possibilities:

Tip: The details of how you draw these conclusions are explained later — for now, just try to understand the logic of what's going on.

- Your **observed data** is **really unlikely** under the null hypothesis, H_0.

  - If your observed data is **really unlikely** when you assume that H_0 is true, then you might start to think 'Well, maybe H_0 isn't true after all.'

  - It could be that your observed data is actually **much** more likely to happen under your **alternative hypothesis**. Then you'd perhaps think H_1 is more likely to be true than H_0.

  - In this case, you would **reject H_0** in favour of H_1.

  - This **doesn't** mean that H_0 is **definitely false**. After all, as long as your observed data isn't impossible under H_0, then H_0 could still be true. All it means is that 'on the balance of probabilities', H_1 seems to be **more likely** to be true than H_0.

Tip: 'Under the null hypothesis' / 'under H_0' just means 'assuming that the null hypothesis is true'.

Tip: How unlikely your results need to be before you reject H_0 is called the **significance level** — it's explained on p128.

- The **observed data isn't** especially unlikely under the null hypothesis, H_0.

  - If your observed data could easily have come about under H_0, then you **can't reject H_0**.

  - In this case, you would '**fail to reject H_0**'.

  - However, this is **not** the same as saying that you have evidence that H_0 is **true** — all it means is that H_0 appears to be **believable**, and that you have **no evidence** that it's false.

  - But it's not really any better than having collected no data at all — you didn't have evidence to disbelieve the null hypothesis before you did your experiment... and you still don't. That's all this conclusion means.

Because the conclusion of 'not rejecting H_0' is so 'weak' (i.e. you might as well not have bothered to collect any data), it's actually more interesting and 'meaningful' when you can 'reject H_0' in favour of H_1.

This is why the alternative hypothesis H_1 is usually 'more interesting' than the null hypothesis H_0.

Tip: Remember... the choice is between '**rejecting H_0**' and '**not rejecting H_0**'. You **never** 'accept H_0'.

- For example, in the example with Aisha and her coin (p123-124), it was the **alternative** hypothesis that contained the claim that the coin was **biased**.

- It's also why H_0 often says something that you think is **false**. Your aim is to gather evidence to reject H_0 in favour of H_1 (and this is why H_1 might be what you actually **believe**).

- If Aisha **rejects H_0**:

  - She has **evidence** that H_0 is false (i.e. that the coin is biased).
  - Although she **can't** be certain, H_1 appears **more likely** to be true.

- If Aisha **fails to reject H_0**:

  - She has **no** evidence that H_0 is false (i.e. that the coin is biased).
  - H_0 **could** be true, but she has no evidence to say so.
  - H_0 **could** also be false, but she has no evidence for that either.

Tip: A hypothesis test **can** provide evidence that H_1 is likely to be true, but it **can't** provide evidence that H_0 is likely to be true.

Example 1

A 4-sided spinner has sides labelled A–D. Adam thinks that the spinner is biased towards side A. He wants to do a hypothesis test to test this theory.

a) Write down a suitable null hypothesis to test Adam's theory.

The parameter Adam's interested in is the probability, p, that the spinner will land on side A.

The null hypothesis must give a **specific value** to p, and it's the statement that Adam is trying to get evidence to **reject**.

Adam thinks the spinner is biased. So his null hypothesis should be that the spinner is **unbiased**, and that each side has a probability of 0.25 of being spun. So:

$$H_0: \ p = 0.25$$

Tip: The question will usually give you a hint about what H_1 should be. Here it says Adam suspects it is biased towards side A, which means he thinks p is greater than 0.25

b) Write down a suitable alternative hypothesis.

If the spinner is biased towards side A, then the probability, p, of spinning A will be greater than 0.25. So:

$$H_1: \ p > 0.25$$

(This is the hypothesis that Adam actually believes.)

c) State whether this test is one- or two-tailed.

The alternative hypothesis specifies that p is greater than 0.25, so the test is one-tailed .

The population parameter won't always be a probability.

Example 2

In a particular post office, people usually join the queue at an average rate of 2 per minute. The manager of the post office wants to test whether the rate at which people join the queue is different between the hours of 1 pm and 2 pm.

a) Write down a suitable null hypothesis.

The manager is interested in the population parameter λ, the rate at which people join the post-office queue between 1 pm and 2 pm.

The null hypothesis must give a **specific value** to λ. So:

$$H_0: \lambda = 2$$

Tip: The manager's null hypothesis is that the number of people joining the queue between 1 pm and 2 pm is the same as at other times.

b) Write down a suitable alternative hypothesis.

The manager wants to test for **any** difference (rather than just an increase or just a decrease). So:

$$H_1: \lambda \neq 2$$

c) State whether this test is one- or two-tailed.

The alternative hypothesis only specifies that λ is not equal to 2, so the test is two-tailed .

Q1 Over the last few years Jules has had a 90% success rate in germinating her geranium plants. This year she has bought an improved variety of seeds and hopes for even better results.

a) Which quantity is Jules investigating?

b) What value has this quantity taken over the last few years?

c) Write down a suitable null hypothesis.

d) Write down a suitable alternative hypothesis.

e) State whether this test is one- or two-tailed.

Q2 A cat catches mice at an average rate of 1.5 per day. Its owner has put a bell on its collar and wants to test if the cat now catches fewer mice.

a) State the quantity that the owner is investigating.

b) What value did this quantity take before?

c) Write down a suitable null hypothesis using parts a) and b).

d) Write down a suitable alternative hypothesis.

e) State whether this test is one- or two-tailed.

Q3 The school health team checks teenagers for the presence of an antibody before vaccinating them. Usually 35% of teenagers have the antibody present. The team is to visit a remote Scottish island and they think that the proportion of teenagers with the antibody may be different.

a) Write down the quantity that is being investigated.

b) Formulate the null and alternative hypotheses, H_0 and H_1.

c) State whether this test is one- or two-tailed.

Q4 The local council found that only 16% of residents were aware that grants were available to help pay to insulate their houses. The council ran a campaign to publicise the grants, and now want to test whether there is an increased awareness in the area.

Write down suitable null and alternative hypotheses involving the quantity q, the proportion of residents aware of the grants.

Q5 A village shop sells chilli chutney at an average rate of 16 jars per week. The owner has changed the packaging of the chutney and wants to know if the rate at which chilli chutney is sold has changed. Write down suitable null and alternative hypotheses.

Q6 It is claimed that the proportion of members of a particular gym who watch Australian soaps is 40%. Boyd wants to test his theory that the proportion is higher. Write down suitable null and alternative hypotheses.

Significance Levels

- You've seen that you would reject H_0 if the data you collect is 'really unlikely' under H_0. But you need to decide exactly **how unlikely** your results will need to be before you decide to reject H_0.

- The **significance level** of a test shows how far you're prepared to believe that unlikely results are just down to **chance**, rather than because the assumption in H_0 is wrong.

> The **significance level** of a test (α) determines **how unlikely** your data needs to be under the null hypothesis (H_0) before you reject H_0.

Tip: If your results under H_0 have a probability lower than α, then you can say that your results are **significant**.

- For example, your significance level could be $\alpha = 0.05$ (or 5%). This would mean that you would **only** reject H_0 if your observed data fell into the **most extreme 5%** of possible outcomes.

- You'll usually be told what significance level to use, but the most common values are $\alpha = 0.05$ (or 5%) and $\alpha = 0.01$ (or 1%).

Tip: Significance levels can be written as percentages or decimals.

- The value of α also determines the strength of the evidence that the test has provided if you reject H_0 — the **lower** the value of α, the **stronger the evidence** you have that H_0 is false.
  - For example, if you use $\alpha = 0.05$ and your data lets you reject H_0, then you have evidence that H_0 is false.
  - But if you use $\alpha = 0.01$ and your data lets you reject H_0, then you have **stronger** evidence that H_0 is false.

- Also, the **lower** the value of α, the **lower** the probability of **incorrectly rejecting H_0** when it is in fact **true** — i.e. of getting extreme data due to chance rather than because H_0 was false.

- But although a **low** value of α sounds like a good thing, there's an important **disadvantage** to using a low significance level — you're **less likely to be able to reject H_0**. This means your experiment is more likely to end up 'failing to reject H_0' and concluding nothing.

Test statistics

To see if your results are **significant**, you need to find their probability under H_0. The way you do this is to '**summarise**' your data in something called a **test statistic**.

> A **test statistic** for a hypothesis test is a statistic calculated from **sample data**, which is used to **decide** whether or not to reject H_0.

Tip: This is one reason why you spent so much time learning all about the binomial and Poisson distributions.

See Chapter 1 (for binomial) and Chapter 2 (for Poisson) if you need to remind yourself of any details.

- In S2, the sampling distribution of the test statistics you'll use will be one of the following:
  - a binomial distribution $B(n, p)$
  - a Poisson distribution $Po(\lambda)$

- Once you've found your test statistic (x), you then need to work out the probability of a value **at least as extreme** as x using the parameter in your null hypothesis.

- If this probability is less than the significance level α, you can reject H_0.

Deciding whether or not to reject H_0

1. Comparing the probability of the test statistic with α

Right... back to Aisha and her coin. Let's assume first that Aisha is carrying out a **one-tailed test** to check if the coin is biased **towards heads**.

- For this one-tailed test, Aisha's null and alternative hypotheses will be:
  $$H_0: p = 0.5 \quad \text{and} \quad H_1: p > 0.5$$

- Aisha's going to use a significance level of $\alpha = 0.05$.
- Aisha then throws the coin 30 times and records the number of heads.
- Her test statistic X is the **number of heads** she throws — so X follows a binomial distribution $B(n, p)$. In fact, under H_0, $X \sim B(30, 0.5)$.

First suppose Aisha records **19 heads** — i.e. $X = 19$.
- The probability of a result **at least as extreme** as $X = 19$ is $P(X \geq 19)$.
- Under H_0, this is $1 - P(X < 19) = 1 - P(X \leq 18) = 1 - 0.8998 = 0.1002$
- This value of 0.1002 is **not less than** the significance level α, so she **cannot reject H_0**.
- Aisha has **no evidence** at the 5% level of significance that the coin is biased in favour of heads.

Suppose instead that Aisha records **20 heads** — i.e. $X = 20$.
- The probability of a result **at least as extreme** as $X = 20$ is $P(X \geq 20)$.
- Under H_0, this is $1 - P(X < 20) = 1 - P(X \leq 19) = 1 - 0.9506 = 0.0494$
- This value of 0.0494 is **less than** the significance value α, so she **can reject H_0**.
- Aisha has **evidence** at the 5% level of significance that the coin is biased in favour of heads.

Before moving on, look at the graph of the **probability function** for your test statistic.

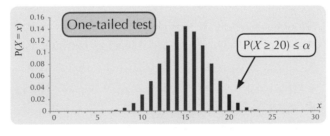

- The red bars form the 'one tail' of the test statistic's distribution where values of the test statistic would lead you to reject H_0 in favour of H_1.
- Notice how they're at the 'high' end of the distribution — this is because H_1 was of the form: $H_1: p > 0.5$ (meaning that very high values of X are more likely under H_1 than under H_0).
- If Aisha had chosen her alternative hypothesis to be: $H_1: p < 0.5$, then the values that would lead her to reject H_0 would be at the 'low' end.

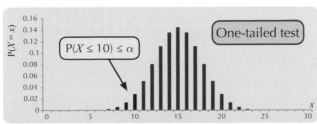

Tip: Remember... n is the number of trials (here, $n = 30$). And p is the probability of success in each of those trials, which we're assuming to be 0.5 (because we're assuming that H_0 is true — see p123).

Tip: A result 'at least as extreme as 19' means '19 or more' here. See below for more details.

Tip: In fact, any value for X of 20 or more would lead Aisha to reject H_0.

Tip: Remember... under H_0, $X \sim B(30, 0.5)$.

Tip: If Aisha's alternative hypothesis had been $H_1: p < 0.5$, then she would reject H_0 for values of X of 10 or under. This is because for $B(30, 0.5)$, $P(X \leq 10) = 0.0494 < \alpha$, but $P(X \leq 11) = 0.1002 > \alpha$.

Now assume that Aisha is carrying out a **two-tailed test** to check if the coin is biased towards **either heads or tails**.

Most of what follows is the same as for the one-tailed test, but there's one important difference.

- For this two-tailed test, Aisha's null and alternative hypotheses will be: $H_0: p = 0.5$ and $H_1: p \neq 0.5$
- Again, Aisha's going to use a significance level of $\alpha = 0.05$.
- Aisha then throws the coin 30 times and records the number of heads.
- Her test statistic X is the **number of heads** she throws — so X follows a binomial distribution $B(n, p)$. In fact, under H_0, $X \sim B(30, 0.5)$.

So up to this point, things are pretty much identical to the one-tailed test. But now think about which 'extreme' outcomes for the test statistic would favour H_1 over H_0.

- This time, extreme outcomes at **either** the 'high' end **or** the 'low' end of the distribution would favour your alternative hypothesis, $H_1: p \neq 0.5$.
- But the significance level is the **total** probability of the results that would lead to you reject H_0. So for a two-tailed test, you have to **divide α by 2** and use half of the significance level ($\frac{\alpha}{2} = 0.025$) at each end of the distribution.

So suppose Aisha records **20 heads** — i.e. $X = 20$.
- The probability of a result **at least as extreme** as $X = 20$ is $P(X \geq 20)$.
- Under H_0, this is $1 - P(X < 20) = 1 - P(X \leq 19) = 1 - 0.9506 = 0.0494$
- This value of 0.0494 is **not less than** $\frac{\alpha}{2}$, so she **cannot reject H_0**.
- Aisha has **no evidence** at the 5% level of significance that the coin is biased (in either direction).

Suppose instead that Aisha records **21 heads** — i.e. $X = 21$.
- The probability of a result **at least as extreme** as $X = 21$ is $P(X \geq 21)$.
- Under H_0, this is $1 - P(X < 21) = 1 - P(X \leq 20) = 1 - 0.9786 = 0.0214$
- This value of 0.0214 is **less than** $\frac{\alpha}{2}$, so she **can reject H_0**.
- Aisha has **evidence** at the 5% level of significance that the coin is biased (towards either heads or tails).

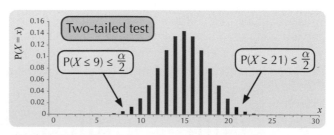

- Notice how in this two-tailed test, Aisha needs 21 heads to reject H_0, whereas in the one-tailed test, she only needed 20 heads.
- This is why you need to be careful when you choose your alternative hypothesis. Choosing the wrong H_1 can make it harder to reject H_0.

2. Finding the critical region

When Aisha was deciding whether to reject H_0 or not reject H_0, she:
1. worked out her test statistic using her data,
2. then calculated the probability (under H_0) of getting a value for the test statistic at least as extreme as the value she had found.

Finding the **critical region** is another way of doing a hypothesis test. It involves working out in advance all the values of the test statistic that would lead you to reject H_0.

> The **critical region** (CR) is the **set** of all values of the **test statistic** that would cause you to **reject H_0.**

Tip: The critical region is just a set of values that X can take which fall far enough away from what's expected under the null hypothesis to allow you to reject it.

Using a critical region is like doing things the other way round, because you:
1. work out all the values that would make you reject H_0,
2. then work out the value of your test statistic using your data, and check if it is in the critical region (and if it is, then reject H_0).

So if you find the **critical region** first, you can quickly say whether any observed value of the test statistic, X, is **significant**.

■ As you've already seen, **one-tailed tests** have a **single critical region**, containing either the highest or lowest values. Here are the graphs from pages 129 and 130 again — the values of x which are **red** would all cause you to reject H_0, so they are the values that make up the critical region.

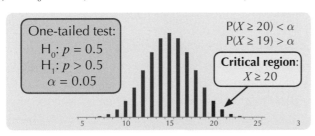

One-tailed test:
$H_0: p = 0.5$
$H_1: p > 0.5$
$\alpha = 0.05$

$P(X \geq 20) < \alpha$
$P(X \geq 19) > \alpha$

Critical region:
$X \geq 20$

Tip: When $X = 19$, Aisha couldn't reject H_0 (see p129), so $X = 19$ is **not** in the critical region.

But $X = 20$ **is** in the critical region, since in this case Aisha **could** reject H_0.

$X = 20$ is called the **critical value** — it's the value on the 'edge' of the critical region.

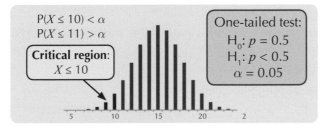

$P(X \leq 10) < \alpha$
$P(X \leq 11) > \alpha$

Critical region:
$X \leq 10$

One-tailed test:
$H_0: p = 0.5$
$H_1: p < 0.5$
$\alpha = 0.05$

Tip: For this test, $X = 10$ is the **critical value**.

■ A **two-tailed test** has a **critical region** that's split into two 'tails' — one tail at each end of the distribution. Again, the **red** values of x make up the two parts of the critical region.

Tip: Remember... use a two-tailed test if you're testing for a difference, but you're not sure how it'll differ (i.e. whether it will be bigger or smaller).

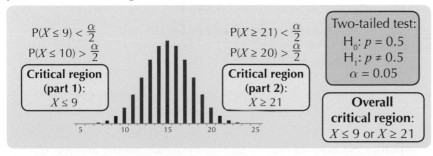

$P(X \leq 9) < \dfrac{\alpha}{2}$
$P(X \leq 10) > \dfrac{\alpha}{2}$

Critical region (part 1):
$X \leq 9$

$P(X \geq 21) < \dfrac{\alpha}{2}$
$P(X \geq 20) > \dfrac{\alpha}{2}$

Critical region (part 2):
$X \geq 21$

Two-tailed test:
$H_0: p = 0.5$
$H_1: p \neq 0.5$
$\alpha = 0.05$

Overall critical region:
$X \leq 9$ or $X \geq 21$

Tip: The actual significance level is usually different from the original level of significance when the test statistic is a **discrete** random variable (as it is here).

This is because the value of $P(X \leq x)$ 'jumps' as the value of x changes, so it's usually impossible to find a critical region containing values with a probability of **exactly** α.

Once you've calculated the critical region, you can easily find what's called the **actual significance level**.

- The **actual significance level** of the test is usually **slightly different** from the significance level you use to find the critical region in the first place.
- The **actual significance level** of a test is the **probability** of **rejecting H$_0$** when it is true. So the actual significance level is the probability of **incorrectly rejecting H$_0$**.
- You find the actual significance level by calculating the **probability** of X taking a value in the **critical region** (assuming H$_0$ is true).

Back to Aisha and her coin for the final time...

- Aisha's one-tailed test has a critical region of $X \geq 20$ (see p131). She found this using a significance level $\alpha = 0.05$.
- But the **actual significance level** of this test is $P(X \geq 20) = \boxed{0.0494}$
- So the probability of Aisha rejecting H$_0$ when it is true is 0.0494.
- In other words, this means that there is a probability of 0.0494 of Aisha **incorrectly** rejecting H$_0$ — i.e. of the test producing this kind of **wrong result**.

The actual significance level of a **one-tailed test** will always be **less than or equal to** α.

Tip: In a two-tailed test, you need to remember to find the probability of each end of the critical region and add them up.

- Similarly, Aisha's two-tailed test has a critical region of $X \geq 21$ or $X \leq 9$ (see p131). She found this using a significance level $\alpha = 0.05$.
- But the **actual significance level** of this test is $P(X \geq 21) + P(X \leq 9) = 0.0214 + 0.0214 = \boxed{0.0428}$
- So the probability of Aisha rejecting H$_0$ when it's true this time is 0.0428.
- In other words, there is a probability of 0.0428 of Aisha **incorrectly** rejecting H$_0$ — i.e. of the test producing this kind of **wrong result**.

There are actually **two** different ways that you might be asked to find a critical region for a **two-tailed test**.

- You might be asked to find the critical region so that the probability in each tail is **no greater than** $\frac{\alpha}{2}$.
- Or you might be asked to find the critical region so that the probability in each tail is **as close as possible to** $\frac{\alpha}{2}$. In this case, the **total** probability in the two tails **might** be slightly **greater** than α.

So that's what hypothesis tests are, and how they work.

There are loads of examples of the kinds you might meet in the exams in the next few sections.

4. Hypothesis Tests for a Binomial Distribution

In the previous section, a binomial example was used to demonstrate all the general theory of hypothesis testing. This section will go through lots more binomial examples, and there'll be loads of practice too. There's not much to actually learn here — it's just applying what you already know.

Learning Objective:

- Be able to conduct hypothesis tests about probabilities or proportions using a test statistic with a binomial distribution — both by testing for significance and by finding critical regions.

Setting up the test

In S2, test statistics in hypothesis tests will only follow either binomial or Poisson distributions.

The question will be about a **binomial distribution** if it is about an event that happens with a **constant probability** or about the **proportion** of a population.

In the last section, you saw that there were **two** different methods you could be asked to use in a hypothesis-test question — **testing for significance** and **finding a critical region**.

In both cases, you'll always **set up** the hypothesis to test in the same way. Follow this step-by-step method:

- Identify the **population parameter**
  — for a binomial distribution it's always p, a **probability** of success, or **proportion** of a population.
- Write down the **null** hypothesis (H_0)
  — H_0: $p = a$ for some constant a.
- Write down the **alternative** hypothesis (H_1)
  — H_1 will either be H_1: $p < a$ or H_1: $p > a$ (one-tailed test)
    or H_1: $p \neq a$ (two-tailed test)
- State the **test statistic**, X
  — always just the number of '**successes**' in the sample.
- Write down the **sampling distribution** of the test statistic under H_0
  — $X \sim B(n, p)$ where n is the sample size.
- State the **significance level,** α
  — you'll usually be given this.

Example

Naomi wants to test whether a coin is more likely to land on heads than tails. She plans to flip it 15 times and record the results. Write down suitable null and alternative hypotheses. Define the test statistic, X, and give its sampling distribution under the null hypothesis.

- The population parameter p = probability of the coin landing on heads.
- The null hypothesis will be that the coin is unbiased, so H_0: $p = 0.5$.
- Naomi believes the coin is more likely to land on heads, so her alternative hypothesis is H_1: $p > 0.5$.
- The test statistic is X = the number of heads in the sample of 15 throws.
- The sampling distribution of X under H_0 is **binomial** with $p = 0.5$ and 15 trials so $X \sim B(15, 0.5)$.

Tip: This test is about the **probability** of the coin landing on heads, so the test statistic will have a binomial distribution.

Tip: Remember...
to test for significance,
you need to find the
probability that the test
statistic is 'at least as
extreme' as your results.
See p128-130 for the
general theory on testing
for significance.

Tip: The binomial
probability function (p8)
says that if $X \sim B(n, p)$,
then

$$P(X = x) = \binom{n}{x} p^x (1 - p)^{n-x}$$

for $x = 0, 1, 2, ..., n$.

Testing for significance

If you're asked to test an observed value for significance, you need to work out the probability (under H_0) of X being at least as extreme as the observed value using either the **binomial tables** or the **binomial probability function**, and then compare it to α for a one-tailed test, or $\frac{\alpha}{2}$ if it's a two-tailed test.

- The binomial **tables** are quicker if you can use them, because they show the cumulative distribution function $P(X \le x)$ — this lets you quickly find the probability of results '**at least as extreme**' as the observed value.

- The binomial **probability function** only gives $P(X = x)$, so you'll have to work out the various probabilities separately and add them up to get $P(X \le x)$ — but it's useful when the tables don't include the probability you need.

The next three examples will guide you through one-tailed hypothesis tests from forming the hypotheses to the final conclusion.

Example 1

A student believes that a five-sided spinner is biased towards landing on 5. He spins the spinner 20 times and it lands on 5 ten times. Using a 5% level of significance, test the hypothesis that the spinner is biased towards landing on 5.

- Identify the **population parameter**:

  p = the probability of the spinner landing on 5

- Formulate the **null** and **alternative** hypotheses for p.
  The null hypothesis will be that the spinner is not biased, so $H_0: p = 0.2$
  The alternative hypothesis will be that the spinner is more likely to land on 5, so $H_1: p > 0.2$ ← What the student actually thinks.

- State the **test statistic** X — the number of 5s, and its **sampling distribution** under H_0.

  Let X = number of times the spinner lands on a **5** in the **sample**.
  Under H_0, $X \sim B(20, 0.2)$.

  [number of trials] [probability of a 5 under H_0]

- State the **significance level** of the test. It's 5% here so $\alpha = 0.05$.

- Test for **significance** — you're interested in the probability of X being **at least as extreme** as the value you've observed, i.e. the probability of X being 10 or more, under the null hypothesis.

  Under the null hypothesis $p = 0.2$.

Tip: The full set of
binomial tables is given
on pages 159-163.
These tables are also
in the formula booklet
you'll get in your exam.

  Using the binomial tables
  $P(X \ge 10) = 1 - P(X < 10)$
  $= 1 - P(X \le 9)$
  $= 1 - 0.9974$
  $= 0.0026$

Binomial Cumulative Distribution Function
Values show $P(X \le x)$, where $X \sim B(n, p)$

	$p =$	0.05	0.10	0.15	0.20
$n = 20, x = 0$		0.3585	0.1216	0.0388	0.0115
		...	...	...	...
8		1.0000	0.9999	0.9987	0.9900
9		1.0000	1.0000	0.9998	0.9974
10		1.0000	1.0000	1.0000	0.9994

Since $0.0026 < 0.05$, the result **is significant**.

- Write your **conclusion** — you will either reject the null hypothesis H_0 or have insufficient evidence to do so.

> There is evidence at the 5% level of significance to reject H_0 and to support the student's claim that the spinner is biased towards landing on 5.

Tip: Make sure you always state your conclusion. Just showing whether the result is significant is not enough.

Example 2

Pen-Gu Inc. sells stationery to 60% of the schools in the country. The manager of Pen-Gu Inc. claims that there has recently been a decrease in the number of schools buying their stationery. She rings 30 schools at random and finds that 16 buy Pen-Gu Inc. stationery. Test her claim using a 1% significance level.

- Identify the **population parameter**:

    p = the probability of a school buying their stationery.

- Formulate the **null** and **alternative** hypotheses for p.

    If the number of schools buying their stationery has not changed, then $H_0: p = 0.6$

    If the number of schools buying their stationery has decreased, then $H_1: p < 0.6$

- State the **test statistic** X, and its **sampling distribution** under H_0.

    Let X = number of **schools** in the sample who buy Pen-Gu Inc. stationery.
    Under H_0, $X \sim \mathbf{B(30, 0.6)}$.

- State the **significance level** of the test. It's 1% here so $\alpha = 0.01$.

- Test for **significance** — you're interested in the probability of X being **at least as extreme** as the value you've observed, i.e. the probability of X being 16 or less, under the null hypothesis.

    The value of p under H_0 is greater than 0.5, so you need to do a bit of fiddling to be able to use the binomial tables.

    Let Y = number of schools in the sample who do **not** buy Pen-Gu Inc. stationery. Then $Y \sim B(30, 0.4)$.

Tip: When the null hypothesis is of the form $p = a$ and a is greater than 0.5, you'll need to manipulate the probabilities slightly to be able to use the tables. This method of using the tables was on p14-15.

    Using the binomial tables:
    $P(X \leq 16) = P(Y \geq 14)$
    $\qquad = 1 - P(Y < 14)$
    $\qquad = 1 - P(Y \leq 13)$
    $\qquad = 1 - 0.7145$
    $\qquad = 0.2855$

    Binomial Cumulative Distribution Function
    Values show $P(X \leqslant x)$, where $X \sim B(n, p)$

$p =$	...	0.35	0.40
$n = 30, x = \cdots$	...	...	...
12	...	0.7802	0.5785
13	...	0.8737	0.7145
14	...	0.9348	0.8246

    Since $0.2855 > 0.01$, the result is **not significant**.

- Write your **conclusion**:

> There is insufficient evidence at the 1% level of significance to reject H_0 in favour of the manager's claim.

Tip: Always say:
'**there is sufficient evidence to reject H_0**'
or
'**there is insufficient evidence to reject H_0**'
Never talk about 'accepting H_0' or 'rejecting H_1'.

If you can't use the tables for your value of p, you have to use the **binomial probability function** to work things out.

Example 3

The proportion of pupils at a school who support the local football team is found to be 1 in 3. Nigel attends a school nearby and claims that there is less support for the same local team at his school. In a random sample of 20 pupils from Nigel's school, 3 support the local team. Use a 5% level of significance to test Nigel's claim.

- Let p = proportion of pupils who support the local team.

- Formulate the **hypotheses**: $H_0: p = \frac{1}{3}$ $H_1: p < \frac{1}{3}$

- Let X = number of sampled pupils supporting the team. Under H_0, $X \sim B(20, \frac{1}{3})$.

- The **significance level** is $\alpha = 0.05.$

- Now you need to find the probability under H_0 of getting a value less than or equal to 3. The tables don't have values for $p = \frac{1}{3}$, so you need to work out the probabilities individually and add them up:

  > Use the binomial probability function for each probability.

  $$P(X \leq 3) = P(X = 0) + P(X = 1) + P(X = 2) + P(X = 3)$$

  $$= \left(\frac{2}{3}\right)^{20} + 20\left(\frac{1}{3}\right)\left(\frac{2}{3}\right)^{19} + 190\left(\frac{1}{3}\right)^2\left(\frac{2}{3}\right)^{18} + 1140\left(\frac{1}{3}\right)^3\left(\frac{2}{3}\right)^{17}$$

  $$= 0.0604$$

  $0.0604 > 0.05$, so the result is not significant.

  > There is insufficient evidence at the 5% level of significance to reject H_0 and to support Nigel's claim that there is less support for the team.

Tip: This is a test of the **proportion** of pupils who support a team, so the test statistic will have a binomial distribution.

Tip: Here you need to use:
$$P(X = x) = \binom{20}{x}\left(\frac{1}{3}\right)^x\left(\frac{2}{3}\right)^{20-x}$$

With two-tailed tests, the only difference is the value that you compare the probability to in the test for significance.

Example 4

A wildlife photographer is taking photographs of a rare blue poison dart frog. He's established over a long period of time that the probability that he'll sight a blue poison dart frog during any day of searching is 0.05. He moves to another part of the rainforest believing that the probability will be different. During his first 6 days searching he spots the frog on 3 of the days. Use a 1% level of significance to test his claim.

- Let p = probability that the wildlife photographer will spot a blue poison dart frog in a day of searching.

- Formulate the **hypotheses**: $H_0: p = 0.05$ $H_1: p \neq 0.05$

- Let X = number of sampled days that he spots a frog.
  Under H_0, $X \sim B(6, 0.05)$.

- The **significance level** is $\alpha = 0.01$. So $\frac{\alpha}{2} = 0.005$.

- Test for **significance** — you're interested in the probability of X being **at least as extreme** as the value you've observed.

  Since the test is two-tailed, you need to work out **which** 'tail' you are working in — i.e. do you need to find the probability that X is less than, or more than, the observed value?

  Under H_0, the expected number of days on which a frog is seen is 0.3. 3 is greater than this expected value, so you're interested in the probability of X being **3 or more**, under the null hypothesis.

  Using the binomial tables:

  $P(X \geq 3)$ $= 1 - P(X < 3)$

  $= 1 - P(X \leq 2)$

  $= 1 - 0.9978$

  $= 0.0022$

  Binomial Cumulative Distribution Function
  Values show $P(X \leq x)$, where $X \sim B(n, p)$

$p =$	0.05	0.10
$n = 6$, $x = 0$	0.7351	0.5314
1	0.9672	0.8857
2	0.9978	0.9842

  Tip: If the observed value was less than the expected value under H_0, you'd want to find the probability that X was less than or equal to that value.

  Since $0.0022 \leq 0.005$, the result **is significant**.

- Write your **conclusion**:

  There is sufficient evidence at the 1% level of significance to reject H_0 in favour of the wildlife photographer's claim.

Exercise 4.1

Q1 Charlotte claims she can read Milly's mind. To test this claim Milly chooses a number from 1 to 5 and concentrates on it while Charlotte attempts to read her mind. Charlotte is right on 4 out of 10 occasions.

   a) Write down the population parameter and suitable null and alternative hypotheses.

   b) Define the test statistic and write down its sampling distribution under the null hypothesis.

   c) Are these results significant at a 5% level of significance?

Q1 Hint: Charlotte thinks she can do better than just guessing a number between 1 and 5.

Q2 Last year 45% of students said that the chicken dinosaurs at school dinner were good value. After this year's price increase Ellen says fewer people think they are good value. She asked 50 people and found only 16 said that chicken dinosaurs were good value. Test Ellen's claim at the 5% level.

Q3 In the past, 25% of John's violin pupils have gained distinctions in their exams. He's using a different examination board and wants to know if the percentage of distinctions will be significantly different. His first 12 exam candidates gained 6 distinctions. Test whether the percentage of distinctions is significantly different at the 1% level.

Q3 Hint: Remember the differences in the hypothesis test method when the test is two-tailed.

Q4 Matt is a keen birdwatcher. Over time he has found that 15% of the birds he sees are classified as 'rare'. He has bought a new type of birdseed and is not sure whether it will attract more or fewer rare birds. On the first day only 2 out of 40 of the birds were rare. Test whether the percentage of rare birds is significantly different at the 10% level.

Q5 10% of customers at a village newsagent's buy Pigeon Spotter Magazine. The owner has just opened a new shop in a different village and wants to know whether this proportion will be different in the new shop. One day 8 out of a random sample of 50 customers bought Pigeon Spotter Magazine. Is this significant at the 5% level?

Q6 Pete's Driving School advertises that 70% of its clients pass the driving test at their first attempt. Hati and three of her friends failed. Four other of her friends did pass first time. She complained that the advertisement was misleading and that the percentage was actually lower. Test whether there is evidence to support Hati's complaint at the 1% level.

Critical regions

- Remember that the critical region is just the **set of all values** which are **significant** under H_0. You use the binomial tables (or the binomial probability function) to find it.

- If the test is **one-tailed**, the critical region will be at only **one end** of the distribution. If the test is **two-tailed**, the critical region will be **split in two** with a bit at each end.

- For a two-tailed test, you could either be asked to make the probability of rejection in the tails **less than** $\frac{\alpha}{2}$, or **as close** to $\frac{\alpha}{2}$ as possible.

- The **actual significance level** is the probability (under H_0) that H_0 is rejected, which is found by calculating the **probability** that the observed value of the test statistic will fall in the critical region.

Tip: Make sure you always read the question to see which one of these it wants you to use — it'll cost you valuable marks if you don't.

> ## Example 1
>
> A company manufactures kettles. Its records over the years show that 20% of its kettles will be faulty. Simon claims that the proportion of faulty kettles must be lower than this. He takes a sample of 30 kettles to test his claim.
>
> a) Find the critical region for a test of Simon's claim at the 5% level.
>
> - Let p = the probability that a kettle is faulty.
>
> - Formulate the hypotheses:
> $$H_0: p = 0.2 \qquad H_1: p < 0.2$$
>
> - The test statistic is X = the number of faulty kettles in the sample, and under H_0 the sampling distribution is $X \sim B(30, 0.2)$.

- Use the binomial tables to find the two values of x for which $P(X \leq x)$ is either side of the significance level 0.05.

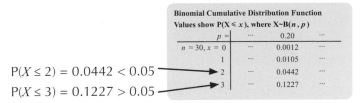

Binomial Cumulative Distribution Function
Values show $P(X \leqslant x)$, where $X \sim B(n, p)$

$p =$	$\cdots$	0.20	$\cdots$
$n = 30, x = 0$	$\cdots$	0.0012	$\cdots$
1	$\cdots$	0.0105	$\cdots$
2	$\cdots$	0.0442	$\cdots$
3	$\cdots$	0.1227	$\cdots$

$P(X \leq 2) = 0.0442 < 0.05$
$P(X \leq 3) = 0.1227 > 0.05$

So the critical region is the set of values $X \leq 2$.

Tip: If you're asked to do this for a probability that isn't in the binomial c.d.f. tables, you'll need to use the binomial probability function — see p8.

Tip: The number $X = 2$ in this example is called the critical value.

b) **State the actual significance level.**

The actual significance level is the probability that H_0 will be rejected when it is true, which is $P(X \leq 2) = $ 0.0442

c) **Simon found that 1 kettle in his sample was faulty. Say whether this is significant evidence to reject H_0.**

1 lies in the critical region, so it is significant evidence to reject H_0 in favour of H_1.

Tip: Testing the hypothesis using the sample data is easy once you've found the critical region — just see if the observed value of the test statistic lies in the critical region.

Example 2

Records show that the proportion of trees in a wood that suffer from a particular leaf disease is 15%. Chloe thinks that recent weather conditions might have affected this proportion. She examines a random sample of 20 of the trees.

a) **Using a 10% level of significance, find the critical region for a two-tailed test of Chloe's theory. The probability of rejection in each tail should be as close to 0.05 as possible.**

- Let p = proportion of trees with the leaf disease.

- Formulate the hypotheses: $H_0: p = 0.15$ $H_1: p \neq 0.15$

- Let X = number of sampled trees with the disease. Under H_0, $X \sim B(20, 0.15)$.

- The significance level $\alpha = 0.1$.

- This is a two-tailed test, so you're interested in both ends of the sampling distribution.

  The **lower tail** is the set of 'low' values of X with a total probability as close to 0.05 as possible.

  The **upper tail** is the set of 'high' values of X with a total probability as close to 0.05 as possible.

- Using the binomial tables:

  Lower tail: $P(X \leq 0) = 0.0388 < 0.05$
  $P(X \leq 1) = 0.1756 > 0.05$

  Find the two values so that $P(X \leq x)$ is either side of 0.05 and then see which is closer.

Tip: Be careful — this test is two-tailed, and it asks for the probability of rejection to be as close to $\frac{\alpha}{2}$ as possible.

<u>Upper tail</u>: You need to find X such that $P(X \geq x)$ is as close to 0.05 as possible.

$$P(X \geq 6) = 1 - P(X \leq 5) = 1 - 0.9327 = 0.0673 > 0.05$$
$$P(X \geq 7) = 1 - P(X \leq 6) = 1 - 0.9781 = 0.0219 < 0.05$$

You want the probability to be **as close as possible** to 0.05, so the lower tail is $X \leq 0$ and the upper tail is $X \geq 6$ because 0.0673 is closer to 0.05 than 0.0219 is.

So the critical region is $X = 0$ or $X \geq 6$.

b) **Find the actual significance level of a test based on your critical region from part a).**

The actual significance level is found by adding the probabilities (under H_0) of the test statistic falling in each part of the critical region.

$$P(X = 0) + P(X \geq 6) = 0.0388 + 0.0673$$
$$= 0.1061$$

You could also give this as 10.61%

c) **Chloe finds that 8 of the sampled trees have the leaf disease. Comment on this finding.**

The observed value of 8 is in the critical region. So there is evidence at the 10% level of significance to reject H_0 and to support Chloe's theory that there has been a change in the proportion of affected trees.

Exercise 4.2

Q1 A primary school hopes to increase the percentage of pupils reaching the top level in reading from its current value of 25% by limiting the time pupils spend watching TV.
Twenty parents will be limiting their child's use of TV.

a) Using a 5% level, find the critical region for a one-tailed test of whether the proportion of pupils reaching the top reading level has increased.

b) State the actual significance level.

Q2 Miss Cackle wishes to decrease the percentage of pupils giving up her potion-making class after year 9 from its current level of 20%. Over the last 3 years she has tried a new teaching method in one of her classes of 30 pupils. Using a 5% significance level, find the critical region for a test of whether the number of pupils giving up potions after year 9 has decreased. State the actual significance level.

Q3 Politicians are testing for a difference in local councils' rubbish collection service between the North and the South. They've found that 40% of the northern councils provide a weekly service. They have randomly chosen 25 councils in the south of the country to investigate. Find the critical region for a test of whether the number of councils providing weekly collections is significantly different in the south at the 5% level. The probability of each tail should be as close to 2.5% as possible. Calculate the actual significance level.

Q4 A travel agent thinks that fewer people are booking their holidays early this year. In the past, 35% have booked their summer holiday by February 1st. She intends to ask 15 people on 2nd February whether they have booked their summer holiday.

a) Find the critical region for a test at the 5% level of whether fewer people are booking their holidays early this year.

b) State the actual significance level.

c) The travel agent finds that 3 of the people she asked had already booked their summer holiday.
Is this result significant at the 5% level?

Q5 A new drug is to be tested on 50 people to see if they report an improvement in their symptoms. In the past it has been found that with a placebo treatment, 15% of people report an improvement, so the new drug has to be significantly better than this. Find the critical region for a test at the 1% level of significance of whether the new drug is significantly better than a placebo. The probability of the tail should be less than 1%. State the actual significance level.

Q6 Tests conducted on five-year-old girls have found that 5% of them believe that they have magical powers. A group of 50 five-year-old boys are to be tested to see if the same proportion of boys believe that they have magical powers. Find the critical region for a test at the 10% level of whether the proportion of boys who believe they have magical powers is different from that of girls. The probability of each tail should be as close to 5% as possible.
Calculate the actual significance level.

Q7 The British Furniture Company's top salesman has persuaded 60% of customers to take out a loyalty card. He has been on a motivational course and aims to improve even further. On his first day's work after the course he serves 12 customers.

a) Using a 5% level of significance, find the critical region for a test of whether the salesman has improved.

b) State the actual significance level.

c) He persuades 10 customers to take out a loyalty card.
Is this result significant at the 5% level?

5. Hypothesis Tests for a Poisson Distribution

You can also use hypothesis tests for testing theories about the rate at which events happen. This time, the test statistic will have a Poisson distribution instead of a binomial one — but the method's pretty much the same.

Setting up the test

A hypothesis test on the **mean**, λ, of a **Poisson distribution** is similar to a test of the probability or proportion, p, of a binomial distribution. Use it when the question is about the rate at which an event happens.

- Identify the **population parameter**
  — it's always λ, the rate at which an event happens in a certain unit of time or space.
- Write down the **null** hypothesis (H_0)
  — H_0: $\lambda = a$ for some constant a.
- Write down the **alternative** hypothesis (H_1)
  — H_1 will either be H_1: $\lambda < a$ or H_1: $\lambda > a$ (one-tailed test)
          or H_1: $\lambda \neq a$ (two-tailed test).
- State the **test statistic**, X
  — always just the number of times the event happens in the sampled period of time or space.
- Write down the **sampling distribution** of the test statistic under H_0
  — $X \sim Po(t\lambda)$ for some constant t, that depends on the sampled period of time or space.
- State the **significance level**, α
  — you'll usually be given this.

Tip: This value of t is just the multiplier to get from the unit of time and space that the population parameter λ is defined for, to the sampled period of time and space.
It just uses the additive property for Poisson distributions — see p33.

Then, as usual, you can either test an observed value of X for **significance**, or find the **critical region**, which gives all significant values of X.

Testing for significance

Tip: See p128-130 for the general theory on testing for significance.

Just like in the binomial case, testing an observed value for significance just means working out the probability of X being at least as extreme as the observed value and comparing it to α for a one-tailed test, or $\frac{\alpha}{2}$ if it's a two-tailed test.

The only difference is that X follows a Poisson distribution.

Tip: See p36 for how to use the Poisson tables.

- The Poisson **tables** show the cumulative distribution function $P(X \leq x)$ — so you can often use these to work out the probabilities.
- The Poisson **probability function** gives $P(X = x)$, so you can use this when the Poisson tables don't include the parameter you need.

Tip: The Poisson probability function (p29) says:
If $X \sim Po(\lambda)$, then
$$P(X = x) = \frac{e^{-\lambda}\lambda^x}{x!}$$

Example 1

During the interval of a musical, programmes are usually sold at a rate of 5 per minute. The musical's composer has promised to sign programmes in the interval and he believes this will increase the rate of programmes sold during the interval. On the first day that this happens, 11 programmes are sold in the first minute.
Test the composer's claim at a 5% significance level.

- Let λ = the rate at which programmes are sold per minute.

- Form the hypotheses: $H_0: \lambda = 5$ $H_1: \lambda > 5$

- Let X = number of programmes sold in a minute.
  Under H_0, $X \sim Po(5)$.

- The significance level is $\alpha = 0.05$ and this is a one-tailed test.

- Test for significance — to find the probability of X taking a value greater than or equal to 11 under H_0, use the Poisson tables (see p164):

$$P(X \geq 11) = 1 - P(X < 11)$$
$$= 1 - P(X \leq 10)$$
$$= 1 - 0.9863$$
$$= 0.0137$$

Since $0.0137 < 0.05$, the result is significant.

Poisson Cumulative Distribution Function
Values show $P(X \leq x)$, where $X \sim Po(\lambda)$

$\lambda =$	4.5	5.0
$x =$ 0	0.0111	0.0067
1	0.0611	0.0404
2	0.1736	0.1247
3	0.3423	0.2650
4	0.5321	0.4405
5	0.7029	0.6160
6	0.8311	0.7622
7	0.9134	0.8666
8	0.9597	0.9319
9	0.9829	0.9682
10	0.9933	0.9863
11	0.9976	0.9945

There is evidence at the 5% level of significance to reject H_0 and to suggest that the rate of programme sales has increased.

Tip: This test is about the **rate** of programmes sold, so the test statistic will follow a Poisson distribution.

Tip: $X \sim Po(5)$, since under H_0, $\lambda = 5$ is the rate of programmes sold per minute.

Example 2

A bookshop sells copies of the book 'All you've never wanted to know about the Poisson distribution' at a (surprisingly high) rate of 5 a week. The shop's manager decides to reduce the price of the book.
In the first two weeks after the price change, 16 copies are sold. Use a 5% level of significance to test whether there is evidence to suggest that sales of the book have increased.

- Let λ = the rate at which copies of the book are sold per week.

- Form the hypotheses: $H_0: \lambda = 5$ $H_1: \lambda > 5$

- Let X = number of copies sold in two weeks.
  Under H_0, $X \sim Po(2 \times 5)$, i.e. $X \sim Po(10)$.

Be careful — you've been given λ as the rate per week, but X is the number sold in 2 weeks, so you'll need to double λ.

Tip: The mention of 'rate' should make you think 'Poisson distribution'.

Tip: This is where the value of t in the step-by-step method on p142 comes in. If books are sold at a rate of 5 a week, then the number sold in 2 weeks will have a Poisson distribution with parameter $2 \times 5 = 10$.

- The significance level is $\alpha = 0.05$.

- Test for significance — find the probability using the tables:

$$P(X \geq 16) = 1 - P(X < 16)$$
$$= 1 - P(X \leq 15)$$
$$= 1 - 0.9513$$
$$= 0.0487$$

and since $0.0487 < 0.05$, the result is significant.

- Don't forget the **conclusion**:

> There is evidence at the 5% level of significance to reject H_0 and to suggest that sales have increased.

Use the Poisson probability function if the value of λ isn't in the Poisson tables.

Example 3

Anna suffers from an average of 4.8 sports injuries per year. She has started doing some exercises which she hopes will decrease the number of sports injuries she gets (although there is a risk they could lead to an increase in the number of injuries). In the first 18 months of doing these exercises she has 4 sports injuries. Using a 5% level of significance, test whether the frequency of her sports injuries has changed.

- Let λ = the number of sports injuries Anna gets per year.

- Form the hypotheses: $H_0: \lambda = 4.8$ $H_1: \lambda \neq 4.8$

- Let X = sports injuries Anna gets in eighteen months.
  Under H_0, $X \sim Po(4.8 \times 1.5)$, i.e. $X \sim Po(7.2)$.

> You'll need to multiply the parameter by 1.5 (the number of years in 18 months).

Tip: The Greek letter κ (rather than λ) has been used in the Poisson probability function here, because λ represents the average rate of injuries Anna gets in 1 year.

- The significance level is $\alpha = 0.05$. So $\frac{\alpha}{2} = 0.025$.

- Test for significance. Since the number of injuries Anna suffers (4) is less than the expected number under H_0 (= 7.2), you need to find the probability of X taking a value less than or equal to 4. The Poisson parameter 7.2 is not in the Poisson tables, so you'll need to use the probability function.

$$P(X = x) = \frac{e^{-\kappa} \kappa^x}{x!}$$

Tip: This is just the summation:
$$\sum_{x=0}^{4} \frac{e^{-7.2}(7.2)^x}{x!}$$
You might be able to put it into your calculator if you have a $\boxed{\sum_{\square}^{\square}\square}$ button.

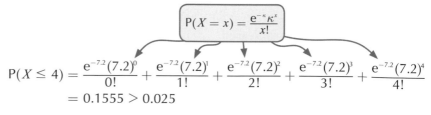

$$P(X \leq 4) = \frac{e^{-7.2}(7.2)^0}{0!} + \frac{e^{-7.2}(7.2)^1}{1!} + \frac{e^{-7.2}(7.2)^2}{2!} + \frac{e^{-7.2}(7.2)^3}{3!} + \frac{e^{-7.2}(7.2)^4}{4!}$$
$$= 0.1555 > 0.025$$

so the result is not significant.

> There is no evidence at the 5% level of significance to reject H_0 and to suggest that the exercises have changed the rate of injury.

Q1 University authorities have received an average of 9 complaints a week, from people living next to student halls, about noise. They banned the students from using their common room as punishment and expect this to lead to an improvement. They wish to test if there has been a decrease in complaints.

a) Identify the population parameter and write down the null and alternative hypotheses.

b) Write down the test statistic and its sampling distribution.

The following week only 4 complaints were received.

c) Does this represent a significant improvement at the 5% level?

Q2 Harriet manages to spill cups of coffee at an average rate of 3 cups a day. On Thursday, she spilt 6 cups of coffee. Test at the 10% level whether she is getting clumsier.

Q3 Samples of pond water have been examined under a microscope by a biologist investigating a particular micro-organism. She found that on average each sample contained 8 of these micro-organisms. She takes a sample from a different pond and is not sure whether the results will be different. There are 15 micro-organisms in her first sample. Is this significant at the 5% level?

Q4 Sahdat has always suffered from an average of 2 headaches a week. Lately, however, he has been attending relaxation classes and he has only had 3 headaches in the last 4 weeks. Does this represent a significant improvement? Test this at the 5% level.

Q5 On average a headmaster uses the word 'excellence' 30 times in a 20-minute speech. Recently he gave a 5-minute talk and used 'excellence' 15 times. Has he changed his use of the word? Test this at the 5% level.

Q6 Hayley is not good at grammar. On average she makes 37 mistakes in a 10-page document. She has been having grammar lessons from a friend and the first page of her latest essay had only 1 grammatical error. Is this evidence of an improvement at the 1% level?

Critical regions

Tip: Remember... the Poisson probability function is:

If $X \sim Po(\lambda)$, then
$$P(X = x) = \frac{e^{-\lambda}\lambda^x}{x!}$$
for $x = 0, 1, 2, 3...$

Finding the **critical region** for a Poisson distribution is just the same as doing it for a binomial, except you use the Poisson **probability function** or **tables** to find the probabilities.

- The critical region is at **one end** of the distribution for **one-tailed** tests, but will be in **two parts** (one part at either end) for **two-tailed** tests.

- For a two-tailed test, you could either be asked to make the probability of rejection in the tails **less than** $\frac{\alpha}{2}$, or **as close** to $\frac{\alpha}{2}$ as possible.

- The **actual significance level** is still the probability of H_0 being rejected when it is **true** (i.e. of being rejected **incorrectly**).

Example 1

During March, lambs are normally born at an average rate of 4.5 per week on Ceara's farm. This year, the weather has been a lot better and Ceara thinks that more lambs will be born in March. She counts the number of lambs born in the first fortnight of March to test her theory. Find the critical region for the one-tailed test of the hypothesis that there has been an increase, using a 5% level of significance. State the actual significance level.

- Let λ = the number of lambs born per week.

- Then H_0: $\lambda = 4.5$ and H_1: $\lambda > 4.5$.

- This is a one-tailed test with $\alpha = 0.05$.

- Let X be the number of lambs born in a fortnight on Ceara's farm. Then under H_0, $X \sim Po(9)$.

- Your critical region will be at the high end of the distribution. Look for the lowest value, x, with $P(X \geq x) < 0.05$.
$$P(X \geq 15) = 1 - P(X < 15) = 1 - P(X \leq 14) = 1 - 0.9585 = 0.0415$$
$$P(X \geq 14) = 1 - P(X < 14) = 1 - P(X \leq 13) = 1 - 0.9261 = 0.0739$$

- This means the critical region is $\boxed{X \geq 15.}$

- The actual significance level is $P(X \geq 15) = \boxed{0.0415.}$

Tip: Under H_0, the number of lambs born per week follows $Po(4.5)$, so the number of lambs born in 2 weeks will follow a Poisson distribution with parameter $2 \times 4.5 = 9$.

Tip: The critical value here is $X = 15$.

Example 2

A local astronomy club usually receives reports of UFO sightings at a rate of 8 per year. Eric thinks that a recent TV series about UFO sightings may change the rate at which sightings are reported to the club. He records the total number of reports received over a period of 6 months.

a) **Find the critical region for a two-tailed test of the hypothesis that the number of reported UFO sightings has changed, using a 5% significance level. The probability in each tail should be less than 2.5%.**

- Let λ = the rate at which UFO sightings are reported per year.

- Then H_0: $\lambda = 8$ and H_1: $\lambda \neq 8$.

- This is a two-tailed test with $\alpha = 0.05$, so $\frac{\alpha}{2} = 0.025$.

- Let X be the number of UFO sightings reported to the club in 6 months. Then under H_0, $X \sim \text{Po}(4)$.

- Since this is a two-tailed test, you need to look at both ends of the distribution.

  For the lower tail, look for the biggest possible value, x, such that $P(X \leq x) \leq 0.025$.

  $$P(X \leq 0) = 0.0183$$

  $$P(X \leq 1) = 0.0916$$

  $P(X \leq 0)$ is less than 0.025, so the critical region at the low end of the distribution is $X = 0$.

  For the upper tail, look for the smallest possible value, x, such that $P(X \geq x) \leq 0.025$.

  $$P(X \geq 9) = 1 - P(X \leq 8) = 1 - 0.9786 = 0.0214$$

  $$P(X \geq 8) = 1 - P(X \leq 7) = 1 - 0.9489 = 0.0511$$

  $P(X \geq 9)$ is less than 0.025, so the critical region at the high end of the distribution is $X \geq 9$.

- The critical region is $\boxed{X = 0 \text{ or } X \geq 9.}$

> **Tip:** You need to find the biggest possible value of x with $P(X \leq x) \leq 0.025$. So find 2 consecutive values in the table x_1 and x_2, where:
> a) $P(X \leq x_1) \leq 0.025$ and
> b) $P(X \leq x_2) > 0.025$.
>
> Then the critical value will be x_1.

b) **State the actual significance level.**

The actual significance level is $0.0183 + 0.0214 = \boxed{0.0397.}$

c) **Eric records 11 reports of UFO sightings. Is this result significant at the 5% level?**

This result lies in the critical region, so it is significant at the 5% level. There is significant evidence to reject H_0 in favour of the alternative hypothesis that the number of reports has changed.

Q1 Lionel is very proud of the state of his front lawn. However, he usually finds he has to dig out an average of 6 new dandelion plants every spring. This year he has experimented with a new top dressing applied to the lawn and believes that he will have fewer dandelions in spring.

a) Find the critical region for the test of the hypothesis that there's been a decrease in dandelions this spring at the 5% level of significance.

b) State the actual significance level.

Q2 Calls to a helpline generally come in at the rate of 7 a day. After a television programme mentions the helpline, calls are expected to increase. The number of calls is recorded on the first day. Find the critical region for the test of the hypothesis that the number of calls has increased, at the 5% level of significance. State the actual significance level.

Q3 The number of left-handed pupils at Mr Twist's school averages 8 per year group. The school has just changed its admissions policy and Mr Twist thinks that the number will change. Mr Twist records the number of left-handed pupils in the new year group.

a) Find the critical region for the test of the hypothesis that there has been significant change in the number of left-handed pupils at the 5% level. The probability in each tail should be as close to 0.025 as possible.

b) Calculate the actual significance level.

Twelve pupils are found to be left-handed.

c) Is this result significant evidence at the 5% level that the number of left-handed pupils per year has changed?

Q4 The owners of Ziggy the dog are trying to house-train her using the Happy Paws Puppy Training Scheme. Before the scheme, Ziggy's owners expected an average of 2 'accidents' an hour. After several weeks they think there's been an improvement so they monitor Ziggy over a 5-hour period.

a) Find the critical region for the test of the hypothesis that there's been a significant decrease in 'accidents' at the 5% level of significance.

b) State the actual significance level.

c) Ziggy has 1 'accident' while the owners are monitoring her. Is this a significant result at the 5% level of significance?

Q5 A saleswoman normally makes 35 sales in each 5-day working week. She goes to an advanced sales course hoping to improve. When she comes back her sales will be checked carefully for the first day. What is the critical region for the test of the hypothesis that she has improved at the 1% level? State the actual significance level.

6. Hypothesis Tests Involving Approximate Distributions

If the binomial sample size (n) or the Poisson mean (λ) is very large then the tables won't work and using the probability function will be time-consuming. When this happens, you can use an approximation of the distribution to make the numbers easier— just like you've seen in chapters 2 and 4.

Learning Objective:

- Be able to use approximations of the binomial and Poisson distributions to test hypotheses.

Using approximations

Approximations using a Poisson distribution

You should remember from Chapter 2 that you can sometimes use a **Poisson** distribution as an **approximation** to a binomial distribution.

> If $X \sim B(n, p)$, and:
> 1) n is **large**,
> 2) p is **small**,
> then X can be approximated by **Po(np)**.

The **mean** (expected value) of the binomial distribution $B(n, p)$ is np.

Tip: The bigger the value of n and the smaller the value of p, the better the approximation will be. For more on this approximation see pages 40-41.

You can use the same approximation to carry out a hypothesis test.

Example

May has a crazy, 20-sided dice which she thinks might be biased towards the number 1. She rolls the dice 100 times and gets twelve 1s. Test May's theory at the 1% level of significance.

- Start by working through the normal hypothesis test method.

  - If the dice is unbiased, $P(1) = 1 \div 20 = 0.05$.
  - So, $H_0: p = 0.05$ and $H_1: p > 0.05$, where p is the probability of rolling a 1.
  - Let X = number of ones in 100 rolls. Under H_0, $X \sim B(100, 0.05)$.
  - $\alpha = 0.01$.

- Now for the approximation. You can't look up $n = 100$ in the tables, but n is big and p is quite small, so X can be approximated by Po(5).

  $$np = 100 \times 0.05 = 5$$

- So using the **Poisson** tables:

  $P(X \geq 12) = 1 - P(X \leq 11) = 1 - 0.9945 = 0.0055 < 0.01,$

  So this result is significant at the 1% level.
  There is very strong evidence to reject H_0 and to support May's claim that the dice is biased towards the number 1.

Tip: The evidence provided by this test is much stronger than the evidence provided by a test using a 5% or 10% significance level. So you can be more confident that you've correctly rejected H_0.

Approximations using a normal distribution

You saw in Chapter 4 that the **normal** distribution can be used to **approximate** both the **binomial** distribution and the **Poisson** distribution in certain cases.

Tip: Even if p isn't that close to 0.5, as long as $np > 5$ and $nq > 5$, the normal approximation of the binomial should work.

> If $X \sim \mathbf{B}(\textbf{\textit{n}}, \textbf{\textit{p}})$, and:
>
> 1) n is **large**,
>
> 2) p is **close** to **0.5**,
>
> then X can be approximated by $Y \sim \mathrm{N}(\textbf{\textit{np}}, \textbf{\textit{npq}})$ where $\textbf{\textit{q}} = \mathbf{1} - \textbf{\textit{p}}$.

> If $X \sim \mathbf{Po}(\boldsymbol{\lambda})$, and λ is **large**,
>
> then X can be approximated by $Y \sim \mathrm{N}(\boldsymbol{\lambda}, \boldsymbol{\lambda})$.

So if either n or λ is **too big** for you to do a hypothesis test, check to see if you can **approximate** it with a **normal** distribution.

Remember... because the binomial and Poisson distributions are both **discrete** but the normal distribution is **continuous**, you need to use a **continuity correction**.

Tip: See p97 for more on continuity corrections.

You should have learnt the following **continuity corrections** in Chapter 4:

Binomial or Poisson	Normal
$P(X = b)$	$P(b - 0.5 < Y < b + 0.5)$
$P(X \leq b)$	$P(Y < b + 0.5)$
$P(X < b)$	$P(Y < b - 0.5)$
$P(X \geq b)$	$P(Y > b - 0.5)$
$P(X > b)$	$P(Y > b + 0.5)$

Example 1

An automated sewing machine produces faults randomly, at an average rate of 5 per day. The machine is improved, and in a random five-day period, 20 faults are found. Using a suitable approximation, test at the 5% significance level whether the number of faults has decreased.

- Start by working through the normal hypothesis test method.

  - Let λ = the rate of faults per day.
  - H_0: $\lambda = 5$ and H_1: $\lambda < 5$,
  - Let X = number of faults in five days. Under H_0, $X \sim \mathrm{Po}(25)$.
  - $\alpha = 0.05$.

- λ is large, so you can approximate X with:

$$Y \sim N(25, 25)$$

Tip: This works better the bigger λ is, but it should be fine for any $\lambda > 10$.

- Apply the continuity correction: $P(X \leq 20) \approx P(Y < 20.5)$

$$P(Y < 20.5) = P\left(Z < \frac{20.5 - 25}{\sqrt{25}}\right)$$
$$= P(Z < -0.9) = 1 - P(Z \leq 0.9)$$
$$= 1 - 0.8159 = 0.1841 > 0.05$$

Tip: Don't forget to include the continuity correction. Here $X \leq 20$ becomes $Y < 20.5$.

So there's insufficient evidence at the 5% level of significance to reject H_0. There's insufficient evidence to say that the number of faults has decreased.

Example 2

45% of the employees of a large company use social networking sites in work time. The managing director has increased the length of the lunch break and thinks this will change the percentage of employees using social networking sites while working. To test this theory he monitors the computer use of 200 members of staff and finds that 100 of them visit social networking sites during working hours. Using a suitable approximation, test his theory at the 5% significance level.

- H_0: $p = 0.45$ and H_1: $p \neq 0.45$, where p is the proportion of employees who use social networking sites during working hours.

- Let X = number of employees out of the 200-employee sample who visit social networking sites. Under H_0, $X \sim B(200, 0.45)$.

- $\alpha = 0.05$, but the test is two-tailed so you'll need $\frac{\alpha}{2} = 0.025$.

- n is large and p is close to 0.5 so use a **normal** approximation
    $Y \sim N(200 \times 0.45, 200 \times 0.45 \times 0.55) = N(90, 49.5)$

- Apply a **continuity correction**: $P(X \geq 100) \approx P(Y > 99.5)$

$$
\begin{aligned}
P(X \geq 100) &= P(Y > 99.5) \\
&= 1 - P(Y \leq 99.5) \\
&= 1 - P\left(Z \leq \frac{99.5 - 90}{\sqrt{49.5}}\right) \\
&= 1 - P(Z \leq 1.35) \\
&= 1 - 0.9115 \\
&= 0.0885 > 0.025
\end{aligned}
$$

Tip: Use the normal distribution tables (p157-158) to find values of $P(Z < z)$.

So there's insufficient evidence at the 5% level of significance to reject H_0. There's insufficient evidence to say that the number of employees using social networking sites has changed from 45%.

Q1 Troy is a professional golfer and usually only misses 3% of his putts. Recently he believes he's improved. He's missed only 4 out of the last 300 practice putts. Use a suitable approximate distribution to test at the 5% level whether he has made a significant improvement.

Q2 Harpreet loses her mobile signal on average 14 times a day. Yesterday seemed particularly bad because she lost her signal 22 times. Use a suitable approximate distribution to test her claim at the 5% level that there has been a significant worsening.

Q3 5% of the trees in a wood are home to a rare species of butterfly and so the wood has been granted a special preservation status. Campaigners have now turned their attention to a neighbouring wood and have found that 3 out of 80 trees are home to the same species of butterfly. Use a suitable approximate distribution to test at the 5% level whether this is significantly different from the first wood.

Q4 Over the last few years 70% of young people have said they expect to own their own home some day. Malcolm thinks that the recent surge in youth unemployment may have reduced this figure. He asked 90 randomly selected young people and 56 said they expected to own their own home some day. Use a suitable approximate distribution to test, at the 5% level, Malcolm's claim that there has been a significant decrease in the proportion of young people expecting to own their own home.

Q5 A Scottish Safari Park is open from Wednesday through to Saturday and has an average of 60 visitors a day. They decide to open the park on Sundays as well but don't know whether to expect more or fewer visitors. On a randomly chosen Sunday only 46 visitors turn up. Use a suitable approximate distribution to test at the 5% level whether this represents a significant decrease in the usual number of visitors.

Q6 Longford Lodge Farm supplies eggs to a local restaurant. Generally only 1% of the eggs are cracked when they arrive. However, a randomly selected sample of 200 eggs contained 6 that were cracked. Use a suitable approximate distribution to test at the 5% level whether there has been a significant increase in the proportion of cracked eggs.

Q7 52% of all dragons born are male. Charlie is researching dragons on a remote island in Scotland, and has recorded that 91 out of the last 150 dragons born have been male. Use a suitable approximate distribution to test at the 5% level whether this supports Charlie's theory that the proportion of dragons born on this island that are male is significantly greater than usual.

Review Exercise — Chapter 5

Q1 The manager of a tennis club wants to know if members are happy with the facilities provided. He decides to carry out a survey of a random sample of members.

a) Identify the population the manager is interested in.

b) Identify the sampling units.

c) Suggest a suitable sampling frame.

Q2 For each of the following situations, explain whether it would be more sensible to carry out a census or a sample survey:

a) Marcel is in charge of a packaging department of 8 people. He wants to know the average number of items a person packs per day.

b) A toy manufacturer produces batches of 500 toys. As part of a safety check, they want to test the toys to work out the strength needed to pull them apart.

c) Tara has a biased dice. She wants to find the proportion of dice rolls that will result in a 'three'.

Q3 Amanda has been asked to check a normal pack of 52 cards suspected of being marked. She decides to choose 4 cards at random and subject them to a thorough examination under a microscope.

a) What is the sampling frame?

b) How many sampling units are there?

Q4 Why is it a good idea to use simple random sampling to select a sample?

Q5 The weights of a population of jars of pickled onions have unknown mean μ and standard deviation σ. A random sample of 50 weights $(X_1, ..., X_{50})$ is recorded. For each of the following, say whether or not it's a statistic:

a) $\dfrac{X_{25} + X_{26}}{2}$
   b) $\sum X_i - \sigma$
   c) $\sum X_i^2 + \mu$
   d) $\dfrac{\sum X_i}{50}$

Q6 A machine has been calibrated to fill bags of frozen peas with a mean weight $\mu = 0.5$ kg and a standard deviation $\sigma = 0.05$ kg. It is suspected that the mean and standard deviation have changed over time. 20 bags are weighed, giving weights X_1 to X_{20}. Which of the following are statistics?

a) $\sum X_i$
   b) $\dfrac{\sum(X_i - \mu)}{20}$
   c) $\dfrac{\sum(X_i - 2\sigma)}{20}$
   d) The sample median

Q7 For each of the following, state whether a one-tailed or two-tailed hypothesis test should be used. Define suitable null and alternative hypotheses for each test.

a) Salma thinks a coin might be biased. She wants to find out about p, the proportion of coin tosses that result in 'heads'.

b) The number of errors made by a typist every hour follows a Poisson distribution with mean $\lambda = 20$. After receiving some training, the typist wants to test whether he now makes fewer errors.

Q8 Suggest suitable test statistics for hypothesis tests of:

a) A binomial parameter, p.   b) The mean, λ, of a Poisson distribution.

Q9 a) Carry out the following tests of the binomial parameter p.
Let X represent the number of successes in a random sample of size 20:

(i)   Test $H_0: p = 0.2$ against $H_1: p < 0.2$, at the 5% significance level, using $x = 2$.

(ii) Test $H_0: p = 0.4$ against $H_1: p > 0.4$, at the 1% significance level, using $x = 15$.

b) Carry out the following tests of the Poisson parameter λ. Let X represent the number of events in a given interval and λ be the average rate at which they are assumed to occur in intervals of identical size:

(i)   Test $H_0: \lambda = 7$ against $H_1: \lambda < 7$, at the 5% significance level, using $x = 3$.

(ii) Test $H_0: \lambda = 2.5$ against $H_1: \lambda > 2.5$, at the 10% significance level, using $x = 4$.

Q10 a) Find the critical region for the following test where $X \sim B(10, p)$:
Test $H_0: p = 0.3$ against $H_1: p < 0.3$, at the 5% significance level.

b) Find the critical region for the following test where $X \sim Po(\lambda)$:
Test $H_0: \lambda = 6$ against $H_1: \lambda < 6$, at the 10% significance level.

Q11 Class 8Z were sent outside to do a daisy survey at the end of the summer term. They found that each square metre of the school field contains on average 42 daisies. James and Philip had been absent when the data was collected, so they went out later than the rest of the class. They chose to investigate the shady area at the far end of the school field, where they found 30 daisies in their square metre. Use a suitable approximate distribution to test at the 5% level their theory that significantly fewer daisies grow in the area they investigated.

1   Prize draw tickets are drawn from a container, inside which are large quantities of tickets numbered with '1' or '2'. The tickets correspond to 1 or 2 prizes. 70% have the number 1 and 30% have the number 2.

     A random sample of 3 tickets is drawn from the container. Find the sampling distribution for the median, M, of the numbers on the tickets.

(7 marks)

2   Over a long period of time, the chef at an Italian restaurant has found that there is a probability of 0.2 that a customer ordering a dessert on a weekday evening will order tiramisu. He thinks that the proportion of customers ordering desserts on Saturday evenings who order tiramisu is greater than 0.2.

     a)   State the name of the probability distribution that would be used in a hypothesis test for the value of p, the proportion of Saturday evening dessert eaters ordering tiramisu.

(1 mark)

     A random sample of 20 customers who ordered a dessert on a Saturday evening was taken. 7 of these customers ordered tiramisu.

     b)   (i)   Stating your hypotheses clearly, test the chef's theory at the 5% level of significance.

          (ii)   Find the minimum number of tiramisu orders needed for the result to be significant.

(7 marks)

3   A tennis player serves a fault on her first serve at an average rate of 4 per service game. The player receives some extra coaching. In a randomly selected set of tennis, she serves 12 first-serve faults in 5 service games. She wants to test whether her average rate of first-serve faults has decreased.

     a)   Write down the conditions needed for the number of first-serve faults per service game to be modelled by a Poisson distribution.

(2 marks)

     Assume the conditions you stated in part a) hold.

     b)   Using a suitable approximation, carry out the test at the 5% level of significance.

(6 marks)

4   A machine breaks down at random at an average rate of 6.5 times per month.
     It is serviced and the person carrying out the service claims that the number of
     breakdowns should be lower. The machine's owner wishes to test this claim.
     He forms the null and alternative hypotheses below:

$$H_0: \lambda = 6.5 \text{ and } H_1: \lambda < 6.5$$

a)   Let X represent the number of times in one month that the machine breaks
     down. Find the critical region for this test at the 5% level of significance.
     The probability in the tail should be less than 5%.

(3 marks)

b)   Find the probability of rejecting H_0, assuming that H_0 is true.

(1 mark)

5   a)   Explain what you understand by

     (i)   a survey

(1 mark)

     (ii) a census

(1 mark)

     (iii) a sample

(1 mark)

Every waterproof camera sold by Splash Electronics Ltd. has a unique product code on the
inside cover. Before the company sends a batch of cameras out, they test a random sample
of 15 cameras to see how long they can stay underwater before water leaks in.

b)   (i)   Identify the sampling units for this sample.

(1 mark)

     (ii) Suggest a sampling frame.

(1 mark)

     (iii) Give a reason why the company would test a sample of their cameras rather
           than the whole population.

(1 mark)

6   The residents of a town are being asked their views on a plan to build a wind farm in the
     area. Environmental campaigners claim that 10% of the residents are against the plan.
     A random sample of 50 residents is surveyed.

a)   Using a 10% significance level, find the critical region for a two-tailed test of
     this claim. The probability of rejecting each tail should be as close as possible
     to 5%.

(5 marks)

b)   State the probability of incorrectly rejecting H_0, using your critical region from
     part a).

(2 marks)

It's found that 4 of the sampled residents say they are against the plan.

c)   Comment on this finding in relation to the environmental campaigners' claim.

(2 marks)

S2 Statistical Tables

The normal distribution function

The cumulative distribution function $\Phi(z)$ is tabulated below.

This is defined as $\Phi(z) = \dfrac{1}{\sqrt{2\pi}} \displaystyle\int_{-\infty}^{z} e^{-\frac{1}{2}t^2} dt$.

z	$\Phi(z)$	z	$\Phi(z)$	z	$\Phi(z)$	z	$\Phi(z)$	z	$\Phi(z)$
0.00	0.5000	0.50	0.6915	1.00	0.8413	1.50	0.9332	2.00	0.9772
0.01	0.5040	0.51	0.6950	1.01	0.8438	1.51	0.9345	2.02	0.9783
0.02	0.5080	0.52	0.6985	1.02	0.8461	1.52	0.9357	2.04	0.9793
0.03	0.5120	0.53	0.7019	1.03	0.8485	1.53	0.9370	2.06	0.9803
0.04	0.5160	0.54	0.7054	1.04	0.8508	1.54	0.9382	2.08	0.9812
0.05	0.5199	0.55	0.7088	1.05	0.8531	1.55	0.9394	2.10	0.9821
0.06	0.5239	0.56	0.7123	1.06	0.8554	1.56	0.9406	2.12	0.9830
0.07	0.5279	0.57	0.7157	1.07	0.8577	1.57	0.9418	2.14	0.9838
0.08	0.5319	0.58	0.7190	1.08	0.8599	1.58	0.9429	2.16	0.9846
0.09	0.5359	0.59	0.7224	1.09	0.8621	1.59	0.9441	2.18	0.9854
0.10	0.5398	0.60	0.7257	1.10	0.8643	1.60	0.9452	2.20	0.9861
0.11	0.5438	0.61	0.7291	1.11	0.8665	1.61	0.9463	2.22	0.9868
0.12	0.5478	0.62	0.7324	1.12	0.8686	1.62	0.9474	2.24	0.9875
0.13	0.5517	0.63	0.7357	1.13	0.8708	1.63	0.9484	2.26	0.9881
0.14	0.5557	0.64	0.7389	1.14	0.8729	1.64	0.9495	2.28	0.9887
0.15	0.5596	0.65	0.7422	1.15	0.8749	1.65	0.9505	2.30	0.9893
0.16	0.5636	0.66	0.7454	1.16	0.8770	1.66	0.9515	2.32	0.9898
0.17	0.5675	0.67	0.7486	1.17	0.8790	1.67	0.9525	2.34	0.9904
0.18	0.5714	0.68	0.7517	1.18	0.8810	1.68	0.9535	2.36	0.9909
0.19	0.5753	0.69	0.7549	1.19	0.8830	1.69	0.9545	2.38	0.9913
0.20	0.5793	0.70	0.7580	1.20	0.8849	1.70	0.9554	2.40	0.9918
0.21	0.5832	0.71	0.7611	1.21	0.8869	1.71	0.9564	2.42	0.9922
0.22	0.5871	0.72	0.7642	1.22	0.8888	1.72	0.9573	2.44	0.9927
0.23	0.5910	0.73	0.7673	1.23	0.8907	1.73	0.9582	2.46	0.9931
0.24	0.5948	0.74	0.7704	1.24	0.8925	1.74	0.9591	2.48	0.9934
0.25	0.5987	0.75	0.7734	1.25	0.8944	1.75	0.9599	2.50	0.9938
0.26	0.6026	0.76	0.7764	1.26	0.8962	1.76	0.9608	2.55	0.9946
0.27	0.6064	0.77	0.7794	1.27	0.8980	1.77	0.9616	2.60	0.9953
0.28	0.6103	0.78	0.7823	1.28	0.8997	1.78	0.9625	2.65	0.9960
0.29	0.6141	0.79	0.7852	1.29	0.9015	1.79	0.9633	2.70	0.9965
0.30	0.6179	0.80	0.7881	1.30	0.9032	1.80	0.9641	2.75	0.9970
0.31	0.6217	0.81	0.7910	1.31	0.9049	1.81	0.9649	2.80	0.9974
0.32	0.6255	0.82	0.7939	1.32	0.9066	1.82	0.9656	2.85	0.9978
0.33	0.6293	0.83	0.7967	1.33	0.9082	1.83	0.9664	2.90	0.9981
0.34	0.6331	0.84	0.7995	1.34	0.9099	1.84	0.9671	2.95	0.9984
0.35	0.6368	0.85	0.8023	1.35	0.9115	1.85	0.9678	3.00	0.9987
0.36	0.6406	0.86	0.8051	1.36	0.9131	1.86	0.9686	3.05	0.9989
0.37	0.6443	0.87	0.8078	1.37	0.9147	1.87	0.9693	3.10	0.9990
0.38	0.6480	0.88	0.8106	1.38	0.9162	1.88	0.9699	3.15	0.9992
0.39	0.6517	0.89	0.8133	1.39	0.9177	1.89	0.9706	3.20	0.9993
0.40	0.6554	0.90	0.8159	1.40	0.9192	1.90	0.9713	3.25	0.9994
0.41	0.6591	0.91	0.8186	1.41	0.9207	1.91	0.9719	3.30	0.9995
0.42	0.6628	0.92	0.8212	1.42	0.9222	1.92	0.9726	3.35	0.9996
0.43	0.6664	0.93	0.8238	1.43	0.9236	1.93	0.9732	3.40	0.9997
0.44	0.6700	0.94	0.8264	1.44	0.9251	1.94	0.9738	3.50	0.9998
0.45	0.6736	0.95	0.8289	1.45	0.9265	1.95	0.9744	3.60	0.9998
0.46	0.6772	0.96	0.8315	1.46	0.9279	1.96	0.9750	3.70	0.9999
0.47	0.6808	0.97	0.8340	1.47	0.9292	1.97	0.9756	3.80	0.9999
0.48	0.6844	0.98	0.8365	1.48	0.9306	1.98	0.9761	3.90	1.0000
0.49	0.6879	0.99	0.8389	1.49	0.9319	1.99	0.9767	4.00	1.0000
0.50	0.6915	1.00	0.8413	1.50	0.9332	2.00	0.9772		

Percentage points of the normal distribution

The z-values in the table are those which a random variable
$Z \sim N(0, 1)$ exceeds with probability p, i.e. $P(Z > z) = 1 - \Phi(z) = p$.

p	z	p	z
0.5000	0.0000	0.0500	1.6449
0.4000	0.2533	0.0250	1.9600
0.3000	0.5244	0.0100	2.3263
0.2000	0.8416	0.0050	2.5758
0.1500	1.0364	0.0010	3.0902
0.1000	1.2816	0.0005	3.2905

The binomial cumulative distribution function

The values below show $P(X \leq x)$, where $X \sim B(n, p)$.

		$p =$	0.05	0.10	0.15	0.20	0.25	0.30	0.35	0.40	0.45	0.50
$n = 5$	$x =$	0	0.7738	0.5905	0.4437	0.3277	0.2373	0.1681	0.1160	0.0778	0.0503	0.0313
		1	0.9774	0.9185	0.8352	0.7373	0.6328	0.5282	0.4284	0.3370	0.2562	0.1875
		2	0.9988	0.9914	0.9734	0.9421	0.8965	0.8369	0.7648	0.6826	0.5931	0.5000
		3	1.0000	0.9995	0.9978	0.9933	0.9844	0.9692	0.9460	0.9130	0.8688	0.8125
		4	1.0000	1.0000	0.9999	0.9997	0.9990	0.9976	0.9947	0.9898	0.9815	0.9688
$n = 6$	$x =$	0	0.7351	0.5314	0.3771	0.2621	0.1780	0.1176	0.0754	0.0467	0.0277	0.0156
		1	0.9672	0.8857	0.7765	0.6554	0.5339	0.4202	0.3191	0.2333	0.1636	0.1094
		2	0.9978	0.9842	0.9527	0.9011	0.8306	0.7443	0.6471	0.5443	0.4415	0.3438
		3	0.9999	0.9987	0.9941	0.9830	0.9624	0.9295	0.8826	0.8208	0.7447	0.6563
		4	1.0000	0.9999	0.9996	0.9984	0.9954	0.9891	0.9777	0.9590	0.9308	0.8906
		5	1.0000	1.0000	1.0000	0.9999	0.9998	0.9993	0.9982	0.9959	0.9917	0.9844
$n = 7$	$x =$	0	0.6983	0.4783	0.3206	0.2097	0.1335	0.0824	0.0490	0.0280	0.0152	0.0078
		1	0.9556	0.8503	0.7166	0.5767	0.4449	0.3294	0.2338	0.1586	0.1024	0.0625
		2	0.9962	0.9743	0.9262	0.8520	0.7564	0.6471	0.5323	0.4199	0.3164	0.2266
		3	0.9998	0.9973	0.9879	0.9667	0.9294	0.8740	0.8002	0.7102	0.6083	0.5000
		4	1.0000	0.9998	0.9988	0.9953	0.9871	0.9712	0.9444	0.9037	0.8471	0.7734
		5	1.0000	1.0000	0.9999	0.9996	0.9987	0.9962	0.9910	0.9812	0.9643	0.9375
		6	1.0000	1.0000	1.0000	1.0000	0.9999	0.9998	0.9994	0.9984	0.9963	0.9922
$n = 8$	$x =$	0	0.6634	0.4305	0.2725	0.1678	0.1001	0.0576	0.0319	0.0168	0.0084	0.0039
		1	0.9428	0.8131	0.6572	0.5033	0.3671	0.2553	0.1691	0.1064	0.0632	0.0352
		2	0.9942	0.9619	0.8948	0.7969	0.6785	0.5518	0.4278	0.3154	0.2201	0.1445
		3	0.9996	0.9950	0.9786	0.9437	0.8862	0.8059	0.7064	0.5941	0.4770	0.3633
		4	1.0000	0.9996	0.9971	0.9896	0.9727	0.9420	0.8939	0.8263	0.7396	0.6367
		5	1.0000	1.0000	0.9998	0.9988	0.9958	0.9887	0.9747	0.9502	0.9115	0.8555
		6	1.0000	1.0000	1.0000	0.9999	0.9996	0.9987	0.9964	0.9915	0.9819	0.9648
		7	1.0000	1.0000	1.0000	1.0000	1.0000	0.9999	0.9998	0.9993	0.9983	0.9961
$n = 9$	$x =$	0	0.6302	0.3874	0.2316	0.1342	0.0751	0.0404	0.0207	0.0101	0.0046	0.0020
		1	0.9288	0.7748	0.5995	0.4362	0.3003	0.1960	0.1211	0.0705	0.0385	0.0195
		2	0.9916	0.9470	0.8591	0.7382	0.6007	0.4628	0.3373	0.2318	0.1495	0.0898
		3	0.9994	0.9917	0.9661	0.9144	0.8343	0.7297	0.6089	0.4826	0.3614	0.2539
		4	1.0000	0.9991	0.9944	0.9804	0.9511	0.9012	0.8283	0.7334	0.6214	0.5000
		5	1.0000	0.9999	0.9994	0.9969	0.9900	0.9747	0.9464	0.9006	0.8342	0.7461
		6	1.0000	1.0000	1.0000	0.9997	0.9987	0.9957	0.9888	0.9750	0.9502	0.9102
		7	1.0000	1.0000	1.0000	1.0000	0.9999	0.9996	0.9986	0.9962	0.9909	0.9805
		8	1.0000	1.0000	1.0000	1.0000	1.0000	1.0000	0.9999	0.9997	0.9992	0.9980
$n = 10$	$x =$	0	0.5987	0.3487	0.1969	0.1074	0.0563	0.0282	0.0135	0.0060	0.0025	0.0010
		1	0.9139	0.7361	0.5443	0.3758	0.2440	0.1493	0.0860	0.0464	0.0233	0.0107
		2	0.9885	0.9298	0.8202	0.6778	0.5256	0.3828	0.2616	0.1673	0.0996	0.0547
		3	0.9990	0.9872	0.9500	0.8791	0.7759	0.6496	0.5138	0.3823	0.2660	0.1719
		4	0.9999	0.9984	0.9901	0.9672	0.9219	0.8497	0.7515	0.6331	0.5044	0.3770
		5	1.0000	0.9999	0.9986	0.9936	0.9803	0.9527	0.9051	0.8338	0.7384	0.6230
		6	1.0000	1.0000	0.9999	0.9991	0.9965	0.9894	0.9740	0.9452	0.8980	0.8281
		7	1.0000	1.0000	1.0000	0.9999	0.9996	0.9984	0.9952	0.9877	0.9726	0.9453
		8	1.0000	1.0000	1.0000	1.0000	1.0000	0.9999	0.9995	0.9983	0.9955	0.9893
		9	1.0000	1.0000	1.0000	1.0000	1.0000	1.0000	1.0000	0.9999	0.9997	0.9990

The binomial cumulative distribution function (continued)

		p =	0.05	0.10	0.15	0.20	0.25	0.30	0.35	0.40	0.45	0.50
n = 12	x =	0	0.5404	0.2824	0.1422	0.0687	0.0317	0.0138	0.0057	0.0022	0.0008	0.0002
		1	0.8816	0.6590	0.4435	0.2749	0.1584	0.0850	0.0424	0.0196	0.0083	0.0032
		2	0.9804	0.8891	0.7358	0.5583	0.3907	0.2528	0.1513	0.0834	0.0421	0.0193
		3	0.9978	0.9744	0.9078	0.7946	0.6488	0.4925	0.3467	0.2253	0.1345	0.0730
		4	0.9998	0.9957	0.9761	0.9274	0.8424	0.7237	0.5833	0.4382	0.3044	0.1938
		5	1.0000	0.9995	0.9954	0.9806	0.9456	0.8822	0.7873	0.6652	0.5269	0.3872
		6	1.0000	0.9999	0.9993	0.9961	0.9857	0.9614	0.9154	0.8418	0.7393	0.6128
		7	1.0000	1.0000	0.9999	0.9994	0.9972	0.9905	0.9745	0.9427	0.8883	0.8062
		8	1.0000	1.0000	1.0000	0.9999	0.9996	0.9983	0.9944	0.9847	0.9644	0.9270
		9	1.0000	1.0000	1.0000	1.0000	1.0000	0.9998	0.9992	0.9972	0.9921	0.9807
		10	1.0000	1.0000	1.0000	1.0000	1.0000	1.0000	0.9999	0.9997	0.9989	0.9968
		11	1.0000	1.0000	1.0000	1.0000	1.0000	1.0000	1.0000	1.0000	0.9999	0.9998
n = 15	x =	0	0.4633	0.2059	0.0874	0.0352	0.0134	0.0047	0.0016	0.0005	0.0001	0.0000
		1	0.8290	0.5490	0.3186	0.1671	0.0802	0.0353	0.0142	0.0052	0.0017	0.0005
		2	0.9638	0.8159	0.6042	0.3980	0.2361	0.1268	0.0617	0.0271	0.0107	0.0037
		3	0.9945	0.9444	0.8227	0.6482	0.4613	0.2969	0.1727	0.0905	0.0424	0.0176
		4	0.9994	0.9873	0.9383	0.8358	0.6865	0.5155	0.3519	0.2173	0.1204	0.0592
		5	0.9999	0.9978	0.9832	0.9389	0.8516	0.7216	0.5643	0.4032	0.2608	0.1509
		6	1.0000	0.9997	0.9964	0.9819	0.9434	0.8689	0.7548	0.6098	0.4522	0.3036
		7	1.0000	1.0000	0.9994	0.9958	0.9827	0.9500	0.8868	0.7869	0.6535	0.5000
		8	1.0000	1.0000	0.9999	0.9992	0.9958	0.9848	0.9578	0.9050	0.8182	0.6964
		9	1.0000	1.0000	1.0000	0.9999	0.9992	0.9963	0.9876	0.9662	0.9231	0.8491
		10	1.0000	1.0000	1.0000	1.0000	0.9999	0.9993	0.9972	0.9907	0.9745	0.9408
		11	1.0000	1.0000	1.0000	1.0000	1.0000	0.9999	0.9995	0.9981	0.9937	0.9824
		12	1.0000	1.0000	1.0000	1.0000	1.0000	1.0000	0.9999	0.9997	0.9989	0.9963
		13	1.0000	1.0000	1.0000	1.0000	1.0000	1.0000	1.0000	1.0000	0.9999	0.9995
		14	1.0000	1.0000	1.0000	1.0000	1.0000	1.0000	1.0000	1.0000	1.0000	1.0000
n = 20	x =	0	0.3585	0.1216	0.0388	0.0115	0.0032	0.0008	0.0002	0.0000	0.0000	0.0000
		1	0.7358	0.3917	0.1756	0.0692	0.0243	0.0076	0.0021	0.0005	0.0001	0.0000
		2	0.9245	0.6769	0.4049	0.2061	0.0913	0.0355	0.0121	0.0036	0.0009	0.0002
		3	0.9841	0.8670	0.6477	0.4114	0.2252	0.1071	0.0444	0.0160	0.0049	0.0013
		4	0.9974	0.9568	0.8298	0.6296	0.4148	0.2375	0.1182	0.0510	0.0189	0.0059
		5	0.9997	0.9887	0.9327	0.8042	0.6172	0.4164	0.2454	0.1256	0.0553	0.0207
		6	1.0000	0.9976	0.9781	0.9133	0.7858	0.6080	0.4166	0.2500	0.1299	0.0577
		7	1.0000	0.9996	0.9941	0.9679	0.8982	0.7723	0.6010	0.4159	0.2520	0.1316
		8	1.0000	0.9999	0.9987	0.9900	0.9591	0.8867	0.7624	0.5956	0.4143	0.2517
		9	1.0000	1.0000	0.9998	0.9974	0.9861	0.9520	0.8782	0.7553	0.5914	0.4119
		10	1.0000	1.0000	1.0000	0.9994	0.9961	0.9829	0.9468	0.8725	0.7507	0.5881
		11	1.0000	1.0000	1.0000	0.9999	0.9991	0.9949	0.9804	0.9435	0.8692	0.7483
		12	1.0000	1.0000	1.0000	1.0000	0.9998	0.9987	0.9940	0.9790	0.9420	0.8684
		13	1.0000	1.0000	1.0000	1.0000	1.0000	0.9997	0.9985	0.9935	0.9786	0.9423
		14	1.0000	1.0000	1.0000	1.0000	1.0000	1.0000	0.9997	0.9984	0.9936	0.9793
		15	1.0000	1.0000	1.0000	1.0000	1.0000	1.0000	1.0000	0.9997	0.9985	0.9941
		16	1.0000	1.0000	1.0000	1.0000	1.0000	1.0000	1.0000	1.0000	0.9997	0.9987
		17	1.0000	1.0000	1.0000	1.0000	1.0000	1.0000	1.0000	1.0000	1.0000	0.9998
		18	1.0000	1.0000	1.0000	1.0000	1.0000	1.0000	1.0000	1.0000	1.0000	1.0000

The binomial cumulative distribution function (continued)

		$p =$	0.05	0.10	0.15	0.20	0.25	0.30	0.35	0.40	0.45	0.50
$n = 25$	$x =$	0	0.2774	0.0718	0.0172	0.0038	0.0008	0.0001	0.0000	0.0000	0.0000	0.0000
		1	0.6424	0.2712	0.0931	0.0274	0.0070	0.0016	0.0003	0.0001	0.0000	0.0000
		2	0.8729	0.5371	0.2537	0.0982	0.0321	0.0090	0.0021	0.0004	0.0001	0.0000
		3	0.9659	0.7636	0.4711	0.2340	0.0962	0.0332	0.0097	0.0024	0.0005	0.0001
		4	0.9928	0.9020	0.6821	0.4207	0.2137	0.0905	0.0320	0.0095	0.0023	0.0005
		5	0.9988	0.9666	0.8385	0.6167	0.3783	0.1935	0.0826	0.0294	0.0086	0.0020
		6	0.9998	0.9905	0.9305	0.7800	0.5611	0.3407	0.1734	0.0736	0.0258	0.0073
		7	1.0000	0.9977	0.9745	0.8909	0.7265	0.5118	0.3061	0.1536	0.0639	0.0216
		8	1.0000	0.9995	0.9920	0.9532	0.8506	0.6769	0.4668	0.2735	0.1340	0.0539
		9	1.0000	0.9999	0.9979	0.9827	0.9287	0.8106	0.6303	0.4246	0.2424	0.1148
		10	1.0000	1.0000	0.9995	0.9944	0.9703	0.9022	0.7712	0.5858	0.3843	0.2122
		11	1.0000	1.0000	0.9999	0.9985	0.9893	0.9558	0.8746	0.7323	0.5426	0.3450
		12	1.0000	1.0000	1.0000	0.9996	0.9966	0.9825	0.9396	0.8462	0.6937	0.5000
		13	1.0000	1.0000	1.0000	0.9999	0.9991	0.9940	0.9745	0.9222	0.8173	0.6550
		14	1.0000	1.0000	1.0000	1.0000	0.9998	0.9982	0.9907	0.9656	0.9040	0.7878
		15	1.0000	1.0000	1.0000	1.0000	1.0000	0.9995	0.9971	0.9868	0.9560	0.8852
		16	1.0000	1.0000	1.0000	1.0000	1.0000	0.9999	0.9992	0.9957	0.9826	0.9461
		17	1.0000	1.0000	1.0000	1.0000	1.0000	1.0000	0.9998	0.9988	0.9942	0.9784
		18	1.0000	1.0000	1.0000	1.0000	1.0000	1.0000	1.0000	0.9997	0.9984	0.9927
		19	1.0000	1.0000	1.0000	1.0000	1.0000	1.0000	1.0000	0.9999	0.9996	0.9980
		20	1.0000	1.0000	1.0000	1.0000	1.0000	1.0000	1.0000	1.0000	0.9999	0.9995
		21	1.0000	1.0000	1.0000	1.0000	1.0000	1.0000	1.0000	1.0000	1.0000	0.9999
		22	1.0000	1.0000	1.0000	1.0000	1.0000	1.0000	1.0000	1.0000	1.0000	1.0000
$n = 30$	$x =$	0	0.2146	0.0424	0.0076	0.0012	0.0002	0.0000	0.0000	0.0000	0.0000	0.0000
		1	0.5535	0.1837	0.0480	0.0105	0.0020	0.0003	0.0000	0.0000	0.0000	0.0000
		2	0.8122	0.4114	0.1514	0.0442	0.0106	0.0021	0.0003	0.0000	0.0000	0.0000
		3	0.9392	0.6474	0.3217	0.1227	0.0374	0.0093	0.0019	0.0003	0.0000	0.0000
		4	0.9844	0.8245	0.5245	0.2552	0.0979	0.0302	0.0075	0.0015	0.0002	0.0000
		5	0.9967	0.9268	0.7106	0.4275	0.2026	0.0766	0.0233	0.0057	0.0011	0.0002
		6	0.9994	0.9742	0.8474	0.6070	0.3481	0.1595	0.0586	0.0172	0.0040	0.0007
		7	0.9999	0.9922	0.9302	0.7608	0.5143	0.2814	0.1238	0.0435	0.0121	0.0026
		8	1.0000	0.9980	0.9722	0.8713	0.6736	0.4315	0.2247	0.0940	0.0312	0.0081
		9	1.0000	0.9995	0.9903	0.9389	0.8034	0.5888	0.3575	0.1763	0.0694	0.0214
		10	1.0000	0.9999	0.9971	0.9744	0.8943	0.7304	0.5078	0.2915	0.1350	0.0494
		11	1.0000	1.0000	0.9992	0.9905	0.9493	0.8407	0.6548	0.4311	0.2327	0.1002
		12	1.0000	1.0000	0.9998	0.9969	0.9784	0.9155	0.7802	0.5785	0.3592	0.1808
		13	1.0000	1.0000	1.0000	0.9991	0.9918	0.9599	0.8737	0.7145	0.5025	0.2923
		14	1.0000	1.0000	1.0000	0.9998	0.9973	0.9831	0.9348	0.8246	0.6448	0.4278
		15	1.0000	1.0000	1.0000	0.9999	0.9992	0.9936	0.9699	0.9029	0.7691	0.5722
		16	1.0000	1.0000	1.0000	1.0000	0.9998	0.9979	0.9876	0.9519	0.8644	0.7077
		17	1.0000	1.0000	1.0000	1.0000	0.9999	0.9994	0.9955	0.9788	0.9286	0.8192
		18	1.0000	1.0000	1.0000	1.0000	1.0000	0.9998	0.9986	0.9917	0.9666	0.8998
		19	1.0000	1.0000	1.0000	1.0000	1.0000	1.0000	0.9996	0.9971	0.9862	0.9506
		20	1.0000	1.0000	1.0000	1.0000	1.0000	1.0000	0.9999	0.9991	0.9950	0.9786
		21	1.0000	1.0000	1.0000	1.0000	1.0000	1.0000	1.0000	0.9998	0.9984	0.9919
		22	1.0000	1.0000	1.0000	1.0000	1.0000	1.0000	1.0000	1.0000	0.9996	0.9974
		23	1.0000	1.0000	1.0000	1.0000	1.0000	1.0000	1.0000	1.0000	0.9999	0.9993
		24	1.0000	1.0000	1.0000	1.0000	1.0000	1.0000	1.0000	1.0000	1.0000	0.9998
		25	1.0000	1.0000	1.0000	1.0000	1.0000	1.0000	1.0000	1.0000	1.0000	1.0000

The binomial cumulative distribution function (continued)

	$p =$	0.05	0.10	0.15	0.20	0.25	0.30	0.35	0.40	0.45	0.50
$n = 40$ $x =$	0	0.1285	0.0148	0.0015	0.0001	0.0000	0.0000	0.0000	0.0000	0.0000	0.0000
	1	0.3991	0.0805	0.0121	0.0015	0.0001	0.0000	0.0000	0.0000	0.0000	0.0000
	2	0.6767	0.2228	0.0486	0.0079	0.0010	0.0001	0.0000	0.0000	0.0000	0.0000
	3	0.8619	0.4231	0.1302	0.0285	0.0047	0.0006	0.0001	0.0000	0.0000	0.0000
	4	0.9520	0.6290	0.2633	0.0759	0.0160	0.0026	0.0003	0.0000	0.0000	0.0000
	5	0.9861	0.7937	0.4325	0.1613	0.0433	0.0086	0.0013	0.0001	0.0000	0.0000
	6	0.9966	0.9005	0.6067	0.2859	0.0962	0.0238	0.0044	0.0006	0.0001	0.0000
	7	0.9993	0.9581	0.7559	0.4371	0.1820	0.0553	0.0124	0.0021	0.0002	0.0000
	8	0.9999	0.9845	0.8646	0.5931	0.2998	0.1110	0.0303	0.0061	0.0009	0.0001
	9	1.0000	0.9949	0.9328	0.7318	0.4395	0.1959	0.0644	0.0156	0.0027	0.0003
	10	1.0000	0.9985	0.9701	0.8392	0.5839	0.3087	0.1215	0.0352	0.0074	0.0011
	11	1.0000	0.9996	0.9880	0.9125	0.7151	0.4406	0.2053	0.0709	0.0179	0.0032
	12	1.0000	0.9999	0.9957	0.9568	0.8209	0.5772	0.3143	0.1285	0.0386	0.0083
	13	1.0000	1.0000	0.9986	0.9806	0.8968	0.7032	0.4408	0.2112	0.0751	0.0192
	14	1.0000	1.0000	0.9996	0.9921	0.9456	0.8074	0.5721	0.3174	0.1326	0.0403
	15	1.0000	1.0000	0.9999	0.9971	0.9738	0.8849	0.6946	0.4402	0.2142	0.0769
	16	1.0000	1.0000	1.0000	0.9990	0.9884	0.9367	0.7978	0.5681	0.3185	0.1341
	17	1.0000	1.0000	1.0000	0.9997	0.9953	0.9680	0.8761	0.6885	0.4391	0.2148
	18	1.0000	1.0000	1.0000	0.9999	0.9983	0.9852	0.9301	0.7911	0.5651	0.3179
	19	1.0000	1.0000	1.0000	1.0000	0.9994	0.9937	0.9637	0.8702	0.6844	0.4373
	20	1.0000	1.0000	1.0000	1.0000	0.9998	0.9976	0.9827	0.9256	0.7870	0.5627
	21	1.0000	1.0000	1.0000	1.0000	1.0000	0.9991	0.9925	0.9608	0.8669	0.6821
	22	1.0000	1.0000	1.0000	1.0000	1.0000	0.9997	0.9970	0.9811	0.9233	0.7852
	23	1.0000	1.0000	1.0000	1.0000	1.0000	0.9999	0.9989	0.9917	0.9595	0.8659
	24	1.0000	1.0000	1.0000	1.0000	1.0000	1.0000	0.9996	0.9966	0.9804	0.9231
	25	1.0000	1.0000	1.0000	1.0000	1.0000	1.0000	0.9999	0.9988	0.9914	0.9597
	26	1.0000	1.0000	1.0000	1.0000	1.0000	1.0000	1.0000	0.9996	0.9966	0.9808
	27	1.0000	1.0000	1.0000	1.0000	1.0000	1.0000	1.0000	0.9999	0.9988	0.9917
	28	1.0000	1.0000	1.0000	1.0000	1.0000	1.0000	1.0000	1.0000	0.9996	0.9968
	29	1.0000	1.0000	1.0000	1.0000	1.0000	1.0000	1.0000	1.0000	0.9999	0.9989
	30	1.0000	1.0000	1.0000	1.0000	1.0000	1.0000	1.0000	1.0000	1.0000	0.9997
	31	1.0000	1.0000	1.0000	1.0000	1.0000	1.0000	1.0000	1.0000	1.0000	0.9999
	32	1.0000	1.0000	1.0000	1.0000	1.0000	1.0000	1.0000	1.0000	1.0000	1.0000

The binomial cumulative distribution function (continued)

	$p =$	0.05	0.10	0.15	0.20	0.25	0.30	0.35	0.40	0.45	0.50
$n = 50$ $x =$	0	0.0769	0.0052	0.0003	0.0000	0.0000	0.0000	0.0000	0.0000	0.0000	0.0000
	1	0.2794	0.0338	0.0029	0.0002	0.0000	0.0000	0.0000	0.0000	0.0000	0.0000
	2	0.5405	0.1117	0.0142	0.0013	0.0001	0.0000	0.0000	0.0000	0.0000	0.0000
	3	0.7604	0.2503	0.0460	0.0057	0.0005	0.0000	0.0000	0.0000	0.0000	0.0000
	4	0.8964	0.4312	0.1121	0.0185	0.0021	0.0002	0.0000	0.0000	0.0000	0.0000
	5	0.9622	0.6161	0.2194	0.0480	0.0070	0.0007	0.0001	0.0000	0.0000	0.0000
	6	0.9882	0.7702	0.3613	0.1034	0.0194	0.0025	0.0002	0.0000	0.0000	0.0000
	7	0.9968	0.8779	0.5188	0.1904	0.0453	0.0073	0.0008	0.0001	0.0000	0.0000
	8	0.9992	0.9421	0.6681	0.3073	0.0916	0.0183	0.0025	0.0002	0.0000	0.0000
	9	0.9998	0.9755	0.7911	0.4437	0.1637	0.0402	0.0067	0.0008	0.0001	0.0000
	10	1.0000	0.9906	0.8801	0.5836	0.2622	0.0789	0.0160	0.0022	0.0002	0.0000
	11	1.0000	0.9968	0.9372	0.7107	0.3816	0.1390	0.0342	0.0057	0.0006	0.0000
	12	1.0000	0.9990	0.9699	0.8139	0.5110	0.2229	0.0661	0.0133	0.0018	0.0002
	13	1.0000	0.9997	0.9868	0.8894	0.6370	0.3279	0.1163	0.0280	0.0045	0.0005
	14	1.0000	0.9999	0.9947	0.9393	0.7481	0.4468	0.1878	0.0540	0.0104	0.0013
	15	1.0000	1.0000	0.9981	0.9692	0.8369	0.5692	0.2801	0.0955	0.0220	0.0033
	16	1.0000	1.0000	0.9993	0.9856	0.9017	0.6839	0.3889	0.1561	0.0427	0.0077
	17	1.0000	1.0000	0.9998	0.9937	0.9449	0.7822	0.5060	0.2369	0.0765	0.0164
	18	1.0000	1.0000	0.9999	0.9975	0.9713	0.8594	0.6216	0.3356	0.1273	0.0325
	19	1.0000	1.0000	1.0000	0.9991	0.9861	0.9152	0.7264	0.4465	0.1974	0.0595
	20	1.0000	1.0000	1.0000	0.9997	0.9937	0.9522	0.8139	0.5610	0.2862	0.1013
	21	1.0000	1.0000	1.0000	0.9999	0.9974	0.9749	0.8813	0.6701	0.3900	0.1611
	22	1.0000	1.0000	1.0000	1.0000	0.9990	0.9877	0.9290	0.7660	0.5019	0.2399
	23	1.0000	1.0000	1.0000	1.0000	0.9996	0.9944	0.9604	0.8438	0.6134	0.3359
	24	1.0000	1.0000	1.0000	1.0000	0.9999	0.9976	0.9793	0.9022	0.7160	0.4439
	25	1.0000	1.0000	1.0000	1.0000	1.0000	0.9991	0.9900	0.9427	0.8034	0.5561
	26	1.0000	1.0000	1.0000	1.0000	1.0000	0.9997	0.9955	0.9686	0.8721	0.6641
	27	1.0000	1.0000	1.0000	1.0000	1.0000	0.9999	0.9981	0.9840	0.9220	0.7601
	28	1.0000	1.0000	1.0000	1.0000	1.0000	1.0000	0.9993	0.9924	0.9556	0.8389
	29	1.0000	1.0000	1.0000	1.0000	1.0000	1.0000	0.9997	0.9966	0.9765	0.8987
	30	1.0000	1.0000	1.0000	1.0000	1.0000	1.0000	0.9999	0.9986	0.9884	0.9405
	31	1.0000	1.0000	1.0000	1.0000	1.0000	1.0000	1.0000	0.9995	0.9947	0.9675
	32	1.0000	1.0000	1.0000	1.0000	1.0000	1.0000	1.0000	0.9998	0.9978	0.9836
	33	1.0000	1.0000	1.0000	1.0000	1.0000	1.0000	1.0000	0.9999	0.9991	0.9923
	34	1.0000	1.0000	1.0000	1.0000	1.0000	1.0000	1.0000	1.0000	0.9997	0.9967
	35	1.0000	1.0000	1.0000	1.0000	1.0000	1.0000	1.0000	1.0000	0.9999	0.9987
	36	1.0000	1.0000	1.0000	1.0000	1.0000	1.0000	1.0000	1.0000	1.0000	0.9995
	37	1.0000	1.0000	1.0000	1.0000	1.0000	1.0000	1.0000	1.0000	1.0000	0.9998
	38	1.0000	1.0000	1.0000	1.0000	1.0000	1.0000	1.0000	1.0000	1.0000	1.0000

The Poisson cumulative distribution function

The values below show $P(X \le x)$, where $X \sim Po(\lambda)$.

$\lambda =$	0.5	1.0	1.5	2.0	2.5	3.0	3.5	4.0	4.5	5.0
$x = $ 0	0.6065	0.3679	0.2231	0.1353	0.0821	0.0498	0.0302	0.0183	0.0111	0.0067
1	0.9098	0.7358	0.5578	0.4060	0.2873	0.1991	0.1359	0.0916	0.0611	0.0404
2	0.9856	0.9197	0.8088	0.6767	0.5438	0.4232	0.3208	0.2381	0.1736	0.1247
3	0.9982	0.9810	0.9344	0.8571	0.7576	0.6472	0.5366	0.4335	0.3423	0.2650
4	0.9998	0.9963	0.9814	0.9473	0.8912	0.8153	0.7254	0.6288	0.5321	0.4405
5	1.0000	0.9994	0.9955	0.9834	0.9580	0.9161	0.8576	0.7851	0.7029	0.6160
6	1.0000	0.9999	0.9991	0.9955	0.9858	0.9665	0.9347	0.8893	0.8311	0.7622
7	1.0000	1.0000	0.9998	0.9989	0.9958	0.9881	0.9733	0.9489	0.9134	0.8666
8	1.0000	1.0000	1.0000	0.9998	0.9989	0.9962	0.9901	0.9786	0.9597	0.9319
9	1.0000	1.0000	1.0000	1.0000	0.9997	0.9989	0.9967	0.9919	0.9829	0.9682
10	1.0000	1.0000	1.0000	1.0000	0.9999	0.9997	0.9990	0.9972	0.9933	0.9863
11	1.0000	1.0000	1.0000	1.0000	1.0000	0.9999	0.9997	0.9991	0.9976	0.9945
12	1.0000	1.0000	1.0000	1.0000	1.0000	1.0000	0.9999	0.9997	0.9992	0.9980
13	1.0000	1.0000	1.0000	1.0000	1.0000	1.0000	1.0000	0.9999	0.9997	0.9993
14	1.0000	1.0000	1.0000	1.0000	1.0000	1.0000	1.0000	1.0000	0.9999	0.9998
15	1.0000	1.0000	1.0000	1.0000	1.0000	1.0000	1.0000	1.0000	1.0000	0.9999
16	1.0000	1.0000	1.0000	1.0000	1.0000	1.0000	1.0000	1.0000	1.0000	1.0000
17	1.0000	1.0000	1.0000	1.0000	1.0000	1.0000	1.0000	1.0000	1.0000	1.0000
18	1.0000	1.0000	1.0000	1.0000	1.0000	1.0000	1.0000	1.0000	1.0000	1.0000
19	1.0000	1.0000	1.0000	1.0000	1.0000	1.0000	1.0000	1.0000	1.0000	1.0000

$\lambda =$	5.5	6.0	6.5	7.0	7.5	8.0	8.5	9.0	9.5	10.0
$x = $ 0	0.0041	0.0025	0.0015	0.0009	0.0006	0.0003	0.0002	0.0001	0.0001	0.0000
1	0.0266	0.0174	0.0113	0.0073	0.0047	0.0030	0.0019	0.0012	0.0008	0.0005
2	0.0884	0.0620	0.0430	0.0296	0.0203	0.0138	0.0093	0.0062	0.0042	0.0028
3	0.2017	0.1512	0.1118	0.0818	0.0591	0.0424	0.0301	0.0212	0.0149	0.0103
4	0.3575	0.2851	0.2237	0.1730	0.1321	0.0996	0.0744	0.0550	0.0403	0.0293
5	0.5289	0.4457	0.3690	0.3007	0.2414	0.1912	0.1496	0.1157	0.0885	0.0671
6	0.6860	0.6063	0.5265	0.4497	0.3782	0.3134	0.2562	0.2068	0.1649	0.1301
7	0.8095	0.7440	0.6728	0.5987	0.5246	0.4530	0.3856	0.3239	0.2687	0.2202
8	0.8944	0.8472	0.7916	0.7291	0.6620	0.5925	0.5231	0.4557	0.3918	0.3328
9	0.9462	0.9161	0.8774	0.8305	0.7764	0.7166	0.6530	0.5874	0.5218	0.4579
10	0.9747	0.9574	0.9332	0.9015	0.8622	0.8159	0.7634	0.7060	0.6453	0.5830
11	0.9890	0.9799	0.9661	0.9467	0.9208	0.8881	0.8487	0.8030	0.7520	0.6968
12	0.9955	0.9912	0.9840	0.9730	0.9573	0.9362	0.9091	0.8758	0.8364	0.7916
13	0.9983	0.9964	0.9929	0.9872	0.9784	0.9658	0.9486	0.9261	0.8981	0.8645
14	0.9994	0.9986	0.9970	0.9943	0.9897	0.9827	0.9726	0.9585	0.9400	0.9165
15	0.9998	0.9995	0.9988	0.9976	0.9954	0.9918	0.9862	0.9780	0.9665	0.9513
16	0.9999	0.9998	0.9996	0.9990	0.9980	0.9963	0.9934	0.9889	0.9823	0.9730
17	1.0000	0.9999	0.9998	0.9996	0.9992	0.9984	0.9970	0.9947	0.9911	0.9857
18	1.0000	1.0000	0.9999	0.9999	0.9997	0.9993	0.9987	0.9976	0.9957	0.9928
19	1.0000	1.0000	1.0000	1.0000	0.9999	0.9997	0.9995	0.9989	0.9980	0.9965
20	1.0000	1.0000	1.0000	1.0000	1.0000	0.9999	0.9998	0.9996	0.9991	0.9984
21	1.0000	1.0000	1.0000	1.0000	1.0000	1.0000	0.9999	0.9998	0.9996	0.9993
22	1.0000	1.0000	1.0000	1.0000	1.0000	1.0000	1.0000	0.9999	0.9999	0.9997

Chapter 1: The Binomial Distribution

1. Binomial Distributions

Exercise 1.1 — Binomial coefficients

Q1 a) All 8 letters are different, so there are $8! = 40\,320$ different arrangements.

b) If all 9 letters were different, there would be $9! = 362\,880$ different arrangements. But since two of the letters are the same, you need to divide this by $2! = 2$. So there are $9! \div 2! = 181\,440$ different arrangements.

c) If all 7 letters were different, there would be $7! = 5040$ different arrangements. But there are 2 Ts and 2 Rs, so you need to divide this by $2!$ twice. So there are $7! \div 2! \div 2! = 1260$ different arrangements.

Q2 $\binom{20}{11} = \frac{20!}{11!9!} = 167\,960$ different ways

Q3 a) $\binom{10}{3} = \binom{10}{7} = \frac{10!}{3!7!} = 120$ ways

b) $\binom{10}{5} = \frac{10!}{5!5!} = 252$ ways

Q4 a) $\binom{11}{4} = \binom{11}{7} = \frac{11!}{4!7!} = 330$ ways

b) $\binom{11}{6} = \binom{11}{5} = \frac{11!}{6!5!} = 462$ ways

c) $\binom{11}{8} = \binom{11}{3} = \frac{11!}{8!3!} = 165$ ways

Exercise 1.2 — The binomial distribution

Q1 a) Not a binomial distribution — the number of trials is not fixed.

b) Here, X will follow a binomial distribution. $X \sim B(2000, 0.005)$.

c) Here, Y will follow a binomial distribution. $Y \sim B(10, 0.5)$.

Q2 The number of trials is fixed (i.e. the 15 acts), each trial can either succeed or fail, X is the total number of successes, and the probability of success is the same each time if the trials are independent. So to model this situation with a binomial distribution, you would need to assume that all the trials are independent.

Q3 The number of trials is fixed, each trial can either succeed or fail, and X is the total number of successes. To make the probability of success the same each time, the cards would need to be replaced, and to make each pick independent you could shuffle the pack after replacing the picked cards. If this is done, then $X \sim B(10, \frac{3}{13})$.

Q4 The number of trials is fixed (650), each trial can either succeed or fail, X is the total number of successes, and the probability of each button falling off is the same if the trials are independent. So to model this situation with a binomial distribution, you would need to assume that all the trials are independent (i.e. the probability of each separate button falling off should not depend on whether any other button has fallen off). If this assumption is satisfied, then $X \sim B(650, 0.001)$.

Exercise 1.3 — Using the binomial probability function

Q1 a) Use the binomial probability function with $n = 10$ and $p = 0.14$.

(i) $P(X = 2) = \binom{10}{2} \times 0.14^2 \times (1 - 0.14)^{10-2}$

$= \frac{10!}{2!8!} \times 0.14^2 \times 0.86^8$

$= 0.264$ (to 3 sig. fig.)

(ii) $P(X = 4) = \binom{10}{4} \times 0.14^4 \times (1 - 0.14)^{10-4}$

$= \frac{10!}{4!6!} \times 0.14^4 \times 0.86^6$

$= 0.0326$ (to 3 sig. fig.)

(iii) $P(X = 5) = \binom{10}{5} \times 0.14^5 \times (1 - 0.14)^{10-5}$

$= \frac{10!}{5!5!} \times 0.14^5 \times 0.86^5$

$= 0.00638$ (to 3 sig. fig.)

b) Use the binomial probability function with $n = 8$ and $p = 0.27$.

(i) $P(X = 3) = \binom{8}{3} \times 0.27^3 \times (1 - 0.27)^{8-3}$

$= \frac{8!}{3!5!} \times 0.27^3 \times 0.73^5$

$= 0.229$ (to 3 sig. fig.)

(ii) $P(X = 5) = \binom{8}{5} \times 0.27^5 \times (1 - 0.27)^{8-5}$

$= \frac{8!}{5!3!} \times 0.27^5 \times 0.73^3$

$= 0.0313$ (to 3 sig. fig.)

(iii) $P(X = 7) = \binom{8}{7} \times 0.27^7 \times (1 - 0.27)^{8-7}$

$= \frac{8!}{7!1!} \times 0.27^7 \times 0.73^1$

$= 0.000611 \text{(to 3 sig. fig.)}$

Q2 a) Use the binomial probability function with $n = 20$ and $p = 0.16$.

(i) $P(X < 2) = P(X = 0) + P(X = 1)$

$= \frac{20!}{0!20!} \times 0.16^0 \times (1 - 0.16)^{20-0}$

$+ \frac{20!}{1!19!} \times 0.16^1 \times (1 - 0.16)^{20-1}$

$= 0.03059... + 0.11653...$

$= 0.147 \text{ (to 3 sig. fig.)}$

(ii) $P(X \le 3) = P(X = 0) + P(X = 1)$

$+ P(X = 2) + P(X = 3)$

$= 0.03059... + 0.11653...$

$+ \frac{20!}{2!18!} \times 0.16^2 \times (1 - 0.16)^{20-2}$

$+ \frac{20!}{3!17!} \times 0.16^3 \times (1 - 0.16)^{20-3}$

$= 0.03059... + 0.11653...$

$+ 0.21087... + 0.24099...$

$= 0.599 \text{ (to 3 sig. fig.)}$

(iii) $P(1 < X \le 4) = P(X = 2) + P(X = 3)$

$+ P(X = 4)$

$= 0.21087... + 0.24099...$

$+ \frac{20!}{4!16!} \times 0.16^4 \times 0.84^{16}$

$= 0.21087... + 0.24099...$

$+ 0.19509...$

$= 0.647 \text{ (to 3 sig. fig.)}$

b) Use the binomial probability function with $n = 30$ and $p = 0.88$.

(i) $P(X > 28) = P(X = 29) + P(X = 30)$

$= \frac{30!}{29!1!} \times 0.88^{29} \times 0.12^1$

$+ \frac{30!}{30!0!} \times 0.88^{30} \times 0.12^0$

$= 0.088369... + 0.021601...$

$= 0.110 \text{ (to 3 sig. fig.)}$

(ii) $P(25 < X < 28) = P(X = 26) + P(X = 27)$

$= \frac{30!}{26!4!} \times 0.88^{26} \times 0.12^4$

$+ \frac{30!}{27!3!} \times 0.88^{27} \times 0.12^3$

$= 0.204693... + 0.222383...$

$= 0.427 \text{ (to 3 sig. fig.)}$

(iii) $P(X \ge 27) = P(X = 27) + P(X = 28)$

$+ P(X = 29) + P(X = 30)$

$= 0.222383...$

$+ \frac{30!}{28!2!} \times 0.88^{28} \times 0.12^2$

$+ 0.088369... + 0.021601...$

$= 0.222383... + 0.174729...$

$+ 0.088369... + 0.021601...$

$= 0.507 \text{ (to 3 sig. fig.)}$

Q3 a) Use the binomial probability function with $n = 5$ and $p = \frac{1}{2}$.

(i) $P(X \le 4) = 1 - P(X > 4) = 1 - P(X = 5)$

$= 1 - \frac{5!}{5!0!} \times \left(\frac{1}{2}\right)^5 \times \left(\frac{1}{2}\right)^0$

$= 1 - 0.03125$

$= 0.969 \text{ (to 3 sig. fig.)}$

(ii) $P(X > 1) = 1 - P(X \le 1)$

$= 1 - P(X = 0) - P(X = 1)$

$= 1 - \frac{5!}{0!5!} \times \left(\frac{1}{2}\right)^0 \times \left(\frac{1}{2}\right)^5$

$- \frac{5!}{1!4!} \times \left(\frac{1}{2}\right)^1 \times \left(\frac{1}{2}\right)^4$

$= 1 - 0.03125 - 0.15625$

$= 0.813 \text{ (to 3 sig. fig.)}$

(iii) $P(1 \le X \le 4) = 1 - P(X = 0) - P(X = 5)$

$= 1 - \frac{5!}{0!5!} \times \left(\frac{1}{2}\right)^0 \times \left(\frac{1}{2}\right)^5$

$- \frac{5!}{5!0!} \times \left(\frac{1}{2}\right)^5 \times \left(\frac{1}{2}\right)^0$

$= 1 - 0.03125 - 0.03125$

$= 0.938 \text{ (to 3 sig. fig.)}$

b) Use the binomial probability function with $n = 8$ and $p = \frac{2}{3}$.

(i) $P(X < 7) = 1 - P(X \ge 7)$

$= 1 - P(X = 7) - P(X = 8)$

$= 1 - \frac{8!}{7!1!} \times \left(\frac{2}{3}\right)^7 \times \left(\frac{1}{3}\right)^1$

$- \frac{8!}{8!0!} \times \left(\frac{2}{3}\right)^8 \times \left(\frac{1}{3}\right)^0$

$= 1 - 0.156073... - 0.039018...$

$= 0.805 \text{ (to 3 sig. fig.)}$

(ii) $P(X \ge 2) = 1 - P(X < 2)$

$= 1 - P(X = 0) - P(X = 1)$

$= 1 - \frac{8!}{0!8!} \times \left(\frac{2}{3}\right)^0 \times \left(\frac{1}{3}\right)^8$

$- \frac{8!}{1!7!} \times \left(\frac{2}{3}\right)^1 \times \left(\frac{1}{3}\right)^7$

$= 1 - 0.00015241...$

$- 0.00243865...$

$= 0.997 \text{ (to 3 sig. fig.)}$

(iii) $P(0 \le X \le 8) = 1$

This must be 1, since X can only take values from 0 to 8.

Q4 $n = 5$ and $p = $ P(roll a six) $= \frac{1}{6}$, so

$$P(2 \text{ sixes}) = \binom{5}{2} \times \left(\frac{1}{6}\right)^2 \times \left(\frac{5}{6}\right)^3 = 0.161 \text{(to 3 sig. fig.)}$$

Q5 a) $X \sim B(12, \frac{1}{3})$

b) $P(X < 3) = P(X = 0) + P(X = 1)$
$$+ P(X = 2)$$
$$= \frac{12!}{0!12!} \times \left(\frac{1}{3}\right)^0 \times \left(\frac{2}{3}\right)^{12-0}$$
$$+ \frac{12!}{1!11!} \times \left(\frac{1}{3}\right)^1 \times \left(\frac{2}{3}\right)^{12-1}$$
$$+ \frac{12!}{2!10!} \times \left(\frac{1}{3}\right)^2 \times \left(\frac{2}{3}\right)^{12-2}$$
$$= 0.00770... + 0.04624...$$
$$+ 0.12717...$$
$$= 0.181 \text{(to 3 sig. fig.)}$$

Q6 a) $X \sim B(10, 0.65)$

b) $P(4 < X \le 7) = P(X = 5) + P(X = 6)$
$$+ P(X = 7)$$
$$= \frac{10!}{5!5!} \times 0.65^5 \times 0.35^5$$
$$+ \frac{10!}{6!4!} \times 0.65^6 \times 0.35^4$$
$$+ \frac{10!}{7!3!} \times 0.65^7 \times 0.35^3$$
$$= 0.15357... + 0.23766...$$
$$+ 0.25221...$$
$$= 0.643 \text{(to 3 sig. fig.)}$$

Q7 Let X represent the number of defective items. Then $X \sim B(15, 0.05)$, and you need to find $P(1 \le X \le 3)$.
$$P(1 \le X \le 3) = P(X = 1) + P(X = 2)$$
$$+ P(X = 3)$$
$$= \frac{15!}{1!14!} \times 0.05^1 \times 0.95^{14}$$
$$+ \frac{15!}{2!13!} \times 0.05^2 \times 0.95^{13}$$
$$+ \frac{15!}{3!12!} \times 0.05^3 \times 0.95^{12}$$
$$= 0.36575... + 0.13475...$$
$$+ 0.03073...$$
$$= 0.531 \text{(to 3 sig. fig.)}$$

2. Using Binomial Tables

Exercise 2.1 — Using tables to find probabilities

Q1 a) $P(X \le 2) = 0.5256$

b) $P(X \le 7) = 0.9996$

c) $P(X \le 9) = 1.0000$

d) $P(X < 5) = P(X \le 4) = 0.9219$

e) $P(X < 4) = P(X \le 3) = 0.7759$

f) $P(X < 6) = P(X \le 5) = 0.9803$

Q2 a) $P(X > 3) = 1 - P(X \le 3) = 1 - 0.0905 = 0.9095$

b) $P(X > 6) = 1 - P(X \le 6) = 1 - 0.6098 = 0.3902$

c) $P(X > 10) = 1 - P(X \le 10) = 1 - 0.9907 = 0.0093$

d) $P(X \ge 5) = 1 - P(X < 5) = 1 - P(X \le 4)$
$$= 1 - 0.2173 = 0.7827$$

e) $P(X \ge 3) = 1 - P(X < 3) = 1 - P(X \le 2)$
$$= 1 - 0.0271 = 0.9729$$

f) $P(X \ge 13) = 1 - P(X < 13) = 1 - P(X \le 12)$
$$= 1 - 0.9997 = 0.0003$$

Q3 a) $P(X = 7) = P(X \le 7) - P(X \le 6)$
$$= 0.6010 - 0.4166 = 0.1844$$

b) $P(X = 12) = P(X \le 12) - P(X \le 11)$
$$= 0.9940 - 0.9804 = 0.0136$$

c) $P(2 < X \le 4) = P(X \le 4) - P(X \le 2)$
$$= 0.1182 - 0.0121 = 0.1061$$

d) $P(10 < X \le 15) = P(X \le 15) - P(X \le 10)$
$$= 1.0000 - 0.9468 = 0.0532$$

e) $P(7 \le X \le 10) = P(X \le 10) - P(X \le 6)$
$$= 0.9468 - 0.4166 = 0.5302$$

f) $P(3 \le X < 11) = P(X \le 10) - P(X \le 2)$
$$= 0.9468 - 0.0121 = 0.9347$$

Q4 Define a new random variable $Y \sim B(25, 0.2)$.

a) $P(X \ge 17) = P(Y \le 8) = 0.9532$

b) $P(X \ge 20) = P(Y \le 5) = 0.6167$

c) $P(X > 14) = P(Y < 11) = P(Y \le 10) = 0.9944$

d) $P(X = 21) = P(Y = 4) = P(Y \le 4) - P(Y \le 3)$
$$= 0.4207 - 0.2340 = 0.1867$$

e) $P(3 \le X < 14) = P(11 < Y \le 22)$
$$= P(Y \le 22) - P(Y \le 11)$$
$$= 1.0000 - 0.9985 = 0.0015$$

f) $P(12 \le X < 18) = P(7 < Y \le 13)$
$$= P(Y \le 13) - P(Y \le 7)$$
$$= 0.9999 - 0.8909 = 0.1090$$

Q5 Let X represent the number of heads. Then $X \sim B(7, 0.5)$, so use the table for $n = 7$.
$P(X > 4) = 1 - P(X \le 4) = 1 - 0.7734 = 0.2266$

Q6 Let X represent the number of faulty items. Then $X \sim B(25, 0.05)$, so use the table for $n = 25$.
$P(X < 6) = P(X \le 5) = 0.9988$

Exercise 2.2 — Using binomial tables 'backwards'

Q1 **a)** Use the table for $n = 8$ and the column for $p = 0.35$. Reading down the column tells you that $P(X \leq 2) = 0.4278$, so $a = 2$.

b) $P(X < b) = 0.9747$, so $P(X \leq b - 1) = 0.9747$. From the table, $P(X \leq 5) = 0.9747$. So $b - 1 = 5$, which means that $b = 6$.

c) $P(X > c) = 0.8309$, so $P(X \leq c) = 1 - P(X > c)$ $= 1 - 0.8309 = 0.1691$. From the table, $P(X \leq 1) = 0.1691$, which means that $c = 1$.

d) $P(X \geq d) = 0.1061$, so $P(X < d) = 1 - P(X \geq d)$ $= 1 - 0.1061 = 0.8939$. This means that $P(X \leq d - 1) = 0.8939$. From the table, $P(X \leq 4) = 0.8939$, which means that $d - 1 = 4$, so $d = 5$.

Q2 **a)** Let X be the score of someone who guesses the answer to each question. Then $X \sim B(30, 0.25)$. Use the table for $n = 30$ and the column for $p = 0.25$.

You need to find the minimum value m for which $P(X \geq m) \leq 0.1$. This is the minimum value m for which $P(X < m) \geq 0.9$, or $P(X \leq m - 1) \geq 0.9$.

$P(X \leq 10) = 0.8943$, but $P(X \leq 11) = 0.9493$. This means that $m - 1 = 11$, so the pass mark should be at least 12.

b) This time you need to find the minimum value m for which $P(X \geq m) < 0.01$. This is the minimum value m for which $P(X < m) > 0.99$, or $P(X \leq m - 1) > 0.99$.

$P(X \leq 12) = 0.9784$, but $P(X \leq 13) = 0.9918$. This means that $m - 1 = 13$, so the pass mark should be at least 14.

Q3 Here, $X \sim B(20, 0.5)$. You need $P(X \geq x) < 0.05$. This means $P(X < x) > 0.95$, or $P(X \leq x - 1) > 0.95$.

Use the table for $n = 20$, and the column for $p = 0.5$. $P(X \leq 13) = 0.9423$, but $P(X \leq 14) = 0.9793$.

This means that $x - 1 = 14$, so x should be at least 15.

3. Mean and Variance
Exercise 3.1 — Mean and variance of the binomial distribution

Q1 **a)** (i) $\mu = 10 \times 0.9 = 9$
(ii) $\sigma^2 = 10 \times 0.9 \times (1 - 0.9) = 0.9$
(iii) $\sigma = \sqrt{0.9} = 0.949$ (to 3 sig. fig.)

b) (i) $\mu = 25 \times 0.7 = 17.5$
(ii) $\sigma^2 = 25 \times 0.7 \times (1 - 0.7) = 5.25$
(iii) $\sigma = \sqrt{5.25} = 2.29$ (to 3 sig. fig.)

c) (i) $\mu = 50 \times 0.05 = 2.5$
(ii) $\sigma^2 = 50 \times 0.05 \times (1 - 0.05) = 2.375$
(iii) $\sigma = \sqrt{2.375} = 1.54$ (to 3 sig. fig.)

d) (i) $\mu = 70 \times 0.85 = 59.5$
(ii) $\sigma^2 = 70 \times 0.85 \times (1 - 0.85) = 8.925$
(iii) $\sigma = \sqrt{8.925} = 2.99$ (to 3 sig. fig.)

e) (i) $\mu = 15 \times 0.1 = 1.5$
(ii) $\sigma^2 = 15 \times 0.1 \times (1 - 0.1) = 1.35$
(iii) $\sigma = \sqrt{1.35} = 1.16$ (to 3 sig. fig.)

f) (i) $\mu = 100 \times 0.35 = 35$
(ii) $\sigma^2 = 100 \times 0.35 \times (1 - 0.35) = 22.75$
(iii) $\sigma = \sqrt{22.75} = 4.77$ (to 3 sig. fig.)

Q2 **a)** $X \sim B(60, 0.6)$

b) Mean of X: $\mu = 60 \times 0.6 = 36$
Variance of X: $\sigma^2 = 60 \times 0.6 \times (1 - 0.6) = 14.4$

Q3 **a)** $Y \sim B(150, p)$
$E(Y) = 150p = 30$, so $p = 30 \div 150 = 0.2$

b) $Var(Y) = np(1 - p) = 150 \times 0.2 \times (1 - 0.2) = 24$

Q4 **a)** $X \sim B(1600, 0.1)$
$E(X) = 1600 \times 0.1 = 160$

b) $\sigma^2 = 1600 \times 0.1 \times (1 - 0.1) = 144$

4. Modelling Real Problems
Exercise 4.1 — Modelling real problems with B(n, p)

Q1 **a)** Each person who passes can be considered a separate trial, where 'success' means they take a leaflet, and 'failure' means they don't. Since there is a fixed number of independent trials (50), a constant probability of success (0.25), and X is the total number of successes, $X \sim B(50, 0.25)$.

b) $P(X > 4) = 1 - P(X \leq 4) = 1 - 0.0021 = 0.9979$

c) $P(X = 10) = P(X \leq 10) - P(X \leq 9)$ $= 0.2622 - 0.1637 = 0.0985$

d) $E(X) = np = 50 \times 0.25 = 12.5$ people

e) $Var(X) = \sigma^2 = 50 \times 0.25 \times (1 - 0.25) = 9.375$ So $\sigma = \sqrt{9.375} = 3.06$ people (to 3 sig. fig.)

Q2 **a)** Let X represent the number of plants in a tray with yellow flowers. Then $X \sim B(15, 0.35)$. Using binomial tables for $n = 15$ and $p = 0.35$: $P(X = 5) = P(X \leq 5) - P(X \leq 4)$ $= 0.5643 - 0.3519 = 0.2124$

b) P(more yellow flowers than white flowers) $= P(X \geq 8) = 1 - P(X < 8) = 1 - P(X \leq 7)$ $= 1 - 0.8868 = 0.1132$

Q3 **a)** $X \sim B(n, 0.15)$. $E(X) = 0.15n = 6$, so $n = 6 \div 0.15 = 40$.

b) Using the binomial table for $n = 40$: $P(X < 6) = P(X \leq 5) = 0.4325$

c) $Y \sim B(m, 0.15)$. $E(Y) = mp = 0.15m = 24$, so $m = 24 \div 0.15 = 160$. $Var(Y) = mp(1 - p) = 160 \times 0.15 \times 0.85$ $= 20.4$

Review Exercise — Chapter 1

Q1 a) There are 21 objects altogether, so if all the balls were different colours, there would be 21! ways to arrange them. But since 15 of the objects are identical, you need to divide this figure by 15!. So there are 21! ÷ 15! = 39 070 080 possible arrangements.

b) There are $\dfrac{16!}{4!4!4!4!} = 63\,063\,000$ possible arrangements.

c) There are $\dbinom{12}{7} = \dbinom{12}{5} = \dfrac{12!}{7!5!} = 792$ possible arrangements.

Q2 a) $\text{P(5 heads)} = \dbinom{10}{5} \times 0.5^5 \times 0.5^5$
$= \dfrac{10!}{5!5!} \times 0.5^{10}$
$= 0.246 \text{ (to 3 sig. fig.)}.$

b) $\text{P(9 heads)} = \dbinom{10}{9} \times 0.5^9 \times 0.5$
$= \dfrac{10!}{9!1!} \times 0.5^{10}$
$= 0.00977 \text{ (to 3 sig. fig.)}.$

Q3 a) Binomial — there are a fixed number of independent trials (30) with two possible results ('prime' / 'not prime'), a constant probability of success, and the random variable is the total number of successes.

b) Binomial — there are a fixed number of independent trials (however many students are in the class) with two possible results ('heads' / 'tails'), a constant probability of success, and the random variable is the total number of successes.

c) Not binomial — the probability of being dealt an ace changes with each card dealt, since the total number of cards decreases as each card is dealt.

d) Not binomial — the number of trials is not fixed.

Q4 a) Use tables with $n = 10$ and $p = 0.5$.
If X represents the number of heads, then:
$P(X \geq 5) = 1 - P(X < 5) = 1 - P(X \leq 4)$
$= 1 - 0.3770 = 0.6230$

b) $P(X \geq 9) = 1 - P(X < 9) = 1 - P(X \leq 8)$
$= 1 - 0.9893 = 0.0107$

Q5 a) You can't use tables here (because they don't include $p = 0.27$ or $n = 14$), so you have to use the probability function.
$P(X = 4) = \dbinom{14}{4} \times 0.27^4 \times (1 - 0.27)^{10}$
$= 0.229 \text{ (to 3 sig. fig.)}$

b) $P(X < 2) = P(X = 0) + P(X = 1)$
$= \dbinom{14}{0} \times 0.27^0 \times (1 - 0.27)^{14}$
$\quad + \dbinom{14}{1} \times 0.27^1 \times (1 - 0.27)^{13}$
$= 0.012204... + 0.063195...$
$= 0.0754 \text{ (to 3 sig. fig.)}$

c) $P(5 < X \leq 8) = P(X = 6) + P(X = 7)$
$\qquad\qquad\qquad + P(X = 8)$
$= \dbinom{14}{6} \times 0.27^6 \times (1 - 0.27)^8$
$\quad + \dbinom{14}{7} \times 0.27^7 \times (1 - 0.27)^7$
$\quad + \dbinom{14}{8} \times 0.27^8 \times (1 - 0.27)^6$
$= 0.093823... + 0.039660...$
$\qquad\qquad + 0.012835...$
$= 0.146 \text{ (to 3 sig. fig.)}$

Q6 For parts a)-c), use tables with $n = 25$ and $p = 0.15$.

a) $P(X \leq 3) = 0.4711$

b) $P(X \leq 7) = 0.9745$

c) $P(X \leq 15) = 1.0000$

For parts d)-f), define a new random variable $T = 15 - Y$, with $T \sim B(15, 0.35)$. Then if Y represents the number of successes in 15 trials, T represents the number of failures.
Now you can use tables with $n = 15$ and $p = 0.35$.

d) $P(Y \leq 3) = P(T \geq 12) = 1 - P(T < 12)$
$= 1 - P(T \leq 11) = 1 - 0.9995 = 0.0005$

e) $P(Y \leq 7) = P(T \geq 8) = 1 - P(T < 8)$
$= 1 - P(T \leq 7) = 1 - 0.8868 = 0.1132$

f) $P(Y \leq 15) = 1$ (since 15 is the maximum possible value).
These last few parts (where you can't use the tables directly) are quite awkward, so make sure you get lots of practice.

Q7 From tables:

a) $P(X \leq 15) = 0.9997$

b) $P(X < 4) = P(X \leq 3) = 0.1302$

c) $P(X > 7) = 1 - P(X \leq 7) = 1 - 0.0639 = 0.9361$

For parts d)-f) where $X \sim B(n, p)$ with $p > 0.5$, define a new random variable $Y \sim B(n, q)$, where $q = 1 - p$ and $Y = n - X$. Then use tables.

d) Define $Y \sim B(50, 0.2)$.
Then $P(X \geq 40) = P(Y \leq 10) = 0.5836$

e) Define $Y \sim B(30, 0.3)$.
Then $P(X = 20) = P(Y = 10) = P(Y \leq 10) - P(Y \leq 9)$
$= 0.7304 - 0.5888 = 0.1416$

f) Define $Y \sim B(10, 0.25)$.
Then $P(X = 7) = P(Y = 3) = P(Y \leq 3) - P(Y \leq 2)$
$= 0.7759 - 0.5256 = 0.2503$

Q8 Using the table for $n = 30$ and $p = 0.35$:

a) $a = 13$

b) Since $P(X \geq b) = 0.8762$, you know that
$P(X < b) = 1 - 0.8762 = 0.1238$.
This means that $P(X \leq b - 1) = 0.1238$.
So from tables, $b - 1 = 7$, which gives $b = 8$.

c) $P(X \leq 5) = 0.0233$, but $P(X \leq 6) = 0.0586$.
So the maximum value for c with $P(X \leq c) < 0.05$ must be $c = 5$.

Q9 a) mean $= 20 \times 0.4 = 8$
variance $= 20 \times 0.4 \times 0.6 = 4.8$

b) mean $= 40 \times 0.15 = 6$
variance $= 40 \times 0.15 \times 0.85 = 5.1$

c) mean $= 25 \times 0.45 = 11.25$
variance $= 25 \times 0.45 \times 0.55 = 6.1875$

d) mean $= 50 \times 0.8 = 40$
variance $= 50 \times 0.8 \times 0.2 = 8$

e) mean $= 30 \times 0.7 = 21$
variance $= 30 \times 0.7 \times 0.3 = 6.3$

f) mean $= 45 \times 0.012 = 0.54$
variance $= 45 \times 0.012 \times 0.988 = 0.53352$

Exam-Style Questions — Chapter 1

1 a) **(i)** Define a new random variable $Y \sim B(12, 0.4)$, where $Y = 12 - X$.
Then $P(X < 8) = P(Y > 4) = 1 - P(Y \leq 4)$
$= 1 - 0.4382$ *[1 mark]* $= 0.5618$ *[1 mark]*

(ii) $P(X = 5) = P(Y = 7)$
$= P(Y \leq 7) - P(Y \leq 6)$ *[1 mark]*
$= 0.9427 - 0.8418 = 0.1009$ *[1 mark]*
Or you could use the probability function for (ii):
$$P(X = 5) = \binom{12}{5} \times 0.6^5 \times 0.4^7 = 0.1009$$
(to 4 d.p.).

(iii) $P(3 < X \leq 7) = P(5 \leq Y < 9)$
$= P(5 \leq Y \leq 8)$ *[1 mark]*
$= P(Y \leq 8) - P(Y \leq 4)$ *[1 mark]*
$= 0.9847 - 0.4382 = 0.5465$ *[1 mark]*

b) **(i)** $P(Y = 4) = \dfrac{11!}{4!7!} \times 0.8^4 \times 0.2^7$ *[1 mark]*
$= 0.00173$ (to 3 sig. fig.) *[1 mark]*

(ii) $E(Y) = 11 \times 0.8 = 8.8$ *[1 mark]*

(iii) $Var(Y) = 11 \times 0.8 \times 0.2 = 1.76$ *[1 mark]*

2 a) **(i)** Let X represent the number of apples that contain a maggot.
Then $X \sim B(40, 0.15)$ *[1 mark]*.
$P(X < 6) = P(X \leq 5) = 0.4325$ *[1 mark]*

(ii) $P(X > 2) = 1 - P(X \leq 2)$ *[1 mark]*
$= 1 - 0.0486 = 0.9514$ *[1 mark]*

(iii) $P(X = 12) = P(X \leq 12) - P(X \leq 11)$ *[1 mark]*
$= 0.9957 - 0.9880 = 0.0077$ *[1 mark]*
Or you could use the probability function for (iii):
$$P(X = 12) = \binom{40}{12} \times 0.15^{12} \times 0.85^{28}$$
$$= 0.0077 \text{ (to 4 d.p.)}.$$

b) The probability that a crate contains more than 2 apples with maggots is 0.9514 (from part **a) (ii)**).
So define a random variable Y, where Y is the number of crates that contain more than 2 apples with maggots.
Then $Y \sim B(3, 0.9514)$ *[1 mark]*.
You need to find $P(Y = 2) + P(Y = 3)$. This is:
$$\binom{3}{2} \times 0.9514^2 \times (1 - 0.9514)$$
$$+ \binom{3}{3} \times 0.9514^3 \times (1 - 0.9514)^0 \text{ [1 mark]}$$
$$= 0.1319... + 0.8611...$$
$$= 0.993 \text{ (to 3 d.p.) [1 mark]}$$

3 a) **(i)** The probability of Simon being able to solve each crossword needs to remain the same *[1 mark]*, and all the outcomes need to be independent (i.e. Simon solving or not solving a puzzle one day should not affect whether he will be able to solve it on another day) *[1 mark]*.

(ii) The total number of puzzles he solves (or the number he fails to solve) *[1 mark]*.

b) $P(X = 4) = \frac{18!}{4!14!} \times p^4 \times (1 - p)^{14}$ *[1 mark]*

$P(X = 5) = \frac{18!}{5!13!} \times p^5 \times (1 - p)^{13}$ *[1 mark]*

So $\frac{18!}{4!14!} \times p^4 \times (1 - p)^{14}$

$\qquad = \frac{18!}{5!13!} \times p^5 \times (1 - p)^{13}$ *[1 mark]*

Dividing by things that occur
on both sides gives:

$\frac{1 - p}{14} = \frac{p}{5}$ *[1 mark]*, or $5 = 19p$.

This means $p = \frac{5}{19} = 0.263$ (to 3 sig. fig.)
[1 mark].

4 a) Let the random variable X represent the number
of 'treble-20's the player gets in a set of 3 darts.
Then $X \sim B(3, 0.75)$ *[1 mark]*.
$P(X \geq 2) = P(X = 2) + P(X = 3)$

$P(X = 2) = \binom{3}{2} \times 0.75^2 \times (1 - 0.75)$

$\qquad = 0.421875$

$P(X = 3) = \binom{3}{3} \times 0.75^3 \times (1 - 0.75)^0$

$\qquad = 0.421875$

So $P(X \geq 2) = 0.421875 + 0.421875$
$\qquad = 0.84375 = 0.844$ (to 3 sig. fig.) *[1 mark]*

b) Let the random variable Y represent the number
of sets of darts in which the player gets a
'treble-20' with at least 2 darts.
Then $Y \sim B(5, 0.84375)$ *[1 mark]*.
$E(Y) = np = 5 \times 0.84375$
$\qquad = 4.21875$
$\qquad = 4.22$ (to 3 sig. fig.) *[1 mark]*

c) (i) Now let X represent the number of
'treble-20's the player scores with 30 darts.
Then $X \sim B(30, 0.75)$.
You need to find $P(X \geq 26)$.
Define a new random variable $Y = 30 - X$,
with $Y \sim B(30, 0.25)$.
Then $P(X \geq 26) = P(Y \leq 4)$ *[1 mark]*.
From tables, $P(Y \leq 4) = 0.0979$ *[1 mark]*.

(ii) $P(22 \leq X \leq 25) = P(5 \leq Y \leq 8)$ *[1 mark]*
$\qquad = P(Y \leq 8) - P(Y \leq 4)$ *[1 mark]*
$\qquad = 0.6736 - 0.0979 = 0.5757$ *[1 mark]*

5 a) Let the random variable X represent the number
of bronze coins Jessica picks out in n picks.
Then $X \sim B(n, 0.3)$.
$E(X) = np = 0.3n = 7.5$ *[1 mark]*.
So $n = 7.5 \div 0.3 = 25$ *[1 mark]*.

b) If the ratio of bronze coins : silver coins is 1 : 4,
then Jessica will have picked out 5 bronze coins.
Using tables:
$P(X - 5) = P(X < 5) - P(X \leq 4)$ *[1 mark]*
$\qquad = 0.1935 - 0.0905 = 0.1030$ *[1 mark]*
You could use the probability function here if you prefer.

6 a) (i) Here, $X \sim B(12, 0.06)$.

$P(X = 0) = \binom{12}{0} \times 0.06^0 \times (1 - 0.06)^{12}$

[1 mark]
$\qquad = 0.475920... = 0.476$ (to 3 sig. fig.) *[1 mark]*

(ii) $P(X > 2) = 1 - P(X \leq 2)$
$\qquad = 1 - P(X = 0) - P(X = 1) - P(X = 2)$ *[1 mark]*

$P(X = 1) = \binom{12}{1} \times 0.06^1 \times (1 - 0.06)^{11}$

$\qquad = 0.364534...$

$P(X = 2) = \binom{12}{2} \times 0.06^2 \times (1 - 0.06)^{10}$

$\qquad = 0.127974...$

So $P(X > 2) = 1 - 0.475920... - 0.364534...$
$\qquad - 0.127974...$ *[1 mark]*
$\qquad = 0.031570...$
$\qquad = 0.0316$ (to 3 sig. fig.) *[1 mark]*

b) (i) $Y \sim B(50, 0.0316)$ *[1 mark]*

(ii) $P(Y \geq 1) = 1 - P(Y < 1) = 1 - P(Y = 0)$ *[1 mark]*

$\qquad = 1 - \binom{50}{0} \times 0.0316^0 \times (1 - 0.0316)^{50}$

$\qquad = 1 - 0.20078...$

$\qquad = 0.799$ (to 3 sig. fig.) *[1 mark]*

Chapter 2: The Poisson Distribution

1. Poisson Distributions

Exercise 1.1 — The Poisson distribution

Q1 a) The daisies occur randomly, singly and at a constant average 'rate' of 10 daisies per square metre. So D will follow a Poisson distribution — in fact, $D \sim \text{Po}(10)$.

b) The flaws occur randomly, singly and at a constant average rate of 0.5 flaws per square metre. So F will follow a Poisson distribution — in fact, $F \sim \text{Po}(0.5)$.

c) Because the water has been standing for 24 hours, the gravel particles will not occur randomly throughout the water — they'll have sunk to the bottom. So P does not follow a Poisson distribution.

d) Because the water has just been vigorously stirred, the micro-organisms should be randomly scattered throughout the water. They also occur singly and at a constant average rate of 40 per litre. So M will follow a Poisson distribution — in fact, $M \sim \text{Po}(40)$.

Q2 No, the number of sheep in a randomly chosen square metre of field (X) is unlikely to follow a Poisson distribution. This is because the sheep are probably not randomly scattered, but are likely to be near the corner containing their food.

Exercise 1.2 — Using the Poisson probability function

Q1 a) $P(X = 1) = \frac{e^{-2}2^1}{1!} = 0.271$ (to 3 sig. fig.)

b) $P(X = 0) = \frac{e^{-2}2^0}{0!} = 0.135$ (to 3 sig. fig.)

c) $P(X = 4) = \frac{e^{-2}2^4}{4!} = 0.0902$ (to 3 sig. fig.)

Q2 a) $P(X = 4) = \frac{e^{-3}3^4}{4!} = 0.168$ (to 3 sig. fig.)

b) $P(X \leq 1) = P(X = 0) + P(X = 1)$
$$= \frac{e^{-3}3^0}{0!} + \frac{e^{-3}3^1}{1!}$$
$$= 0.04978... + 0.14936...$$
$$= 0.199 \text{ (to 3 sig. fig.)}$$

c) $P(4 \leq X \leq 6) = P(X = 4) + P(X = 5) + P(X = 6)$
$$= \frac{e^{-3}3^4}{4!} + \frac{e^{-3}3^5}{5!} + \frac{e^{-3}3^6}{6!}$$
$$= 0.16803... + 0.10081... + 0.05040...$$
$$= 0.319 \text{ (to 3 sig. fig.)}$$

Q3 a) $P(X = 3) = \frac{e^{-3.8}3.8^3}{3!} = 0.205$ (to 3 sig. fig.)

b) $P(X < 3) = P(X = 0) + P(X = 1) + P(X = 2)$
$$= \frac{e^{-3.8}3.8^0}{0!} + \frac{e^{-3.8}3.8^1}{1!} + \frac{e^{-3.8}3.8^2}{2!}$$
$$= 0.02237... + 0.08500... + 0.16151...$$
$$= 0.26889... = 0.269 \text{ (to 3 sig. fig.)}$$

c) $P(X \geq 3) = 1 - P(X < 3) = 1 - 0.26889...$
$$= 0.731 \text{ (to 3 sig. fig.)}$$

Q4 $P(X > 3) = 1 - P(X \leq 3)$
$$= 1 - P(X = 0) - P(X = 1) - P(X = 2) - P(X = 3)$$
$$= 1 - \frac{e^{-1.4}1.4^0}{0!} - \frac{e^{-1.4}1.4^1}{1!}$$
$$- \frac{e^{-1.4}1.4^2}{2!} - \frac{e^{-1.4}1.4^3}{3!}$$
$$= 1 - 0.24659... - 0.34523...$$
$$- 0.24166... - 0.11277...$$
$$= 0.0537 \text{ (to 3 sig. fig.)}$$

Q5 a) The flaws occur randomly, singly and at a constant average rate of 0.2 per metre. So $X \sim \text{Po}(0.2)$.

b) (i) $P(X = 0) = \frac{e^{-0.2}0.2^0}{0!} = 0.819$ (to 3 sig. fig.)

(ii) $P(X < 2) = P(X = 0) + P(X = 1)$
$$= \frac{e^{-0.2}0.2^0}{0!} + \frac{e^{-0.2}0.2^1}{1!}$$
$$= 0.81873... + 0.16374...$$
$$= 0.98247... = 0.982 \text{ (to 3 sig. fig.)}$$

Q6 a) If X represents the number of phone calls arriving at the switchboard in a randomly chosen minute, then $X \sim \text{Po}(12)$.
$$P(X = 12) = \frac{e^{-12}12^{12}}{12!} = 0.114 \text{ (to 3 sig. fig.)}$$

b) $P(10 \leq X \leq 13) = P(X = 10) + P(X = 11)$
$$+ P(X = 12) + P(X = 13)$$
$$= \frac{e^{-12}12^{10}}{10!} + \frac{e^{-12}12^{11}}{11!} + \frac{e^{-12}12^{12}}{12!} + \frac{e^{-12}12^{13}}{13!}$$
$$= 0.10483... + 0.11436... + 0.11436...$$
$$+ 0.10557...$$
$$= 0.439 \text{ (to 3 sig. fig.)}$$

Exercise 1.3 — Mean and variance of a Poisson distribution

Q1 a) (i) 9   **(ii)** 9

b) (i) 12   **(ii)** 12

c) (i) 4.3   **(ii)** 4.3

Q2 a) $\mu = 9$, $\sigma^2 = 9$

b) $\sigma = 3$

c) $P(X = \mu + \sigma) = P(X = 12) = \frac{e^{-9}9^{12}}{12!}$
$$= 0.0728 \text{ (to 3 sig. fig.)}$$

Q3 a) $\mu = 16$, $\sigma^2 = 16$

b) $\sigma = 4$

c) $P(X \le \sigma) = P(X \le 4)$
$= P(X = 0) + P(X = 1) + P(X = 2)$
$\quad + P(X = 3) + P(X = 4)$
$= 0.00000... + 0.00000... + 0.00001...$
$\quad + 0.00007... + 0.00030...$
$= 0.0004$ (to 4 d.p.)

Q4 a) The mean of this data is $\bar{x} = \dfrac{\sum fx}{\sum f}$.

And the variance is given by $\dfrac{\sum fx^2}{\sum f} - \bar{x}^2$

It's easiest if you extend the table as below.

Rentals per week (x)	5	6	7	8	9	10	11	12	13
Frequency (f)	4	6	3	8	16	9	3	2	1
fx	20	36	21	64	144	90	33	24	13
x^2	25	36	49	64	81	100	121	144	169
fx^2	100	216	147	512	1296	900	363	288	169

Find the totals of the 2nd and 3rd rows:
$\sum f = 52$ and $\sum fx = 445$
So $\bar{x} = \dfrac{445}{52} = 8.557... = 8.56$ (to 3 sig. fig.)

Find the total of the 5th row:
$\sum fx^2 = 3991$

So variance $= \dfrac{\sum fx^2}{\sum f} - \bar{x}^2 = \dfrac{3991}{52} - (8.557...)^2$
$= 3.515... = 3.52$ (to 3 sig. fig.)

b) The assumption seems to be wrong. The values probably **don't** follow a Poisson distribution, as the mean and the variance are very different.

Exercise 1.4 — Additive property of the Poisson distribution

Q1 a) $X \sim Po(600)$

b) Since 1 mm^2 = 1 cm$^2 \div 100$, $Y \sim Po(6)$

c) $P(Y = 3) = \dfrac{e^{-6}6^3}{3!} = 0.0892$ (to 3 sig. fig.)

Q2 If the random variable X represents the number of potholes in 1 km of road, then $X \sim Po(3)$.
So if Y represents the number of potholes in a randomly chosen 8 km stretch of this road, then $Y \sim Po(8 \times 3) = Po(24)$.
$P(20 \le Y \le 22) = P(Y = 20) + P(Y = 21) + P(Y = 22)$
$= \dfrac{e^{-24}24^{20}}{20!} + \dfrac{e^{-24}24^{21}}{21!} + \dfrac{e^{-24}24^{22}}{22!}$
$= 0.06237... + 0.07128... + 0.07777...$
$= 0.211$ (to 3 sig. fig.)

Q3 a) Let the random variable L represent the number of texts received by Louise in 1 day, and the random variable H represent the number of texts received by Hannah in 1 day. Then $L \sim Po(4)$ and $H \sim Po(2)$.
So the total number of text messages Louise and Hannah receive in 1 day is $L + H$, and $L + H \sim Po(4 + 2) = Po(6)$.
This means that the probability of this total being equal to 5 is $P(L + H = 5) = \dfrac{e^{-6}6^5}{5!}$
$= 0.161$ (to 3 sig. fig.)

b) The total number of texts received by the two girls in 1 week equals $7(L + H)$, where $7(L + H) \sim Po(7 \times 6) = Po(42)$.
So $P(7(L + H) = 44) = \dfrac{e^{-42}42^{44}}{44!}$
$= 0.0573$ (to 3 sig. fig.).

Q4 Let the random variable W represent the number of wizard books sold in 1 day, and the random variable B represent the number of celebrity biographies sold in 1 day. Then $W \sim Po(20)$ and $B \sim Po(15)$.
This means the total number of these types of books sold in a day is
$W + B \sim Po(20 + 15) = Po(35)$
$P(W + B = 40) = \dfrac{e^{-35}35^{40}}{40!} = 0.0447$ (to 3 sig. fig.)

2. Using Poisson Tables

Exercise 2.1 — Using tables to find probabilities

Q1 Use the column for $\lambda = 2$.

a) $P(X \le 3) = 0.8571$

b) $P(X \le 7) = 0.9989$

c) $P(X < 5) = P(X \le 4) = 0.9473$

Q2 Use the column for $\lambda = 7.5$.

a) $P(X > 6) = 1 - P(X \le 6) = 1 - 0.3782 = 0.6218$

b) $P(X = 9) = P(X \le 9) - P(X \le 8)$
$= 0.7764 - 0.6620 = 0.1144$

c) $P(2 \le X \le 8) = P(X \le 8) - P(X \le 1)$
$= 0.6620 - 0.0047 = 0.6573$

Q3 Use the column for $\lambda = 6$.

a) $P(X > 4) = 1 - P(X \le 4) = 1 - 0.2851 = 0.7149$

b) $P(2 < X \le 5) = P(X \le 5) - P(X \le 2)$
$= 0.4457 - 0.0620 = 0.3837$

c) $P(4 \le X < 9) = P(X \le 8) - P(X \le 3)$
$= 0.8472 - 0.1512 = 0.6960$

Q4 Use the column for $\lambda = 5.5$.

a) $P(X > 2) = 1 - P(X \le 2) = 1 - 0.0884 = 0.9116$

b) $P(X = 4) = P(X \le 4) - P(X \le 3)$
$= 0.3575 - 0.2017 = 0.1558$

c) $P(2 \le X \le 7) = P(X \le 7) - P(X \le 1)$
$= 0.8095 - 0.0266 = 0.7829$

Q5 a) Let X represent the number of telephone calls received in a random minute. Then $X \sim \text{Po}(8)$.

Use the Poisson table with $\lambda = 8$.
$P(X = 6) = P(X \leq 6) - P(X \leq 5)$
$\qquad = 0.3134 - 0.1912 = 0.1222$

b) $P(X \geq 3) = 1 - P(X < 3) = 1 - P(X \leq 2)$
$\qquad\qquad\qquad = 1 - 0.0138 = 0.9862$

Q6 a) Let X represent the number of tadpoles in 10 cm³ of water. Then $X \sim \text{Po}(0.1)$. So if Y represents the number of tadpoles in 1 litre of water, then $Y \sim \text{Po}(100 \times 0.1) = \text{Po}(10)$.

So use the Poisson table with $\lambda = 10$.
$P(X < 7) = P(X \leq 6) = 0.1301$

b) $P(X > 15) = 1 - P(X \leq 15) = 1 - 0.9513 = 0.0487$

Exercise 2.2 — Using tables 'backwards'

Q1 Use the column for $\lambda = 5.5$.

a) If $P(X \leq x) = 0.5289$, then $x = 5$.

b) If $P(X < x) = 0.9983$, then $P(X \leq x - 1) = 0.9983$. This means $x - 1 = 13$, i.e. $x = 14$.

Q2 Use the column for $\lambda = 3.5$.

a) If $P(Y > y) = 0.8641$, then $P(Y \leq y) = 1 - 0.8641$ $= 0.1359$. Use tables to find that $y = 1$.

b) If $P(Y \geq y) = 0.1424$, then $P(Y < y) = 1 - 0.1424$ $= 0.8576$. This means $P(Y \leq y - 1) = 0.8576$. Use tables to find that $y - 1 = 5$, i.e. $y = 6$.

Q3 Use the column for $\lambda = 1.5$.
You need to find the largest value of x for which $P(X < x) \leq 0.25$, or $P(X \leq x - 1) \leq 0.25$.
$P(X \leq 0) = 0.2231$, but $P(X \leq 1) = 0.5578$, so the value of x you need is given by $x - 1 = 0$, or $x = 1$.

Q4 $X \sim \text{Po}(8)$, so use the column for $\lambda = 8$.
You need to find the smallest value of x for which $P(X \geq x) < 0.05$.
$P(X \leq 12) = 0.9362$, so $P(X > 12) = P(X \geq 13)$ $= 1 - 0.9362 = 0.0638$.
$P(X \leq 13) = 0.9658$, so $P(X > 13) = P(X \geq 14)$ $= 1 - 0.9658 = 0.0342$.
So the smallest possible value of x where $P(X \geq x) < 0.05$ is $x = 14$.

Q5 If X represents the number of inflatables the company rents out in one hour, then $X \sim \text{Po}(6)$.

If the company is to be at least 90% certain of meeting demand, then it needs at least x inflatables, where $P(X > x) < 0.1$.
This means $P(X \leq x) = 1 - P(X > x) > 0.9$.

Using the column for $\lambda = 6$: $P(X \leq 8) = 0.8472$, but $P(X \leq 9) = 0.9161$, so the company needs at least 9 inflatables.

Q6 If X represents the number of breakdowns in one month, then $X \sim \text{Po}(0.5)$. So if Y represents the number of breakdowns in four months, then $Y \sim \text{Po}(4 \times 0.5) = \text{Po}(2)$.

You need to find the minimum value of y for which $P(Y > y) < 0.1$.

Using the column for $\lambda = 2$: $P(X \leq 3) = 0.8571$, and so $P(X > 3) = 1 - 0.8571 = 0.1429$.
But $P(X \leq 4) = 0.9473$, and so $P(X > 4) = 1 - 0.9473 = 0.0527$.

This means that the minimum value of y for which the supplier has a probability of less than 0.1 of paying the penalty is $y = 4$.

3. The Poisson Approximation of a Binomial Distribution

Exercise 3.1 — Approximating the binomial distribution with a Poisson distribution

Q1 a) No, since p is not very small.

b) No, since n is not very large.

c) Yes, since n is large and p is small.

d) Yes, since n is large and p is small.
But np = 25, and $\lambda = 25$ is not in your Poisson tables, so this last approximation may not be very helpful.

Q2 a) $n = 30$ and $p = 0.1$, so use $\text{Po}(30 \times 0.1) = \text{Po}(3)$.

b) $n = 50$ and $p = 0.05$, so use $\text{Po}(50 \times 0.05) = \text{Po}(2.5)$.

c) $n = 200$ and $p = 0.01$, so use $\text{Po}(200 \times 0.01) = \text{Po}(2)$.

d) $n = 500$ and $p = 0.003$, so use $\text{Po}(500 \times 0.003) = \text{Po}(1.5)$.

Q3 a) $n = 90$ and $p = 0.05$, so use $\text{Po}(90 \times 0.05) = \text{Po}(4.5)$.

From the table for Po(4.5): $P(X \leq 2) = 0.1736$

b) From the table for Po(4.5): $P(X \leq 5) = 0.7029$
So $P(X > 5) = 1 - 0.7029 = 0.2971$

c) From the table for Po(4.5):
$P(X < 4) = P(X \leq 3) = 0.3423$

d) $P(X \geq 5) = 1 - P(X < 5) = 1 - P(X \leq 4)$.
From the table for Po(4.5): $P(X \leq 4) = 0.5321$, so $P(X \geq 5) = 1 - 0.5321 = 0.4679$

Q4 a) $n = 150$ and $p = 0.01$, so use $\text{Po}(150 \times 0.01) = \text{Po}(1.5)$.
Using the table for Po(1.5):
$P(X = 3) = P(X \leq 3) - P(X \leq 2)$
$\qquad\qquad = 0.9344 - 0.8088 = 0.1256$
You could also use the probability function here.

b) Using the table for Po(1.5):
$P(3 < X \leq 5) = P(X \leq 5) - P(X \leq 3)$
$\qquad\qquad\qquad = 0.9955 - 0.9344 = 0.0611$

c) Using the table for Po(1.5):
P(2 ≤ X < 7) = P(X ≤ 6) − P(X ≤ 1)
= 0.9991 − 0.5578 = 0.4413

d) Using the table for Po(1.5):
P(1 < X < 4) = P(X ≤ 3) − P(X ≤ 1)
= 0.9344 − 0.5578 = 0.3766

Q5 a) Using binomial tables for $n = 40$ and $p = 0.1$:
P($X \leq 2$) = 0.2228

b) Using binomial tables for $n = 10$ and $p = 0.4$:
P($Y \leq 2$) = 0.1673

c) Po(4) can be used to approximate both X and Y,
since E(X) = 40 × 0.1 = 4 and E(Y) = 10 × 0.4 = 4.
Using the table for Po(4): P($X \leq 2$) and P($Y \leq 2$)
could both be approximated by 0.2381.

d) Using Po(4) gives a much better approximation to
X than Y because n is larger and p is smaller.

Q6 If the random variable X represents the number of
patients out of the 300 who have contracted the
disease, then $X \sim$ B(300, 0.02). Since n is large and p
is small, the distribution of X can be approximated by
the Poisson distribution Po(300 × 0.02) = Po(6).

Using Poisson tables:
P($X > 10$) = 1 − P($X \leq 10$) = 1 − 0.9574 = 0.0426

Q7 If the random variable X represents the number of
times he is correct, then $X \sim$ B(90, 0.9). This means
that if Y represents the number of times he is wrong,
then $Y \sim$ B(90, 0.1).

Since n is large and p is small, the distribution of
Y can be approximated by the Poisson distribution
Po(90 × 0.1) = Po(9).

Using Poisson tables:
P($X > 85$) = P($Y < 5$) = P($Y \leq 4$) = 0.0550

Q8 If the random variable X represents the number of
incorrectly dialled calls, then $X \sim$ B(600, 0.005).
Since n is large and p is small, the distribution of
X can be approximated by the Poisson distribution
Po(600 × 0.005) = Po(3).

Using Poisson tables:
P($X > 7$) = 1 − P($X \leq 7$) = 1 − 0.9881 − 0.0119

Review Exercise — Chapter 2

Q1 a) $P(X = 2) = \dfrac{e^{-3.1} \times 3.1^2}{2!} = 0.21646...$
$= 0.2165$ (to 4 d.p.).

b) $P(X = 1) = \dfrac{e^{-3.1} \times 3.1}{1!} = 0.13965...$
$= 0.1397$ (to 4 d.p.).

c) $P(X = 0) = \dfrac{e^{-3.1} \times 3.1^0}{0!} = 0.04504....$
$= 0.0450$ (to 4 d.p.).

d) $P(X < 3) = P(X = 0) + P(X = 1) + P(X = 2)$
$= 0.04504... + 0.13965... + 0.21646...$
$= 0.40116... = 0.4012$ (to 4 d.p.)

e) $P(X \geq 3) = 1 - P(X < 3)$
$= 1 - 0.40116... = 0.5988$ (to 4 d.p.).

Q2 a) $P(X = 2) = \dfrac{e^{-8.7} \times 8.7^2}{2!} = 0.00630...$
$= 0.0063$ (to 4 d.p.).

b) $P(X = 1) = \dfrac{e^{-8.7} \times 8.7}{1!} = 0.00144...$
$= 0.0014$ (to 4 d.p.).

c) $P(X = 0) = \dfrac{e^{-8.7} \times 8.7^0}{0!} = 0.00016...$
$= 0.0002$ (to 4 d.p.).

d) $P(X < 3) = P(X = 0) + P(X = 1) + P(X = 2)$
$= 0.00016... + 0.00144... + 0.00630...$
$= 0.00792... = 0.0079$ (to 4 d.p.)

e) $P(X \geq 3) = 1 - P(X < 3)$
$= 1 - 0.00792... = 0.9921$ (to 4 d.p.).

Q3 a) E(X) = Var(X) = 8
standard deviation = $\sigma = \sqrt{8} = 2.828$ (to 3 d.p.).

b) E(X) = Var(X) = 12.11
standard deviation = σ
$= \sqrt{12.11} = 3.480$ (to 3 d.p.).

c) E(X) = Var(X) = 84.2227
standard deviation = σ
$= \sqrt{84.2227} = 9.177$ (to 3 d.p.).

Q4 Using tables:

a) P($X \leq \mu$) = P($X \leq 9$) = 0.5874
P($X \leq \mu - \sigma$) = P($X \leq 6$) = 0.2068

b) P($X \leq \mu$) = P($X \leq 4$) = 0.6288
P($X \leq \mu - \sigma$) = P($X \leq 2$) = 0.2381

Q5 a) The defective products occur randomly, singly and (on average) at a constant rate, and the random variable represents the number of 'events' (i.e. defective products) within a fixed period, so this would follow a Poisson distribution.

b) There is a fixed number of trials in this situation, and so this situation would be modelled by a binomial distribution. (Or you could say it won't follow a Poisson distribution, as the events don't occur at a constant average rate over the 25 trials.)

c) If the random variable represents the number of people joining the queue within a fixed period, and assuming that the people join the queue randomly, singly and (on average) at a constant rate, then this would follow a Poisson distribution.

You do need to make a couple of assumptions here — the Poisson model wouldn't work if you had, say, big groups of factory workers all coming in together a couple of minutes after the lunchtime hooter sounds.

d) The mistakes occur randomly, singly and (on average) at a constant rate, and the random variable represents the number of mistakes within a fixed 'period' (i.e. the number of pages in the document), so this would follow a Poisson distribution.

Q6 a) The number of atoms decaying in an hour would follow the Poisson distribution Po(2000). So the number decaying in a minute would follow Po(2000 ÷ 60) = Po($33\frac{1}{3}$).

b) The number of atoms decaying in a day would follow Po(2000 × 24) = Po(48 000).

Q7 a) If X represents the number of atoms from the first sample decaying per minute, then $X \sim$ Po(60). And if Y represents the number of atoms from the second sample decaying per minute, then $Y \sim$ Po(90). So $X + Y$ (the total number of atoms decaying per minute) $\sim$ Po(60 + 90) = Po(150).

b) The total number of atoms decaying per hour would be distributed as Po(150 × 60) = Po(9000).

Q8 a) $P(X \leq 2) = 0.0138$

b) $P(X \leq 7) = 0.4530$

c) $P(X \leq 5) = 0.1912$

d) $P(X < 9) = P(X \leq 8) = 0.5925$

e) $P(X \geq 8) = 1 - P(X < 8) = 1 - P(X \leq 7)$
$= 1 - 0.4530 = 0.5470$

f) $P(X > 1) = 1 - P(X \leq 1) = 1 - 0.0030 = 0.9970$

g) $P(X > 7) = 1 - P(X \leq 7) = 1 - 0.4530 = 0.5470$

h) $P(X = 6) = P(X \leq 6) - P(X \leq 5)$
$= 0.3134 - 0.1912 = 0.1222$

i) $P(X = 4) = P(X \leq 4) - P(X \leq 3)$
$= 0.0996 - 0.0424 = 0.0572$

j) $P(X = 3) = P(X \leq 3) - P(X \leq 2)$
$= 0.0424 - 0.0138 = 0.0286$

Q9 a) No — n is not very large, and p is not very small.

b) Yes — n is large, and p is small, so approximate with Po(7).

c) Not really — n is large, but p isn't as small as you'd like.

d) Not really — n is quite small (and so you don't really need to approximate it anyway).

e) This is perfect for a Poisson approximation — n is enormous and p is tiny. It should follow Po(0.1) very closely.

f) If Y represents the number of 'successes' in 80 trials, then define a new random variable X representing the number of 'failures' in those 80 trials. Then $X \sim$ B(80, 0.1). Since n is quite large, and p is quite small, you could approximate X with Po(80 × 0.1) = Po(8). Then $Y = 80 - X$.

Q10 If X represents the number of geese in a random square metre of field, then $X \sim$ Po(1) — since the 'rate' at which geese occur is constant, they're randomly scattered, and geese only occur singly.

a) $P(X = 0) = \dfrac{e^{-1} \times 1^0}{0!} = 0.3679$

b) $P(X = 1) = \dfrac{e^{-1} \times 1^1}{1!} = 0.3679$

c) $P(X = 2) = \dfrac{e^{-1} \times 1^2}{2!} = 0.1839$

d) $P(X > 2) = 1 - P(X \leq 2)$
$= 1 - (0.3679 + 0.3679 + 0.1839)$
$= 1 - 0.9197 = 0.0803$

Here, you could use either your Poisson tables or the probability function.

Exam-Style Questions — Chapter 2

1 a) Events need to happen at a constant average rate *[1 mark]* and singly ('one at a time') *[1 mark]*.
You could also have had 'events occur randomly' or 'independently'.

b) (i) If X represents the number of chaffinches visiting the observation spot in an hour, then $X \sim$ Po(7) *[1 mark]*.
Using tables, $P(X < 4) = P(X \leq 3) = 0.0818$ *[1 mark]*.

(ii) $P(X \geq 7) = 1 - P(X < 7) = 1 - P(X \leq 6)$ *[1 mark]*
$= 1 - 0.4497 = 0.5503$ *[1 mark]*

(iii) $P(X = 9) = P(X \leq 9) - P(X \leq 8)$ *[1 mark]*
$= 0.8305 - 0.7291 = 0.1014$ *[1 mark]*

Or you could work this last one out using the formula: $P(X = 9) = \dfrac{e^{-7} 7^9}{9!} = 0.1014$

— you get the same answer either way.

c) The number of birds of any species visiting per hour would follow the distribution Po(22 + 7) = Po(29) *[1 mark]*. So the total number of birds visiting in a random 15-minute period will follow Po(29 ÷ 4) = Po(7.25) *[1 mark]*.

$$P(X = 3) = \frac{e^{-7.25} \times 7.25^3}{3!} \text{ *[1 mark]*}$$
$$= 0.045 \text{ (to 3 d.p.) *[1 mark]*}.$$

2 a) (i) If the mean is 20, then the number of calls per hour follows Po(20). So the number of calls in a random 30-minute period follows Po(20 ÷ 2) = Po(10) *[1 mark]*.

Using tables for $\lambda = 10$:
$P(X = 8) = P(X \le 8) - P(X \le 7)$ *[1 mark]*
$= 0.3328 - 0.2202 = 0.1126$ *[1 mark]*
Or you could work this out using the formula:
$$P(X = 8) = \frac{e^{-10}10^8}{8!} = 0.1126.$$

(ii) $P(X > 8) = 1 - P(X \le 8)$ *[1 mark]*
$= 1 - 0.3328 = 0.6672$ *[1 mark]*

b) In this context, independently means that receiving a phone call at one particular instant does not affect whether or not a call will be received at a different instant *[1 mark]*.

3 a) (i) Let the random variable X represent the number of errors in the document. Then since the document contains 4×5 = 20 lines, $X \sim$ Po(4×1) = Po(4) *[1 mark]*.
$$P(X = 0) = \frac{e^{-4}4^0}{0!} = 0.0183 \text{ (to 4 d.p.)}$$
[1 mark].

Or you could use Poisson tables here:
$P(X = 0) = P(X \le 0) = 0.0183.$

(ii) $P(X > 10) = 1 - P(X \le 10)$
$= 1 - 0.9972$ *[1 mark]*
$= 0.0028$ *[1 mark]*

b) (i) Since the document contains 36×5 = 180 lines, $Y \sim$ Po(36×1) = Po(36) *[1 mark]*.

(ii) Var(Y) = 36
And so the standard deviation of Y is $\sqrt{36} = 6$ *[1 mark]*.

4 a) The number of trials here is fixed (= 400) and the probability of the engineer being unable to fix a fault is constant (= 0.02). This means X (the total number of unsuccessful call-outs) will follow a binomial distribution *[1 mark]*.
In fact, $X \sim$ B(400, 0.02) *[1 mark]*.

b) (i) To approximate a binomial distribution B(n, p) with a Poisson distribution, n should be large *[1 mark]* and p should be small *[1 mark]*.

(ii) Po(400×0.02) = Po(8) *[1 mark]*.

(iii) Mean = 8 and variance = 8 *[1 mark]*.

(iv) P(engineer unable to fix fewer than 10 faults)
$= P(X < 10) = P(X \le 9)$ *[1 mark]*.
Using Poisson tables for $\lambda = 8$:
$P(X \le 9) = 0.7166$ *[1 mark]*.

5 a) (i) Let the random variable M represent the number of people mistyping their password in a randomly chosen 10-minute period. Then $M \sim$ Po($30 \div 6$) = Po(5) *[1 mark]*.
Using Poisson tables for $\lambda = 5$:
$P(M > 10) = 1 - P(M \le 10) = 1 - 0.9863$
$= 0.0137$ *[1 mark]*.

(ii) $P(10 \le M \le 15) = P(M \le 15) - P(M \le 9)$
[1 mark]
$= 0.9999 - 0.9682$
$= 0.0317$ *[1 mark]*

b) (i) Mean $= \dfrac{\sum x}{n} = \dfrac{752}{24} = 31.33$ people per hour (to 2 d.p.) *[1 mark]*.

Variance $= \dfrac{\sum x^2}{n} - \left(\dfrac{\sum x}{n}\right)^2 = \dfrac{24338}{24} - \left(\dfrac{752}{24}\right)^2$

[1 mark]
So variance = 32.31 (to 2 d.p.) *[1 mark]*.

(ii) The mean is approximately equal to the variance, which means a Poisson distribution is appropriate *[1 mark]*.

(iii) If X is the number of people mistyping their password in the randomly chosen hour, then $X \sim$ Po(31.33) *[1 mark]*.

So $P(X = 30) = \dfrac{e^{-31.33} \times 31.33^{30}}{30!}$ *[1 mark]*
$= 0.0706$ (to 3 sig. fig.) *[1 mark]*.

Chapter 3: Continuous Random Variables

1. Probability Density Functions

Exercise 1.1 — Probability density functions

Q1 **a)** **(i)** First check that f(x) cannot be negative.

x^2 is non-negative for all x, so $\frac{1}{2}x^2$ must always be non-negative and f(x) ≥ 0 for all $x \in \mathbb{R}$.

Now you just need to check that the total probability is 1.

$$\int_{-\infty}^{\infty} f(x)\,dx = \int_{-\infty}^{0} f(x)\,dx + \int_{0}^{2} f(x)\,dx + \int_{2}^{\infty} f(x)\,dx$$

$$= \int_{-\infty}^{0} 0\,dx + \int_{0}^{2} \frac{1}{2}x^2\,dx + \int_{2}^{\infty} 0\,dx$$

$$= \int_{0}^{2} \frac{1}{2}x^2\,dx = \left[\frac{x^3}{2 \times 3}\right]_0^2 = \left[\frac{x^3}{6}\right]_0^2$$

$$= \left(\frac{2^3}{6}\right) - \left(\frac{0^3}{6}\right) = \frac{8}{6} = \frac{4}{3}$$

Okay... I'm not going to write in the integrals where the p.d.f. is zero any more — you can see they're always going to disappear.

So the probability is not equal to 1 and f(x) is not a p.d.f.

(ii) The function is not a p.d.f.

b) **(i)** x^2 is positive for all x, so $\frac{3}{4}x^2$ must always be positive and f(x) ≥ 0 for all $x \in \mathbb{R}$.

Now work out the total area:

$$\int_{-\infty}^{\infty} f(x)\,dx = \int_{1}^{2} f(x)\,dx$$

$$= \int_{1}^{2} \frac{3}{4}x^2\,dx$$

$$= \left[\frac{3x^3}{4 \times 3}\right]_1^2 = \left[\frac{x^3}{4}\right]_1^2$$

$$= \left(\frac{2^3}{4}\right) - \left(\frac{1^3}{4}\right) = \frac{7}{4}$$

So the probability is not equal to 1 and f(x) is not a p.d.f.

(ii) The function is not a p.d.f.

c) **(i)** The graph of $y = 1 - \frac{1}{2}x$ looks like this:

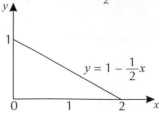

So this function is always non-negative in the range $0 < x < 2$, so f(x) ≥ 0 for all $x \in \mathbb{R}$.

Work out the total area:

$$\int_{-\infty}^{\infty} f(x)\,dx = \int_{0}^{2} f(x)\,dx$$

$$= \int_{0}^{2} \left(1 - \frac{1}{2}x\right)dx$$

$$= \left[x - \frac{x^2}{4}\right]_0^2$$

$$= \left(2 - \frac{2^2}{4}\right) - \left(0 - \frac{0^2}{4}\right)$$

$$= (2 - 1) - 0 = 1$$

So the total area is 1, and this function is a p.d.f.

(ii)

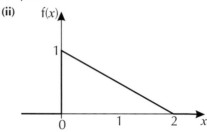

d) **(i)** When x is non-negative, x^3 is non-negative, so $\frac{1}{4}x^3$ is non-negative for $0 < x < 2$ and f(x) ≥ 0 for all $x \in \mathbb{R}$.

Work out the total area:

$$\int_{-\infty}^{\infty} f(x)\,dx = \int_{-\infty}^{0} f(x)\,dx + \int_{0}^{2} f(x)\,dx + \int_{2}^{\infty} f(x)\,dx$$

$$= \int_{-\infty}^{0} 1\,dx + \int_{0}^{2} \frac{1}{4}x^3\,dx + \int_{2}^{\infty} 1\,dx$$

$$= [x]_{-\infty}^{0} + \left[\frac{x^4}{16}\right]_0^2 + [x]_2^{\infty}$$

The first and third integrals are both undefined — they are infinite. So the total area is not equal to 1 and this function is not a p.d.f.

(ii) The function is not a p.d.f.

e) (i) x^2 is always non-negative, so $x^2 + 5$ must also always be non-negative and $f(x) \geq 0$ for all $x \in \mathbb{R}$.

Work out the total area:

$$\int_{-\infty}^{\infty} f(x)\, dx = \int_1^2 f(x)\, dx$$

$$= \int_1^2 (x^2 + 5)\, dx$$

$$= \left[\frac{x^3}{3} + 5x\right]_1^2$$

$$= \left(\frac{2^3}{3} + 5(2)\right) - \left(\frac{1^3}{3} + 5(1)\right)$$

$$= \left(\frac{8}{3} + 10\right) - \left(\frac{1}{3} + 5\right) = \frac{22}{3}$$

So the total area is not 1 and this function is not a p.d.f.

(ii) $f(x)$ is not a p.d.f.

f) (i) $y = \frac{2}{9}(3x - x^2) = \frac{2}{9}x(3 - x)$ is a quadratic with negative x^2-coefficient and roots at $x = 0$ and $x = 3$.

So it looks like this:

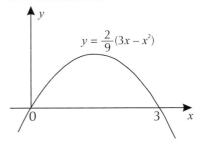

So it is non-negative for $0 < x < 3$, which means $f(x) \geq 0$ for all $x \in \mathbb{R}$.

Work out the total area:

$$\int_{-\infty}^{\infty} f(x)\, dx = \int_0^3 f(x)\, dx$$

$$= \int_0^3 \frac{2}{9}(3x - x^2)\, dx$$

$$= \left[\frac{2}{9}\left(\frac{3x^2}{2} - \frac{x^3}{3}\right)\right]_0^3$$

$$= \left(\frac{2}{9}\left(\frac{3 \times 3^2}{2} - \frac{3^3}{3}\right)\right) - \left(\frac{2}{9}\left(\frac{3 \times 0^2}{2} - \frac{0^3}{3}\right)\right)$$

$$= \left(\frac{2}{9}\left(\frac{27}{2} - \frac{27}{3}\right)\right) - 0 = 1 - 0 = 1$$

So the total area is 1, and this function is a p.d.f.

(ii)

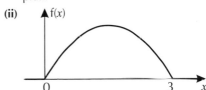

g) (i) The curve with equation

$$y = x^2 - \frac{5}{3} = \left(x + \sqrt{\frac{5}{3}}\right)\left(x - \sqrt{\frac{5}{3}}\right) \text{ is a}$$

quadratic with positive x^2-coefficient and roots at $\pm\sqrt{\frac{5}{3}}$.

So the graph looks like this:

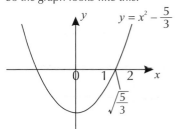

So the function $f(x)$ is negative for $1 \leq x < \sqrt{\frac{5}{3}}$, so the function $f(x)$ is not a p.d.f.

(ii) The function is not a p.d.f.

h) (i) 0.2 is clearly positive and x^2 is non-negative for all x, so $0.5x^2$ is also non-negative. Therefore $f(x) \geq 0$ for all $x \in \mathbb{R}$.

Work out the total area:

$$\int_{-\infty}^{\infty} f(x)\, dx = \int_0^1 f(x)\, dx + \int_1^3 f(x)\, dx$$

$$= \int_0^1 0.2\, dx + \int_1^3 0.5x^2\, dx$$

$$= [0.2x]_0^1 + \left[\frac{0.5x^3}{3}\right]_1^3$$

$$= [0.2 - 0] + \left[\frac{0.5(3)^3}{3} - \frac{0.5(1)^3}{3}\right]$$

$$= 0.2 + \frac{9}{2} - \frac{1}{6} = \frac{68}{15}$$

So the total area is not equal to 1, which means the function is not a p.d.f.

(ii) The function is not a p.d.f.

Q2 a) The total area must be equal to 1, so work the integral out in terms of k and then set it equal to 1 to find k:

$$\int_{-\infty}^{\infty} f(x)\,dx = \int_{1}^{2} f(x)\,dx$$
$$= \int_{1}^{2} kx^2\,dx$$
$$= \left[\frac{kx^3}{3}\right]_{1}^{2}$$
$$= \left(\frac{k(2)^3}{3}\right) - \left(\frac{k(1)^3}{3}\right)$$
$$= \frac{8k}{3} - \frac{k}{3} = \frac{7k}{3}$$

So let $\frac{7k}{3} = 1 \Rightarrow k = \frac{3}{7}$.

b) Find the total area:

$$\int_{-\infty}^{\infty} f(x)\,dx = \int_{0}^{2} f(x)\,dx$$
$$= \int_{0}^{2} kx^3\,dx$$
$$= \left[\frac{kx^4}{4}\right]_{0}^{2}$$
$$= \left(\frac{k(2)^4}{4}\right) - \left(\frac{k(0)^4}{4}\right)$$
$$= 4k$$

So let $4k = 1 \Rightarrow k = \frac{1}{4}$

c)
$$\int_{-\infty}^{\infty} f(x)\,dx = \int_{0}^{1} f(x)\,dx + \int_{1}^{2} f(x)\,dx$$
$$= \int_{0}^{1} k\,dx + \int_{1}^{2} kx\,dx$$
$$= [kx]_{0}^{1} + \left[\frac{kx^2}{2}\right]_{1}^{2}$$
$$= [k - 0] + \left[\frac{k(2)^2}{2} - \frac{k(1)^2}{2}\right]$$
$$= k + \left[2k - \frac{k}{2}\right] = \frac{5k}{2}$$

So let $\frac{5k}{2} = 1 \Rightarrow k = \frac{2}{5}$

d)
$$\int_{-\infty}^{\infty} f(x)\,dx = \int_{0}^{1} f(x)\,dx + \int_{1}^{2} f(x)\,dx$$
$$= \int_{0}^{1} \frac{1}{3}\,dx + \int_{1}^{2} k(1 - x^2)\,dx$$
$$= \left[\frac{1}{3}x\right]_{0}^{1} + \left[k\left(x - \frac{x^3}{3}\right)\right]_{1}^{2}$$
$$= \left[\frac{1}{3} - 0\right]$$
$$\quad + \left[\left(k\left(2 - \frac{2^3}{3}\right)\right) - \left(k\left(1 - \frac{1^3}{3}\right)\right)\right]$$
$$= \frac{1}{3} + \left[\left(-\frac{2}{3}k\right) - \left(\frac{2}{3}k\right)\right]$$
$$= \frac{1}{3} - \frac{4}{3}k$$

So $\frac{1}{3} - \frac{4}{3}k = 1 \Rightarrow \frac{4}{3}k = -\frac{2}{3} \Rightarrow k = -\frac{2}{4} = -\frac{1}{2}$

Exercise 1.2 — Finding probabilities from probability density functions

Q1 a) $f(x) = 1 - \frac{1}{2}x$ when $0 < X < 1$, so just integrate this expression between the limits.

$$P(0 < X < 1) = \int_{0}^{1}\left(1 - \frac{1}{2}x\right)dx = \left[x - \frac{x^2}{4}\right]_{0}^{1}$$
$$= \left(1 - \frac{1^2}{4}\right) - \left(0 - \frac{0^2}{4}\right)$$
$$= \frac{3}{4} - 0 = \frac{3}{4}$$

b) $f(x) = 1 - \frac{1}{2}x$ when $\frac{1}{2} < X < 1$, so:

$$P\left(\frac{1}{2} < X < 1\right) = \int_{\frac{1}{2}}^{1}\left(1 - \frac{1}{2}x\right)dx = \left[x - \frac{x^2}{4}\right]_{\frac{1}{2}}^{1}$$
$$= \left(1 - \frac{1^2}{4}\right) - \left(\frac{1}{2} - \frac{\left(\frac{1}{2}\right)^2}{4}\right)$$
$$= \frac{3}{4} - \frac{7}{16} = \frac{5}{16}$$

Q2 $f(x) = 2(1 - x)$ when $0.25 < X < 0.75$ so:

$$P(0.25 < X < 0.75) = \int_{0.25}^{0.75} 2(1 - x)\,dx$$
$$= \int_{0.25}^{0.75}(2 - 2x)\,dx = [2x - x^2]_{0.25}^{0.75}$$
$$= (2(0.75) - (0.75)^2)$$
$$\quad - (2(0.25) - (0.25)^2)$$
$$= 0.5$$

Q3 a) $P(X < 1) = \int_{-\infty}^{1} f(x)\,dx = \int_{-\infty}^{0} 0\,dx + \int_{0}^{1}\frac{1}{4}x^3\,dx$

$$= \int_{0}^{1}\frac{1}{4}x^3\,dx = \left[\frac{x^4}{16}\right]_{0}^{1} = \left(\frac{1^4}{16}\right) - \left(\frac{0^4}{16}\right)$$
$$= \frac{1}{16}$$

b) $P(1 < X < 2) = \int_{1}^{2} f(x)\,dx = \int_{1}^{2}\frac{1}{4}x^3\,dx$

$$= \left[\frac{x^4}{16}\right]_{1}^{2} = \left(\frac{2^4}{16}\right) - \left(\frac{1^4}{16}\right)$$
$$= 1 - \frac{1}{16} = \frac{15}{16}$$

You could do part b) more quickly if you notice that it has to be '1 − answer to part a)' (since the area under the graph between x = 0 and x = 2 has to be 1).

Q4 $P(1 < X < 2) = \int_{1}^{2}\frac{2}{9}(3x - x^2)\,dx$

$$= \frac{2}{9}\int_{1}^{2}(3x - x^2)\,dx = \frac{2}{9}\left[\left(\frac{3x^2}{2} - \frac{x^3}{3}\right)\right]_{1}^{2}$$
$$= \frac{2}{9}\left[\left(\frac{3(2)^2}{2} - \frac{2^3}{3}\right) - \left(\frac{3(1)^2}{2} - \frac{1^3}{3}\right)\right]$$
$$= \frac{2}{9}\left[\frac{10}{3} - \frac{7}{6}\right] = \frac{2}{9}\left(\frac{13}{6}\right) = \frac{13}{27}$$

Q5 a) $P(X < 1) = \int_{-\infty}^{1} f(x)\,dx = \int_{-\infty}^{0} 0\,dx + \int_{0}^{1}\frac{2}{5}\,dx$

$$= \int_{0}^{1}\frac{2}{5}\,dx = \left[\frac{2}{5}x\right]_{0}^{1} = \frac{2}{5} - 0 = \frac{2}{5}$$

If you want, you could do this without integrating — the area you're finding is just the area of a rectangle with width 1 and height 2/5.

b) $P\left(\frac{1}{2} < X < \frac{3}{2}\right) = \int_{\frac{1}{2}}^{\frac{3}{2}} f(x)\,dx = \int_{\frac{1}{2}}^{1} \frac{2}{5}\,dx + \int_{1}^{\frac{3}{2}} \frac{2}{5}x\,dx$

$= \left[\frac{2}{5}x\right]_{\frac{1}{2}}^{1} + \left[\frac{x^2}{5}\right]_{1}^{\frac{3}{2}}$

$= \left[\left(\frac{2}{5} \times 1\right) - \left(\frac{2}{5} \times \frac{1}{2}\right)\right]$

$\quad + \left[\left(\frac{\left(\frac{3}{2}\right)^2}{5}\right) - \left(\frac{(1)^2}{5}\right)\right]$

$= \frac{1}{5} + \left[\frac{9}{20} - \frac{1}{5}\right] = \frac{9}{20}$

Notice that we had to split this function into two different integrals and add them together. This is because between $\frac{1}{2}$ and $\frac{3}{2}$ the function is defined differently for different values of x.

Q6 a) $P(0 < X < 1.5) = \int_{0}^{1.5} f(x)\,dx$

$= \int_{0}^{1} \frac{1}{3}\,dx + \int_{1}^{1.5} \frac{1}{3}(2x-1)\,dx$

$= \left[\frac{1}{3}x\right]_{0}^{1} + \left[\frac{1}{3}(x^2 - x)\right]_{1}^{1.5}$

$= \left[\frac{1}{3} - 0\right]$

$\quad + \left(\frac{1}{3}((1.5)^2 - (1.5))\right) - \left(\frac{1}{3}(1^2 - 1)\right)$

$= \frac{1}{3} + \left[\frac{1}{4} - 0\right] = \frac{7}{12}$

b) $P(X = 1) = 0$ because the probability of X being equal to an exact value is always 0.

2. Cumulative Distribution Functions

Exercise 2.1 — Cumulative distribution functions

Q1 a) $F(x)$ is not a c.d.f. To be a c.d.f. it must have $0 \le F(x) \le 1$ for all x, but if $x = 2$, $F(2) = -1$.

b) The graph of $F(x)$ looks like this:

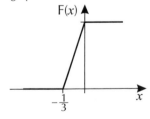

You can see from the graph that it is non-decreasing, it all joins up and it lies between 0 and 1. It satisfies all the properties of a c.d.f., so $F(x)$ is a c.d.f.

c) The graph of $F(x)$ looks like this:

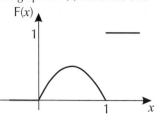

$F(x)$ is decreasing for $0.5 < x < 1$ and it doesn't 'join up' at $x = 1$. So $F(x)$ isn't a c.d.f.

Q2 a) If $x < 0$, $F(x) = 0$ and if $x > 2$, $F(x) = 1$.

For $0 \le x \le 2$:

$F(x) = \int_{-\infty}^{x} f(t)\,dt = \int_{-\infty}^{0} 0\,dt + \int_{0}^{x}\left(1 - \frac{1}{2}t\right)dt$

$= 0 + \left[t - \frac{t^2}{4}\right]_{0}^{x} = x - \frac{x^2}{4}$

So

$$F(x) = \begin{cases} 0 & x < 0 \\ x - \frac{x^2}{4} & 0 \le x \le 2 \\ 1 & x > 2 \end{cases}$$

b) If $x < 0$, $F(x) = 0$ and if $x > 1$, $F(x) = 1$.

For $0 \le x \le 1$:

$F(x) = \int_{-\infty}^{x} f(t)\,dt = \int_{-\infty}^{0} f(t)\,dt + \int_{0}^{x} f(t)\,dt$

$= \int_{-\infty}^{0} 0\,dt + \int_{0}^{x} 2(1 - t)\,dt$

$= 0 + \left[2\left(t - \frac{t^2}{2}\right)\right]_{0}^{x} = [2t - t^2]_{0}^{x} = 2x - x^2$

So

$$F(x) = \begin{cases} 0 & x < 0 \\ 2x - x^2 & 0 \le x \le 1 \\ 1 & x > 1 \end{cases}$$

c) If $x < 1$, $F(x) = 0$ and if $x > 2$, $F(x) = 1$.

For $1 \le x \le 2$:

$F(x) = \int_{-\infty}^{x} f(t)\,dt = \int_{-\infty}^{1} f(t)\,dt + \int_{1}^{x} f(t)\,dt$

$= \int_{-\infty}^{1} 0\,dt + \int_{1}^{x} \frac{3}{7}t^2\,dt$

$= 0 + \left[\frac{3t^3}{7 \times 3}\right]_{1}^{x} = \frac{x^3}{7} - \frac{1}{7}$

So

$$F(x) = \begin{cases} 0 & x < 1 \\ \frac{x^3}{7} - \frac{1}{7} & 1 \le x \le 2 \\ 1 & x > 2 \end{cases}$$

d) If $x < 0$, $F(x) = 0$ and if $x > 2$, $F(x) = 1$.

For $0 \leq x \leq 2$:

$$F(x) = \int_{-\infty}^{x} f(t)\, dt = \int_{-\infty}^{0} f(t)\, dt + \int_{0}^{x} f(t)\, dt$$

$$= \int_{-\infty}^{0} 0 \, dt + \int_{0}^{x} \tfrac{1}{4}(6t^2 - 3t^3)\, dt$$

$$= 0 + \left[\tfrac{1}{4}\left(2t^3 - \tfrac{3t^4}{4} \right) \right]_{0}^{x}$$

$$= \tfrac{1}{4}\left(2x^3 - \tfrac{3x^4}{4} \right) = \tfrac{x^3}{2} - \tfrac{3x^4}{16}$$

So

$$F(x) = \begin{cases} 0 & x < 0 \\ \dfrac{x^3}{2} - \dfrac{3x^4}{16} & 0 \leq x \leq 2 \\ 1 & x > 2 \end{cases}$$

e) If $x < 0$, $F(x) = 0$ and if $x > 3$, $F(x) = 1$.

For $0 \leq x \leq 3$:

$$F(x) = \int_{-\infty}^{x} f(t)\, dt = \int_{-\infty}^{0} f(t)\, dt + \int_{0}^{x} f(t)\, dt$$

$$= \int_{-\infty}^{0} 0 \, dt + \int_{0}^{x} \tfrac{2}{9}(3t - t^2)\, dt$$

$$= 0 + \left[\tfrac{2}{9}\left(\tfrac{3t^2}{2} - \tfrac{t^3}{3} \right) \right]_{0}^{x}$$

$$= \left[\tfrac{t^2}{3} - \tfrac{2t^3}{27} \right]_{0}^{x} = \tfrac{x^2}{3} - \tfrac{2x^3}{27}$$

So

$$F(x) = \begin{cases} 0 & x < 0 \\ \dfrac{x^2}{3} - \dfrac{2x^3}{27} & 0 \leq x \leq 3 \\ 1 & x > 3 \end{cases}$$

Q3 a) For $x < 0$, $F(x) = 0$.

For $0 \leq x < 1$:

$$F(x) = \int_{-\infty}^{x} f(t)\, dt = \int_{-\infty}^{0} f(t)\, dt + \int_{0}^{x} f(t)\, dt$$

$$= F(0) + \int_{0}^{x} \tfrac{2}{5}\, dt = 0 + \left[\tfrac{2}{5}t \right]_{0}^{x} = \tfrac{2}{5}x$$

This tells you that $F(1) = \tfrac{2}{5}$

For $1 \leq x \leq 2$:

$$F(x) = \int_{-\infty}^{x} f(t)\, dt = \int_{-\infty}^{1} f(t)\, dt + \int_{1}^{x} f(t)\, dt$$

$$= F(1) + \int_{1}^{x} \tfrac{2}{5}t\, dt = \tfrac{2}{5} + \left[\tfrac{2t^2}{5 \times 2} \right]_{1}^{x}$$

$$= \tfrac{2}{5} + \left[\tfrac{t^2}{5} \right]_{1}^{x} = \tfrac{2}{5} + \left(\tfrac{x^2}{5} - \tfrac{1}{5} \right) = \tfrac{1}{5}(x^2 + 1)$$

$F(2) = \tfrac{1}{5}(4 + 1) = 1$, so the pieces join up.

So

$$F(x) = \begin{cases} 0 & x < 0 \\ \dfrac{2}{5}x & 0 \leq x < 1 \\ \dfrac{1}{5}(x^2 + 1) & 1 \leq x \leq 2 \\ 1 & x > 2 \end{cases}$$

b) For $x \leq 0$, $F(x) = 0$.

For $0 < x < 1$:

$$F(x) = \int_{-\infty}^{x} f(t)\, dt = \int_{-\infty}^{0} f(t)\, dt + \int_{0}^{x} f(t)\, dt$$

$$= F(0) + \int_{0}^{x} \tfrac{1}{3}\, dt = 0 + \left[\tfrac{1}{3}t \right]_{0}^{x} = \tfrac{1}{3}x$$

This tells you that $F(1) = \tfrac{1}{3}$

For $1 \leq x \leq 2$:

$$F(x) = \int_{-\infty}^{x} f(t)\, dt = \int_{-\infty}^{1} f(t)\, dt + \int_{1}^{x} f(t)\, dt$$

$$= F(1) + \int_{1}^{x} \tfrac{1}{3}(2t - 1)\, dt = \tfrac{1}{3} + \left[\tfrac{1}{3}(t^2 - t) \right]_{1}^{x}$$

$$= \tfrac{1}{3} + \left[\left(\tfrac{1}{3}(x^2 - x) \right) - \left(\tfrac{1}{3}(1^2 - 1) \right) \right]$$

$$= \tfrac{1}{3} + \left[\left(\tfrac{1}{3}(x^2 - x) \right) - 0 \right]$$

$$= \tfrac{1}{3}(x^2 - x + 1)$$

$F(2) = \tfrac{1}{3}(4 - 2 + 1) = \tfrac{3}{3} = 1$, so the pieces join up.

So

$$F(x) = \begin{cases} 0 & x \leq 0 \\ \dfrac{1}{3}x & 0 < x < 1 \\ \dfrac{1}{3}(x^2 - x + 1) & 1 \leq x < 2 \\ 1 & x \geq 2 \end{cases}$$

c) For $x < 0$, $F(x) = 0$.

For $0 \leq x < 1$:

$$F(x) = \int_{-\infty}^{x} f(t)\, dt = \int_{-\infty}^{0} f(t)\, dt + \int_{0}^{x} f(t)\, dt$$

$$= F(0) + \int_{0}^{x} \tfrac{1}{3}\, dt = 0 + \left[\tfrac{1}{3}t \right]_{0}^{x} = \tfrac{1}{3}x$$

This tells you $F(1) = \tfrac{1}{3}$.

For $1 \leq x \leq 2$:

$$F(x) = \int_{-\infty}^{x} f(t)\, dt = \int_{-\infty}^{1} f(t)\, dt + \int_{1}^{x} f(t)\, dt$$

$$= F(1) + \int_{1}^{x} -\tfrac{1}{2}(1 - t^2)\, dt$$

$$= \tfrac{1}{3} + \left[-\tfrac{1}{2}\left(t - \tfrac{t^3}{3} \right) \right]_{1}^{x}$$

$$= \tfrac{1}{3} + \left[\tfrac{t^3}{6} - \tfrac{t}{2} \right]_{1}^{x} = \tfrac{1}{3} + \left[\left(\tfrac{x^3}{6} - \tfrac{x}{2} \right) - \left(\tfrac{1}{6} - \tfrac{1}{2} \right) \right]$$

$$= \tfrac{x^3}{6} - \tfrac{x}{2} + \tfrac{2}{3} = \tfrac{1}{6}(x^3 - 3x + 4)$$

$F(2) = \tfrac{1}{6}(8 - 6 + 4) = 1$, so the pieces join up.

So

$$F(x) = \begin{cases} 0 & x < 0 \\ \dfrac{1}{3}x & 0 \leq x < 1 \\ \dfrac{1}{6}(x^3 - 3x + 4) & 1 \leq x \leq 2 \\ 1 & x > 2 \end{cases}$$

You could have done this using the constants of integration approach... but you should have ended up with the same final answer.

Exercise 2.2 — Finding probability density functions by differentiating

Q1 a) $f(x) = \frac{d}{dx}(F(x)) = \begin{cases} 0 & x < 0 \\ 6x - 6x^2 & 0 \le x \le 1 \\ 0 & x > 1 \end{cases}$

$= \begin{cases} 6x - 6x^2 & 0 \le x \le 1 \\ 0 & \text{otherwise} \end{cases}$

b) $f(x) = \frac{d}{dx}(F(x)) = \begin{cases} 0 & x < 0 \\ \frac{1}{4}(3x^2 + 6x) & 0 \le x \le 1 \\ 0 & x > 1 \end{cases}$

$= \begin{cases} \frac{3}{4}(x^2 + 2x) & 0 \le x \le 1 \\ 0 & \text{otherwise} \end{cases}$

c) $f(x) = \frac{d}{dx}(F(x)) = \begin{cases} 0 & x < 0 \\ \frac{1}{4} & 0 \le x < 1 \\ \frac{1}{5}x^3 & 1 \le x \le 2 \\ 0 & x > 2 \end{cases}$

$= \begin{cases} \frac{1}{4} & 0 \le x < 1 \\ \frac{1}{5}x^3 & 1 \le x \le 2 \\ 0 & \text{otherwise} \end{cases}$

Q2 a) $f(x) = \frac{d}{dx}(F(x)) = \begin{cases} 0 & x < 1 \\ \frac{2}{3}x & 1 \le x \le 2 \\ 0 & x > 2 \end{cases}$

$= \begin{cases} \frac{2}{3}x & 1 \le x \le 2 \\ 0 & \text{otherwise} \end{cases}$

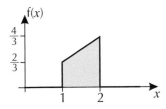

b) $f(x) = \frac{d}{dx}(F(x)) = \begin{cases} 0 & x < 0 \\ \frac{1}{3} & 0 \le x < 2 \\ \frac{2}{3} - \frac{1}{6}x & 2 \le x \le 4 \\ 0 & x > 4 \end{cases}$

$= \begin{cases} \frac{1}{3} & 0 \le x < 2 \\ \frac{2}{3} - \frac{1}{6}x & 2 \le x \le 4 \\ 0 & \text{otherwise} \end{cases}$

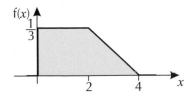

Exercise 2.3 — Finding probabilities using a cumulative distribution function

Q1 a) $P(X \le 0.2) = F(0.2)$
$= \frac{1}{4}((0.2)^3 + 3(0.2)^2) = 0.032$

b) $P(X < 0.5) = P(X \le 0.5) = F(0.5)$
$= \frac{1}{4}((0.5)^3 + 3(0.5)^2) = 0.219 \,(3 \text{ d.p.})$

c) $P(0.3 \le X \le 0.8) = P(X \le 0.8) - P(X < 0.3)$
$= P(X \le 0.8) - P(X \le 0.3)$
$= F(0.8) - F(0.3)$
$= \frac{1}{4}((0.8)^3 + 3(0.8)^2)$
$\quad - \frac{1}{4}((0.3)^3 + 3(0.3)^2)$
$= 0.534$

Q2 a) $P(X \le 1) = F(1) = \frac{1}{3}(1) = \frac{1}{3}$

b) $P(X > 3) = 1 - P(X \le 3) = 1 - F(3)$
$= 1 - \left(\frac{2}{3}(3) - \frac{1}{12}(3)^2 - \frac{1}{3}\right)$
$= 1 - \left(2 - \frac{3}{4} - \frac{1}{3}\right) = \frac{1}{12}$

c) $P(1 \le X \le 2) = P(X \le 2) - P(X < 1)$
$= P(X \le 2) - P(X \le 1)$
$= F(2) - F(1)$
$= \left(\frac{2}{3}(2) - \frac{1}{12}(2)^2 - \frac{1}{3}\right) - \frac{1}{3}(1)$
$= \left(\frac{4}{3} - \frac{1}{3} - \frac{1}{3}\right) - \frac{1}{3}$
$= \frac{1}{3}$

Remember... the different 'pieces' of a c.d.f. must join smoothly, so you can check your value of F(2) using the definition of F(x) for $0 \le x < 2$ (which is a slightly easier formula).

Q3 a) For $x < 0$, $F(x) = 0$ and for $x > 4$, $F(x) = 1$.
For $0 \le x \le 4$:
$F(x) = \int_{-\infty}^{x} f(t)\, dt = \int_{-\infty}^{0} f(t)\, dt + \int_{0}^{x} f(t)\, dt$
$= \int_{-\infty}^{0} 0\, dt + \int_{0}^{x} \frac{1}{8}t\, dt$
$= 0 + \left[\frac{t^2}{8 \times 2}\right]_{0}^{x} = \frac{x^2}{16}$

So
$F(x) = \begin{cases} 0 & x < 0 \\ \frac{x^2}{16} & 0 \le x \le 4 \\ 1 & x > 4 \end{cases}$

b) (i) $P(X < 1) = P(X \le 1) - F(1) = \frac{1^2}{16} = 0.0625$

(ii) $P(2 < X < 3) = P(X < 3) - P(X \le 2)$
$= P(X \le 3) - P(X \le 2)$
$= F(3) - F(2)$
$= \frac{3^2}{16} - \frac{2^2}{16} = \frac{5}{16} = 0.3125$

Q4 a) $\int \frac{1}{12}\,dx = \frac{1}{12}x + C_1$

b) The above integral equals F(x) for $0 \le x \le 1$.
So if F(0) = 0, then $C_1 = 0$.

c) $\int -\frac{1}{3}(1-x^3)\,dx = -\frac{1}{3}\left(x - \frac{x^4}{4}\right) + C_2$

$$= -\frac{x}{3} + \frac{x^4}{12} + C_2$$

d) The above integral equals F(x) for $1 < x \le 2$.
So if F(2) = 1, then

$$-\frac{2}{3} + \frac{2^4}{12} + C_2 = 1 \Rightarrow \frac{2}{3} + C_2 = 1 \Rightarrow C_2 = \frac{1}{3}$$

e)
$$F(x) = \begin{cases} 0 & x < 0 \\ \frac{1}{12}x & 0 \le x \le 1 \\ \frac{x^4}{12} - \frac{x}{3} + \frac{1}{3} & 1 < x \le 2 \\ 1 & x > 2 \end{cases}$$

f) (i) $P(X < 0.5) = F(0.5) = 0.5 \div 12 = \frac{1}{24}$
(ii) $P(X > 1.5) = 1 - P(X \le 1.5) = 1 - F(1.5)$
$= 1 - 0.2552... = 0.745$ (to 3 d.p.).

Q5 a) For $x < 0$, $F(x) = 0$ and for $x > 5$, $F(x) = 1$.
For $0 \le x < 3$:

$$F(x) = \int_{-\infty}^{x} f(t)\,dt = \int_{-\infty}^{0} f(t)\,dt + \int_{0}^{x} f(t)\,dt$$

$$= F(0) + \int_{0}^{x} \frac{1}{4}\,dt = 0 + \left[\frac{1}{4}t\right]_0^x = \frac{1}{4}x$$

This tells you that $F(3) = \frac{3}{4}$.
For $3 \le x \le 5$:

$$F(x) = \int_{-\infty}^{x} f(t)\,dt = \int_{-\infty}^{3} f(t)\,dt + \int_{3}^{x} f(t)\,dt$$

$$= F(3) + \int_{3}^{x} \frac{1}{8}(5-t)\,dt$$

$$= \frac{3}{4} + \left[\frac{1}{8}\left(5t - \frac{t^2}{2}\right)\right]_3^x$$

$$= \frac{3}{4} + \left[\frac{1}{8}\left(5x - \frac{x^2}{2}\right) - \frac{1}{8}\left(15 - \frac{9}{2}\right)\right]$$

$$= \frac{5x}{8} - \frac{x^2}{16} - \frac{9}{16}$$

When $x = 5$, $F(x) = \frac{25}{8} - \frac{25}{16} - \frac{9}{16} = 1$, so the pieces match up.
So
$$F(x) = \begin{cases} 0 & x < 0 \\ \frac{1}{4}x & 0 \le x < 3 \\ \frac{5x}{8} - \frac{x^2}{16} - \frac{9}{16} & 3 \le x \le 5 \\ 1 & x > 5 \end{cases}$$

b) (i) $P(X < 2) = P(X \le 2) = F(2) = \frac{1}{4}(2) = 0.5$
(ii) $P(X > 4) = 1 - P(X \le 4) = 1 - F(4)$
$= 1 - \left(\frac{5(4)}{8} - \frac{(4)^2}{16} - \frac{9}{16}\right) = \frac{1}{16} = 0.0625$
(iii) $P(1 \le X \le 3) = P(X \le 3) - P(X \le 1)$
$= F(3) - F(1) = \frac{1}{4}(3) - \frac{1}{4}(1) = 0.5$
(iv) $P(X = 4.5) = 0$
The probability of a continuous random variable taking any single value is 0.

3. Mean and Variance

Exercise 3.1 — Mean of a continuous random variable

Q1 a) $E(X) = \int_{-\infty}^{\infty} xf(x)\,dx = \int_0^2 x\left(1 - \frac{1}{2}x\right)dx$

$$= \int_0^2 \left(x - \frac{1}{2}x^2\right)dx = \left[\frac{x^2}{2} - \frac{x^3}{6}\right]_0^2$$

$$= \left(\frac{2^2}{2} - \frac{2^3}{6}\right) - \left(\frac{0^2}{2} - \frac{0^3}{6}\right) = \frac{2}{3}$$

b) $E(X) = \int_{-\infty}^{\infty} xf(x)\,dx = \int_0^2 x\left(\frac{1}{4}x^3\right)dx$

$$= \int_0^2 \frac{1}{4}x^4\,dx = \left[\frac{x^5}{20}\right]_0^2 = \frac{32}{20} = \frac{8}{5}$$

c) $E(X) = \int_{-\infty}^{\infty} xf(x)\,dx = \int_0^3 x\left(\frac{2}{9}(3x - x^2)\right)dx$

$$= \int_0^3 \left(\frac{2}{9}(3x^2 - x^3)\right)dx = \left[\frac{2}{9}\left(x^3 - \frac{x^4}{4}\right)\right]_0^3$$

$$= \left(\frac{2}{9}\left(3^3 - \frac{3^4}{4}\right)\right) - \left(\frac{2}{9}\left(0^3 - \frac{0^4}{4}\right)\right) = \frac{3}{2}$$

Q2 a) $\mu = E(X) = \int_{-\infty}^{\infty} xf(x)\,dx = \int_1^2 x\left(\frac{3}{7}x^2\right)dx$

$$= \int_1^2 \frac{3}{7}x^3\,dx = \left[\frac{3x^4}{28}\right]_1^2 = \frac{48}{28} - \frac{3}{28} = \frac{45}{28}$$

$$= 1.607 \text{ (3 d.p.)}$$

b) $E(2X - 1) = 2E(X) - 1 = 2\left(\frac{45}{28}\right) - 1$

$$= \frac{31}{14} = 2.214 \text{ (3 d.p.)}$$

c) $P(X < \mu) = P\left(X < \frac{45}{28}\right) = \int_1^{\frac{45}{28}} \frac{3}{7}x^2\,dx = \left[\frac{3x^3}{7 \times 3}\right]_1^{\frac{45}{28}}$

$$= \left[\frac{x^3}{7}\right]_1^{\frac{45}{28}} = \frac{\left(\frac{45}{28}\right)^3}{7} - \left(\frac{1^3}{7}\right) = 0.450 \text{ (3 d.p.)}$$

Q3 a) $\mu = E(X) = \int_{-\infty}^{\infty} xf(x)\,dx$

$$= \int_0^1 x\left(\frac{2}{5}\right)dx + \int_1^2 x\left(\frac{2}{5}x\right)dx$$

$$= \int_0^1 \frac{2}{5}x\,dx + \int_1^2 \frac{2}{5}x^2\,dx = \left[\frac{x^2}{5}\right]_0^1 + \left[\frac{2x^3}{15}\right]_1^2$$

$$= \left[\left(\frac{1^2}{5}\right) - \left(\frac{0^2}{5}\right)\right] + \left[\left(\frac{2(2)^3}{15}\right) - \left(\frac{2(1)^3}{15}\right)\right]$$

$$= \frac{1}{5} + \left[\frac{16}{15} - \frac{2}{15}\right] = \frac{1}{5} + \frac{14}{15} = \frac{17}{15} = 1.133 \text{ (3 d.p.)}$$

b) $E(4X + 2) = 4E(X) + 2 = 4\left(\frac{17}{15}\right) + 2$

$$= \frac{98}{15} = 6.533 \text{ (3 d.p.)}$$

Q4 a) $\mu = E(X) = \int_{-\infty}^{\infty} xf(x)\,dx$

$$= \int_0^1 x\left(\frac{1}{3}\right)dx + \int_1^2 x\left(-\frac{1}{2}(1 - x^2)\right)dx$$

$$= \int_0^1 \frac{x}{3}\,dx + \int_1^2 \left(-\frac{1}{2}x + \frac{1}{2}x^3\right)dx$$

$$= \left[\frac{x^2}{6}\right]_0^1 + \left[-\frac{x^2}{4} + \frac{x^4}{8}\right]_1^2$$

$$= \left[\left(\frac{1^2}{6}\right) - \left(\frac{0^2}{6}\right)\right] + \left[\left(-\frac{2^2}{4} + \frac{2^4}{8}\right) - \left(-\frac{1^2}{4} + \frac{1^4}{8}\right)\right]$$

$$= \frac{1}{6} + \left[1 + \frac{1}{8}\right]$$

$$= \frac{31}{24} = 1.292 \text{ (3 d.p.)}$$

b) $E(3X - 2) = 3E(X) - 2 = 3\left(\frac{31}{24}\right) - 2$

$= \frac{15}{8} = 1.875$

Q5 a) $\int_0^4 \frac{1}{4}x^2\,dx = \left[\frac{x^3}{12}\right]_0^4 = \left(\frac{4^3}{12}\right) - \left(\frac{0^3}{12}\right) = \frac{16}{3}$

b) $E(X) = \int_{-\infty}^{\infty} xf(x)\,dx = \int_0^4 x\left(\frac{1}{8}x\right)dx = \int_0^4 \frac{1}{8}x^2\,dx$

$= \frac{1}{2}\int_0^4 \frac{1}{4}x^2\,dx = \frac{1}{2}\left(\frac{16}{3}\right) = \frac{16}{6} = \frac{8}{3}$

Exercise 3.2 — Variance of a continuous random variable

Q1 a) Work out $E(X^2)$ first, as you've already worked out $E(X)$ in Exercise 3.1, Q1 part a): $E(X) = \frac{2}{3}$

$E(X^2) = \int_{-\infty}^{\infty} x^2f(x)\,dx = \int_0^2 x^2\left(1 - \frac{1}{2}x\right)dx$

$= \int_0^2 \left(x^2 - \frac{1}{2}x^3\right)dx = \left[\frac{x^3}{3} - \frac{x^4}{8}\right]_0^2$

$= \left(\frac{2^3}{3} - \frac{2^4}{8}\right) - \left(\frac{0^3}{3} - \frac{0^4}{8}\right) = \frac{2}{3}$

$Var(X) = E(X^2) - [E(X)]^2 = \frac{2}{3} - \left(\frac{2}{3}\right)^2 = \frac{2}{9}$

b) Work out $E(X^2)$ first, as you've already worked out $E(X)$ in Exercise 3.1, Q1 part b): $E(X) = \frac{8}{5}$

$E(X^2) = \int_{-\infty}^{\infty} x^2f(x)\,dx = \int_0^2 x^2\left(\frac{1}{4}x^3\right)dx$

$= \int_0^2 \frac{1}{4}x^5\,dx = \left[\frac{x^6}{24}\right]_0^2 = \frac{8}{3}$

$Var(X) = E(X^2) - [E(X)]^2 = \frac{8}{3} - \left(\frac{8}{5}\right)^2 = \frac{8}{75}$

c) Work out $E(X^2)$ first, as you've already worked out $E(X)$ in Exercise 3.1, Q1 part c): $E(X) = \frac{3}{2}$

$E(X^2) = \int_{-\infty}^{\infty} x^2f(x)\,dx = \int_0^3 x^2\left(\frac{2}{9}(3x - x^2)\right)dx$

$= \int_0^3 \left(\frac{2}{9}(3x^3 - x^4)\right)dx = \left[\frac{2}{9}\left(\frac{3x^4}{4} - \frac{x^5}{5}\right)\right]_0^3$

$= \left(\frac{2}{9}\left(\frac{3(3)^4}{4} - \frac{(3)^5}{5}\right)\right) - \left(\frac{2}{9}\left(\frac{3(0)^4}{4} - \frac{(0)^5}{5}\right)\right)$

$= \left(\frac{2}{9}\left(\frac{243}{4} - \frac{243}{5}\right)\right) - 0 = \frac{27}{10}$

$Var(X) = E(X^2) - [E(X)]^2 = \frac{27}{10} - \left(\frac{3}{2}\right)^2 = \frac{9}{20}$

Q2 a) In Exercise 3.1, Q2 a) you showed that $E(X) = \frac{45}{28}$.

$E(X^2) = \int_{-\infty}^{\infty} x^2f(x)\,dx = \int_1^2 x^2\left(\frac{3}{7}x^2\right)dx$

$= \int_1^2 \frac{3}{7}x^4\,dx = \left[\frac{3x^5}{35}\right]_1^2 = \frac{96}{35} - \frac{3}{35} = \frac{93}{35}$

$\sigma^2 = Var(X) = \frac{93}{35} - \left(\frac{45}{28}\right)^2 = \frac{291}{3920} = 0.074\ (3\ \text{d.p.})$

b) $Var(2X) = 2^2Var(X) = 4 \times \frac{291}{3920} = \frac{291}{980}$

$= 0.297\ (3\ \text{d.p.})$

c) $Var(2X + 1) = 2^2Var(X) = \frac{291}{980} = 0.297\ (3\ \text{d.p.})$

d) $\sigma = \sqrt{Var(X)} = \sqrt{\frac{291}{3920}} = 0.272\ (3\ \text{d.p.})$

Q3 a) In Exercise 3.1, Q3 a) you showed that $E(X) = \frac{17}{15}$.

$E(X^2) = \int_{-\infty}^{\infty} x^2f(x)\,dx$

$= \int_0^1 x^2\left(\frac{2}{5}\right)dx + \int_1^2 x^2\left(\frac{2}{5}x\right)dx$

$= \int_0^1 \frac{2}{5}x^2\,dx + \int_1^2 \frac{2}{5}x^3\,dx = \left[\frac{2x^3}{15}\right]_0^1 + \left[\frac{x^4}{10}\right]_1^2$

$= \frac{2}{15} + \left[\left(\frac{2^4}{10}\right) - \left(\frac{1^4}{10}\right)\right] = \frac{2}{15} + \frac{15}{10} = \frac{49}{30}$

So $Var(X) = \frac{49}{30} - \left(\frac{17}{15}\right)^2 = \frac{157}{450} = 0.349\ (3\ \text{d.p.})$

b) $Var(4X + 2) = 4^2Var(X) = 16 \times \frac{157}{450} = \frac{1256}{225}$

$= 5.582\ (3\ \text{d.p.})$

Q4 a) In Exercise 3.1, Q4 a) you showed that $E(X) = \frac{31}{24}$.

$E(X^2) = \int_{-\infty}^{\infty} x^2f(x)\,dx$

$= \int_0^1 x^2\left(\frac{1}{3}\right)dx + \int_1^2 x^2\left(-\frac{1}{2}(1 - x^2)\right)dx$

$= \int_0^1 \frac{x^2}{3}\,dx + \int_1^2 \left(-\frac{1}{2}x^2 + \frac{1}{2}x^4\right)dx$

$= \left[\frac{x^3}{9}\right]_0^1 + \left[-\frac{x^3}{6} + \frac{x^5}{10}\right]_1^2$

$= \frac{1}{9} + \left[\left(-\frac{2^3}{6} + \frac{2^5}{10}\right) - \left(-\frac{1^3}{6} + \frac{1^5}{10}\right)\right]$

$= \frac{1}{9} + \left[\left(-\frac{8}{6} + \frac{32}{10}\right) - \left(-\frac{1}{6} + \frac{1}{10}\right)\right]$

$= \frac{1}{9} + \left[\frac{28}{15} + \frac{1}{15}\right] = \frac{92}{45}$

So $Var(X) = \frac{92}{45} - \left(\frac{31}{24}\right)^2 = \frac{361}{960} = 0.376\ (3\ \text{d.p.})$.

b) $Var(-X) = (-1)^2Var(X) = Var(X) = \frac{361}{960}$

$= 0.376\ (3\ \text{d.p.})$.

c) $Var(3X + 2) = 3^2Var(X) = 9 \times \frac{361}{960} = \frac{1083}{320}$

$= 3.384\ (3\ \text{d.p.})$.

d) $\sigma = \sqrt{Var(X)} = \sqrt{\frac{361}{960}} = 0.613\ (3\ \text{d.p.})$.

4. Mode, Median and Quartiles

Exercise 4.1 — Finding the median and quartiles

Q1 a) Draw a sketch of the p.d.f.:

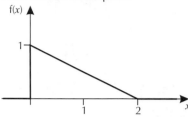

You can see from the graph that the mode is at $x = 0$, where the graph reaches its maximum.

b) Draw a sketch of the p.d.f.:

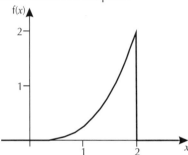

You can see from the graph that the mode is at $x = 2$, where the graph reaches its maximum.

Q2 a) The median is Q_2 where $F(Q_2) = 0.5$

$$\Rightarrow 1 + 3Q_2 = 0.5 \Rightarrow 3Q_2 = -0.5 \Rightarrow Q_2 = -\frac{1}{6}.$$

b) The lower quartile is Q_1 where $F(Q_1) = 0.25$.

$$\Rightarrow 1 + 3Q_1 = 0.25 \Rightarrow 3Q_1 = -0.75 \Rightarrow Q_1 = -\frac{1}{4}.$$

c) The upper quartile is Q_3 where $F(Q_3) = 0.75$.

$$\Rightarrow 1 + 3Q_3 = 0.75 \Rightarrow 3Q_3 = -0.25 \Rightarrow Q_3 = -\frac{1}{12}.$$

So the interquartile range is:
$$Q_3 - Q_1 = -\frac{1}{12} - (-\frac{1}{4}) = \frac{1}{6}.$$

Q3 Before you start working out the quartiles and median, work out the value of $F(x)$ at the end of each 'piece' to see which interval each quartile lies in.

$F(1) = \frac{2}{5} = 0.4$, so the lower quartile lies in $0 \leq x < 1$ and the median and upper quartile lie in $1 \leq x \leq 2$.

a) To find the median, Q_2, let $F(Q_2) = 0.5$.

$1 \leq Q_2 \leq 2$ so $\frac{1}{5}(Q_2^2 + 1) = 0.5 \Rightarrow Q_2^2 + 1 = 2.5$

$\Rightarrow Q_2^2 = 1.5 \Rightarrow Q_2 = \sqrt{1.5} = 1.225$ (3 d.p.).

b) The upper quartile, Q_3, is such that $F(Q_3) = 0.75$

$1 \leq Q_3 \leq 2$ so $\frac{1}{5}(Q_3^2 + 1) = 0.75 \Rightarrow Q_3^2 + 1 = 3.75$

$\Rightarrow Q_3^2 = 2.75 \Rightarrow Q_3 = \sqrt{2.75} = 1.658$ (3 d.p.).

c) $F(Q_1) = 0.25$ and $0 \leq Q_1 < 1$ so $\frac{2}{5}Q_1 = 0.25 \Rightarrow Q_1 = 0.625$.

So the interquartile range is
$Q_3 - Q_1 = 1.658... - 0.625 = 1.033$ (3 d.p.).

Q4 $F(1.56) = 0.496$ (3 d.p.)

$F(1.57) = 0.504$ (3 d.p.)

These are either side of 0.5, so the median lies between these two points.

Q5 a) For $x < 1$, $F(x) = 0$.

For $1 \leq x \leq 3$:

$$F(x) = \int_{-\infty}^{x} f(t)\,dt = \int_{-\infty}^{1} f(t)\,dt + \int_{1}^{x} f(t)\,dt$$

$$= F(1) + \int_{1}^{x} \frac{3}{34}(t^3 - t^2)\,dt = 0 + \left[\frac{3}{34}\left(\frac{t^4}{4} - \frac{t^3}{3}\right)\right]_{1}^{x}$$

$$= \left[\frac{3}{34}\left(\frac{x^4}{4} - \frac{x^3}{3}\right)\right] - \frac{3}{34}\left(\frac{1}{4} - \frac{1}{3}\right) = \frac{3}{34}\left(\frac{x^4}{4} - \frac{x^3}{3} + \frac{1}{12}\right)$$

When $x = 3$:

$F(x) = \frac{3}{34}\left(\frac{81}{4} - \frac{27}{3} + \frac{1}{12}\right) = \frac{3}{34}\left(\frac{34}{3}\right) = 1$,

so the pieces match up.

So

$$F(x) = \begin{cases} 0 & x < 1 \\ \frac{3}{34}\left(\frac{x^4}{4} - \frac{x^3}{3} + \frac{1}{12}\right) & 1 \leq x \leq 3 \\ 1 & x > 3 \end{cases}$$

b) $F(2.6) = 0.498$ (3 d.p.)

$F(2.7) = 0.601$ (3 d.p.)

These are either side of 0.5, so the median lies between these two points.

c) To find the median to one d.p., calculate $F(2.65) = 0.548$ (3 d.p.).

This means the median must be less than 2.65, and so $Q_2 = 2.6$ (to 1 d.p.)

Q6 a) For $x < 1$, $F(x) = 0$

For $1 \leq x \leq 3$:

$$F(x) = \int_{-\infty}^{x} f(t)\,dx = \int_{-\infty}^{1} f(t)\,dt + \int_{1}^{x} f(t)\,dt$$

$$= F(1) + \int_{1}^{x} \frac{1}{2}(3 - t)\,dt = 0 + \left[\frac{1}{2}\left(3t - \frac{t^2}{2}\right)\right]_{1}^{x}$$

$$= \frac{1}{2}\left(3x - \frac{x^2}{2}\right) - \frac{1}{2}\left(3 - \frac{1}{2}\right) = \frac{3x}{2} - \frac{x^2}{4} - \frac{5}{4}$$

$$= \frac{1}{4}(6x - x^2 - 5)$$

For $x = 3$, $F(3) = \frac{1}{4}(6(3) - (3)^2 - 5) = 1$

So the pieces match up and:

$$F(x) = \begin{cases} 0 & x < 1 \\ \frac{1}{4}(6x - x^2 - 5) & 1 \leq x \leq 3 \\ 1 & x > 3 \end{cases}$$

b) To find the median let $F(Q_2) = 0.5$

$\Rightarrow \frac{1}{4}(6Q_2 - Q_2^2 - 5) = 0.5$

$\Rightarrow 6Q_2 - Q_2^2 - 5 = 2$

$\Rightarrow 6Q_2 - Q_2^2 - 7 = 0$

$$\Rightarrow Q_2 = \frac{-6 \pm \sqrt{36 - (4 \times -1 \times -7)}}{-2}$$

$$= 3 \pm \sqrt{2} = 4.414 \text{ or } 1.586 \text{ (3 d.p.)}$$

The mode must be 1.586 as $1 \leq Q_2 \leq 3$.

c) To find the lower quartile, let $F(Q_1) = 0.25$

$\Rightarrow \frac{1}{4}(6Q_1 - Q_1^2 - 5) = 0.25$

$\Rightarrow 6Q_1 - Q_1^2 - 5 = 1$

$\Rightarrow 6Q_1 - Q_1^2 - 6 = 0$

$\Rightarrow Q_1 = \dfrac{-6 \pm \sqrt{36 - (4 \times -1 \times -6)}}{-2}$

$\qquad = 3 \pm \sqrt{3} = 4.7320...$ or $1.2679...$

$\qquad = 4.732$ or $1.268\,(3\,\text{d.p.})$

So the lower quartile is 1.268 since $1 \le Q_1 \le 3$.

To find the upper quartile, let $F(Q_3) = 0.75$

$\Rightarrow \frac{1}{4}(6Q_3 - Q_3^2 - 5) = 0.75$

$\Rightarrow 6Q_3 - Q_3^2 - 5 = 3$

$\Rightarrow 6Q_3 - Q_3^2 - 8 = 0$

$\Rightarrow Q_3 = \dfrac{-6 \pm \sqrt{36 - (4 \times -1 \times -8)}}{-2}$

$\qquad = 2\ \text{or}\ 4$

So the upper quartile is 2 since $1 \le Q_3 \le 3$.

So the interquartile range $Q_3 - Q_1$ is
$2 - 1.2679... = 0.732\ (3\ \text{d.p.})$

d) Draw a sketch of the p.d.f.

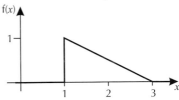

You can see from the graph that the mode is at $x = 1$.

e) The mean is:

$E(X) = \displaystyle\int_{-\infty}^{\infty} x\mathrm{f}(x)\,dx = \int_1^3 x\left(\frac{1}{2}(3 - x)\right)dx$

$\qquad = \displaystyle\int_1^3 \left(\frac{3x}{2} - \frac{x^2}{2}\right)dx = \left[\frac{3x^2}{4} - \frac{x^3}{6}\right]_1^3$

$\qquad = \left(\frac{27}{4} - \frac{27}{6}\right) - \left(\frac{3}{4} - \frac{1}{6}\right) = \frac{5}{3}$

Find $E(X^2)$ before finding the variance:

$E(X^2) = \displaystyle\int_{-\infty}^{\infty} x^2\mathrm{f}(x)\,dx = \int_1^3 x^2\left(\frac{1}{2}(3 - x)\right)dx$

$\qquad = \displaystyle\int_1^3 \left(\frac{3x^2}{2} - \frac{x^3}{2}\right)dx = \left[\frac{x^3}{2} - \frac{x^4}{8}\right]_1^3$

$\qquad = \left(\frac{3^3}{2} - \frac{3^4}{8}\right) - \left(\frac{1^3}{2} - \frac{1^4}{8}\right) = 3$

So the variance is $E(X^2) - [E(X)]^2 = 3 - \left(\frac{5}{3}\right)^2 = \frac{2}{9}$

f) $E(3X - 2) = 3E(X) - 2 = 3\left(\frac{5}{3}\right) - 2 = 3$

$\text{Var}(3X - 2) = 3^2\,\text{Var}(X) = 9 \times \frac{2}{9} = 2$

Review Exercise — Chapter 3

Q1 a) Sketch the p.d.f.:

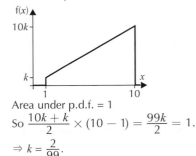

Area under p.d.f. = 1

So $\dfrac{10k + k}{2} \times (10 - 1) = \dfrac{99k}{2} = 1$.

$\Rightarrow k = \dfrac{2}{99}$.

b) Sketch the p.d.f.:

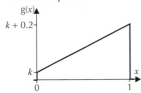

Area under p.d.f. = 1

So $\dfrac{2k + 0.2}{2} \times 1 = k + 0.1 = 1$.

$\Rightarrow k = 0.9$.

Q2 a) Sketch the p.d.f.:

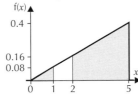

(i) Area under p.d.f. between $x = 0$ and $x = 1$ is:
$1 \times 0.08 \div 2 = 0.04$, so $P(X < 1) = 0.04$.

(ii) Area under p.d.f. between $x = 2$ and $x = 5$ is:
$\dfrac{0.16 + 0.4}{2} \times 3 = 0.84$
so $P(2 \le X \le 5) = 0.84$.

(iii) Area under p.d.f. at the point $x = 4$ is 0.
So $P(X = 4) = 0$.

b) Sketch the p.d.f.:

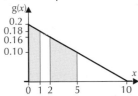

(i) Area under p.d.f. between $x = 0$ and $x = 1$ is:
$\dfrac{0.2 + 0.18}{2} \times 1 = 0.19$, so $P(X < 1) = 0.19$.

(ii) Area under p.d.f. between $x = 2$ and $x = 5$ is:
$\dfrac{0.16 + 0.1}{2} \times 3 = 0.39$
so $P(2 \le X \le 5) = 0.39$.

(iii) Area under p.d.f. at the point $x = 4$ is 0.
So $P(X = 4) = 0$.

Q3 a) $\int_{-\infty}^{\infty} f(x)dx = k\int_0^5 x^2 dx = k\left[\frac{x^3}{3}\right]_0^5 = \frac{125k}{3} = 1,$

so $k = \frac{3}{125}.$

$P(X < 1) = \int_0^1 \frac{3}{125}x^2 dx = \frac{3}{125}\left[\frac{x^3}{3}\right]_0^1 = \frac{1}{125}.$

b) $\int_{-\infty}^{\infty} g(x)dx = \int_0^2 (0.1x^2 + kx)dx$

$= \left[\frac{0.1x^3}{3} + \frac{kx^2}{2}\right]_0^2 = \frac{0.8}{3} + 2k = 1.$

So $k = \frac{1}{2} - \frac{0.4}{3} = \frac{15-4}{30} = \frac{11}{30}$

$P(X < 1) = \int_0^1 \left(0.1x^2 + \frac{11}{30}x\right)dx$

$= \left[\frac{0.1x^3}{3} + \frac{11x^2}{60}\right]_0^1$

$= \frac{0.1}{3} + \frac{11}{60} = \frac{13}{60}$

Q4 a) $\int_{-\infty}^{\infty} f(x)dx = \int_0^2 (0.1x^2 + 0.2)dx$

$= \left[\frac{0.1x^3}{3} + 0.2x\right]_0^2 = \frac{0.8}{3} + 0.4 \neq 1$

So f(x) is not a p.d.f.

b) g(x) < 0 for $-1 \leq x < 0$, so g(x) is not a p.d.f.

Q5 *We'll use the constant of integration method for a change here — see p.62 for a reminder.*

a) Integrate the pieces of the p.d.f., and then make sure the 'joins' are smooth using a suitable constant of integration (k).

$F(x) = \begin{cases} 0 \text{ for } x < 0 \\ 0.04x^2 + k \text{ for } 0 \leq x \leq 5 \\ 1 \text{ for } x > 5 \end{cases}$

Since F(0) = 0 and F(5) = 1, the pieces of this function join smoothly with k = 0.
So

$F(x) = \begin{cases} 0 \text{ for } x < 0 \\ 0.04x^2 \text{ for } 0 \leq x \leq 5 \\ 1 \text{ for } x > 5 \end{cases}$

b) Integrate the pieces of the p.d.f., and then make sure the 'joins' are smooth using a suitable constant of integration (k).

$G(x) = \begin{cases} 0 \text{ for } x < 0 \\ 0.2x - 0.01x^2 + k \text{ for } 0 \leq x \leq 10 \\ 1 \text{ for } x > 10 \end{cases}$

Since G(0) = 0 and G(10) = 1, the pieces of this function join smoothly with k = 0.
So

$G(x) = \begin{cases} 0 \text{ for } x < 0 \\ 0.2x - 0.01x^2 \text{ for } 0 \leq x \leq 10 \\ 1 \text{ for } x > 10 \end{cases}$

c) Integrate the pieces of the p.d.f., and then make sure the 'joins' are smooth using suitable constants of integration (k_1 - k_3).

$H(x) = \begin{cases} 0 \text{ for } x < 0 \\ x^2 + k_1 \text{ for } 0 \leq x \leq 0.5 \\ x + k_2 \text{ for } 0.5 \leq x \leq 1 \\ 3x - x^2 + k_3 \text{ for } 1 \leq x \leq 1.5 \\ 1 \text{ for } x > 1.5 \end{cases}$

H(0) = 0 means that $k_1 = 0$, which then gives H(0.5) = 0.25.
H(0.5) = 0.25 means that $k_2 = -0.25$, giving H(1) = 0.75.
H(1) = 0.75 means that $k_3 = -1.25$, giving H(1.5) = 1.
This means all the joins are now 'smooth'.
So

$H(x) = \begin{cases} 0 \text{ for } x < 0 \\ x^2 \text{ for } 0 \leq x \leq 0.5 \\ x - 0.25 \text{ for } 0.5 \leq x \leq 1 \\ 3x - x^2 - 1.25 \text{ for } 1 \leq x \leq 1.5 \\ 1 \text{ for } x > 1.5 \end{cases}$

d) Integrate the pieces of the p.d.f., and then make sure the 'joins' are smooth using suitable constants of integration (k_1 and k_2).

$M(x) = \begin{cases} 0 \text{ for } x < 2 \\ 0.5x - 0.05x^2 + k_1 \text{ for } 2 \leq x \leq 4 \\ 0.1x + k_2 \text{ for } 4 \leq x \leq 10 \\ 1 \text{ for } x > 10 \end{cases}$

M(2) = 0 means that $k_1 = -0.8$, which gives M(4) = 0.4.
M(4) = 0.4 means that $k_2 = 0$, which gives M(10) = 1.
This means all the joins are now 'smooth'.
So

$M(x) = \begin{cases} 0 \text{ for } x < 2 \\ 0.5x - 0.05x^2 - 0.8 \text{ for } 2 \leq x \leq 4 \\ 0.1x \text{ for } 4 \leq x \leq 10 \\ 1 \text{ for } x > 10 \end{cases}$

Q6 a) Differentiate the different parts of the c.d.f.:

$f(x) = \begin{cases} 4x^3 \text{ for } 0 \leq x \leq 1 \\ 0 \text{ otherwise} \end{cases}$

b)

$g(x) = \begin{cases} \frac{1}{50}(x - 1) \text{ for } 1 \leq x < 6 \\ \frac{3}{8} \text{ for } 6 \leq x \leq 8 \\ 0 \text{ otherwise} \end{cases}$

Q7

$$E(X) = \int_{-\infty}^{\infty} xf(x)\,dx$$

$$= \int_1^2 x\left(\tfrac{2}{3}(x-1)\right)dx + \int_2^3 x\left(\tfrac{2}{3}\right)dx$$

$$= \int_1^2 \tfrac{2}{3}(x^2 - x)\,dx + \int_2^3 \tfrac{2}{3}x\,dx$$

$$= \left[\tfrac{2x^3}{9} - \tfrac{x^2}{3}\right]_1^2 + \left[\tfrac{1}{3}x^2\right]_2^3$$

$$= \left(\tfrac{2(2)^3}{9} - \tfrac{(2)^2}{3}\right) - \left(\tfrac{2(1)^3}{9} - \tfrac{(1)^2}{3}\right)$$

$$+ \left(\tfrac{1}{3}(3)^2\right) - \left(\tfrac{1}{3}(2)^2\right)$$

$$= \tfrac{4}{9} - \left(-\tfrac{1}{9}\right) + 3 - \tfrac{4}{3} = \tfrac{20}{9}$$

Q8 a)

$$E(X) = \int_{-\infty}^{\infty} xf(x)\,dx = \int_0^5 0.08x^2\,dx = 0.08\left[\tfrac{x^3}{3}\right]_0^5$$

$$= \tfrac{125 \times 0.08}{3} = \tfrac{10}{3}$$

$$Var(X) = \int_{-\infty}^{\infty} x^2 f(x)\,dx - \mu^2$$

$$= \int_0^5 0.08x^3\,dx - \left(\tfrac{10}{3}\right)^2$$

$$= 0.08\left[\tfrac{x^4}{4}\right]_0^5 - \left(\tfrac{10}{3}\right)^2 = \tfrac{625 \times 0.08}{4} - \left(\tfrac{10}{3}\right)^2$$

$$= \tfrac{25}{2} - \left(\tfrac{10}{3}\right)^2 = \tfrac{25}{18} = 1.39 \text{ (to 2 d.p.)}.$$

$$E(Y) = \int_{-\infty}^{\infty} yg(y)\,dy = \int_0^{10} 0.02y(10-y)\,dy$$

$$= 0.02\left[5y^2 - \tfrac{y^3}{3}\right]_0^{10}$$

$$= 0.02\left(500 - \tfrac{1000}{3}\right) = 10 - \tfrac{20}{3} = \tfrac{10}{3}$$

$$Var(Y) = \int_{-\infty}^{\infty} y^2 g(y)\,dy - \mu^2$$

$$= \int_0^{10} 0.02y^2(10-y)\,dy - \left(\tfrac{10}{3}\right)^2$$

$$= 0.02\left[\tfrac{10y^3}{3} - \tfrac{y^4}{4}\right]_0^{10} - \left(\tfrac{10}{3}\right)^2$$

$$= 0.02 \times \left(\tfrac{10\,000}{3} - \tfrac{10\,000}{4}\right) - \left(\tfrac{10}{3}\right)^2$$

$$= \tfrac{50}{3} - \left(\tfrac{10}{3}\right)^2 = \tfrac{50}{9} = 5.56 \text{ (to 2 d.p.)}.$$

b)

$$E(4X+2) = 4E(X) + 2 = 4 \times \tfrac{10}{3} + 2 = \tfrac{46}{3}$$

$$E(3Y-4) = 3E(Y) - 4 = 3 \times \tfrac{10}{3} - 4 = 6$$

$$Var(4X+2) = 4^2 \times Var(X)$$

$$= 16 \times \tfrac{25}{18} = \tfrac{200}{9} = 22.22 \text{ (to 2 d.p.)}.$$

$$Var(3Y-4) = 3^2 \times Var(Y) = 9 \times \tfrac{50}{9} = 50$$

c) Sketch the p.d.f.:

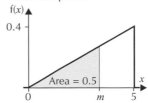

The mode is the value of x where the p.d.f. reaches its maximum, so mode = 5.
The median is Q_2, where:

$$\int_0^{Q_2} 0.08x\,dx = 0.08\left[\tfrac{x^2}{2}\right]_0^{Q_2} = 0.04Q_2^2 = 0.5$$

So the median = $\sqrt{12.5}$ = 3.54 (to 2 d.p.).

You usually work out the median by finding F(x), and then solving F(Q₂) = 0.5, but you haven't been asked to find F(x) here, so just use the integral because by definition $F(Q_2) = \int_{-\infty}^{Q_2} f(x)\,dx$.

d) The lower quartile is Q_1, where:

$$\int_0^{Q_1} 0.08x\,dx = 0.08\left[\tfrac{x^2}{2}\right]_0^{Q_1} = 0.04Q_1^2 = 0.25$$

So $Q_1 = \sqrt{6.25} = 2.5$.
The upper quartile is Q_3, where:

$$\int_0^{Q_3} 0.08x\,dx = 0.08\left[\tfrac{x^2}{2}\right]_0^{Q_3} = 0.04Q_3^2 = 0.75$$

So $Q_3 = \sqrt{18.75}$.
This means the interquartile range is:
$\sqrt{18.75} - 2.5 = 1.83$ (to 2 d.p.).

Q9 a) You need the total area to be 1, so integrate:

$$\int_{-\infty}^{\infty} f(x)\,dx = \int_1^2 k(x^2 - 3x)\,dx = \left[k\left(\tfrac{x^3}{3} - \tfrac{3x^2}{2}\right)\right]_1^2$$

$$= k\left(\tfrac{2^3}{3} - \tfrac{3(2)^2}{2}\right) - k\left(\tfrac{1^3}{3} - \tfrac{3(1)^2}{2}\right)$$

$$= k\left(\tfrac{8}{3} - \tfrac{12}{2} - \tfrac{1}{3} + \tfrac{3}{2}\right) = -\tfrac{13}{6}k$$

So $-\tfrac{13}{6}k = 1 \Rightarrow k = -\tfrac{6}{13}$.
This p.d.f. is non-negative between 1 and 2, so it is valid.

b) For $x < 1$, $F(x) = 0$.

For $1 \leq x \leq 2$:

$$F(x) = \int_{-\infty}^{x} f(t)\,dt = \int_{-\infty}^{1} f(t)\,dt + \int_{1}^{x} f(t)\,dt$$

$$= F(1) + \int_{1}^{x} -\frac{6}{13}(t^2 - 3t)\,dt$$

$$= 0 + \left[-\frac{6}{13}\left(\frac{t^3}{3} - \frac{3t^2}{2}\right) \right]_{1}^{x}$$

$$= -\frac{6}{13}\left(\frac{x^3}{3} - \frac{3x^2}{2}\right) - \left(-\frac{6}{13}\left(\frac{1}{3} - \frac{3}{2}\right)\right)$$

$$= -\frac{1}{13}\left(\frac{6x^3}{3} - \frac{18x^2}{2}\right) - \frac{7}{13}$$

$$= -\frac{1}{13}(2x^3 - 9x^2 + 7)$$

So, $F(2) = -\frac{1}{13}(2(2)^3 - 9(2)^2 + 7) = 1$.

So the pieces join up and

$$F(x) = \begin{cases} 0 & x < 1 \\ -\frac{1}{13}(2x^3 - 9x^2 + 7) & 1 \leq x \leq 2 \\ 1 & x > 2 \end{cases}$$

c) $F(1.5) = -\frac{1}{13}(2(1.5)^3 - 9(1.5)^2 + 7) = 0.5$

So the median is 1.5.

d) $F(1.2) = 0.193$ (3 d.p.), $F(1.3) = 0.294$ (3 d.p.)
So Q_1, where $F(Q_1) = 0.25$, lies between 1.2 and 1.3.

$F(1.7) = 0.706$ (3 d.p.), $F(1.8) = 0.807$ (3 d.p.)
So Q_3, where $F(Q_3) = 0.75$, lies between 1.7 and 1.8.

e) $F(1.25) = 0.243$ (3 d.p.) so $Q_1 = 1.3$ to 1 d.p.
$F(1.75) = 0.757$ (3 d.p.) so $Q_3 = 1.7$ to 1 d.p.

Exam-Style Questions — Chapter 3

1 a) $\int_{-\infty}^{\infty} f(x)\,dx = \frac{1}{k}\int_{0}^{2}(x + 4)\,dx$

$$= \frac{1}{k}\left[\frac{x^2}{2} + 4x\right]_{0}^{2} = \frac{10}{k} \ \textbf{\textit{[1 mark]}}$$

This must be equal to 1 **[1 mark]**.

So $k = 10$ **[1 mark]**.

b) Integrate the pieces of the p.d.f., and then make sure the 'joins' are smooth using a constant of integration (k).
[1 mark].

$$F(x) = \begin{cases} 0 \ \text{for} \ x < 0 \\ 0.05x^2 + 0.4x + k \ \text{for} \ 0 \leq x \leq 2 \\ 1 \ \text{for} \ x > 2 \end{cases}$$

[1 mark for each part correctly found]

All the joins are 'smooth' if $k = 0$, so the c.d.f. is:

$$F(x) = \begin{cases} 0 \ \text{for} \ x < 0 \\ 0.05x^2 + 0.4x \ \text{for} \ 0 \leq x \leq 2 \\ 1 \ \text{for} \ x > 2 \end{cases}$$

[1 mark for final answer]

You must define a c.d.f. for all values of x. Don't just do the tricky bits in the middle and assume you're finished.

c) $E(X) = \int_{-\infty}^{\infty} xf(x)\,dx$

$$= \int_{0}^{2} 0.1(x^2 + 4x)\,dx \ \textbf{\textit{[1 mark]}}$$

$$= 0.1\left[\frac{x^3}{3} + 2x^2\right]_{0}^{2} \ \textbf{\textit{[1 mark]}}$$

$$= 0.1\left(\frac{8}{3} + 8\right) = \frac{32}{30} = \frac{16}{15}$$

$$= 1.067 \ \text{(to 3 d.p.)} \ \textbf{\textit{[1 mark]}}$$

d) (i) $Var(X) = \int_{-\infty}^{\infty} x^2 f(x)\,dx - \mu^2$

$$= 0.1\int_{0}^{2}(x^3 + 4x^2)\,dx - \left(\frac{16}{15}\right)^2 \ \textbf{\textit{[1 mark]}}$$

$$= 0.1\left[\frac{x^4}{4} + \frac{4x^3}{3}\right]_{0}^{2} - \left(\frac{16}{15}\right)^2 \ \textbf{\textit{[1 mark]}}$$

$$= 0.1\left(4 + \frac{32}{3}\right) - \left(\frac{16}{15}\right)^2$$

$$= \frac{22}{15} - \left(\frac{16}{15}\right)^2 = \frac{74}{225}$$

$$= 0.329 \ \text{(to 3 d.p.)}. \ \textbf{\textit{[1 mark]}}$$

(ii) $Var(4X - 2) = 4^2 \times Var(X)$ **[1 mark]**

$$= 16 \times \frac{74}{225} = 5.262 \ \text{(to 3 d.p.)}. \ \textbf{\textit{[1 mark]}}$$

e) Use the c.d.f. from part b) to find the median.
The median is Q_2,
where $0.05Q_2^2 + 0.4Q_2 = 0.5$ **[1 mark]**.
This simplifies to: $Q_2^2 + 8Q_2 - 10 = 0$ **[1 mark]**.
Using the quadratic formula (and choosing the positive answer **[1 mark]**) gives

$$Q_2 = \frac{-8 + \sqrt{104}}{2} = 1.099 \ \text{(to 3 d.p.)} \ \textbf{\textit{[1 mark]}}.$$

f) The mode is at the highest point of the p.d.f. within the range of possible values. Since $f(x)$ has a positive gradient, this must be at the greatest possible value of x, so the mode of X is 2
[1 mark].

2 a)

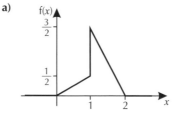

[1 mark]

b) From the graph, the maximum of $f(x)$ is at $x = 1$ so the mode of X is 1 **[1 mark]**.

c) Integrate the pieces of the p.d.f., and then make sure the 'joins' are smooth using constants of integration (k_1 and k_2).
[1 mark].

$$F(x) = \begin{cases} 0 & x < 0 \\ \dfrac{x^2}{4} + k_1 & 0 \le x < 1 \\ -\dfrac{3x^2}{4} + 3x + k_2 & 1 \le x \le 2 \\ 1 & x > 2 \end{cases}$$

[1 mark for each part correctly found]

All the joins are 'smooth' if $k_1 = 0$ and $k_2 = -2$, so the c.d.f. is:

$$F(x) = \begin{cases} 0 & x < 0 \\ \dfrac{x^2}{4} & 0 \le x < 1 \\ -\dfrac{3x^2}{4} + 3x - 2 & 1 \le x \le 2 \\ 1 & x > 2 \end{cases}$$

[1 mark for final answer]

d) $F(1) = \dfrac{1}{4} = 0.25$, so the lower quartile is $Q_1 = 1$ *[1 mark]*.

The upper quartile lies in $1 < Q_3 \le 2$, so let $F(Q_3) = 0.75$ *[1 mark]*.

$$\Rightarrow -\frac{3Q_3^2}{4} + 3Q_3 - 2 = 0.75$$

$$\Rightarrow -\frac{3Q_3^2}{4} + 3Q_3 - \frac{11}{4} = 0$$

$$\Rightarrow -3Q_3^2 + 12Q_3 - 11 = 0$$

$$\Rightarrow Q_3 = \frac{-12 \pm \sqrt{144 - (4 \times -3 \times -11)}}{-6}$$

$$= \frac{6 \pm \sqrt{3}}{3} = 1.423 \text{ or } 2.577 \ (3 \text{ d.p.}) \ [1 \ mark]$$

So the upper quartile is $Q_3 = 1.423$ (3 d.p.) (2.577 is too big) *[1 mark]*.

So the interquartile range is $Q_3 - Q_1 = 1.423 - 1 = 0.423$ (3 d.p.) *[1 mark]*.

3 a) Using the third part of the c.d.f., $F(3) = 0.5$ *[1 mark]*.
So $F(3)$ must also equal 0.5 using the second part of the c.d.f., which means that $2k = 0.5$, or $k = 0.25$ *[1 mark]*.

b) Q_1 is given by $F(Q_1) = 0.25$ *[1 mark]*.
Since $F(3) = 0.5$, the lower quartile must lie in the region described by the second part of the c.d.f., so solve $0.25(Q_1 - 1) = 0.25$, or $Q_1 = 2$ *[1 mark]*.

Q_3 is given by $F(Q_3) = 0.75$ *[1 mark]*. Since $F(3) = 0.5$, the upper quartile must lie in the region described by the third part of the c.d.f., so solve $0.5(Q_3 - 2) = 0.75$, or $Q_3 = 3.5$ *[1 mark]*.

So the interquartile range is $3.5 - 2 = 1.5$ *[1 mark]*.

c) (i) Differentiate to find the p.d.f.:

$$f(x) = \begin{cases} 0.25 & \text{for } 1 \le x < 3 \ [1 \ mark] \\ 0.5 & \text{for } 3 \le x \le 4 \ [1 \ mark] \\ 0 & \text{otherwise } [1 \ mark] \end{cases}$$

(ii)

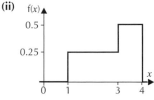

[1 mark]

d) (i) $\mu = \displaystyle\int_{-\infty}^{\infty} xf(x)\,dx$

$$= \int_1^3 0.25x\,dx + \int_3^4 0.5x\,dx \ [1 \ mark]$$

$$= [0.125x^2]_1^3 + [0.25x^2]_3^4 \ [1 \ mark]$$

$$= 1 + \frac{7}{4} = \frac{11}{4} = 2.75 \ [1 \ mark]$$

(ii) $\text{Var}(X) = \sigma^2 = \displaystyle\int_{-\infty}^{\infty} x^2 f(x)\,dx - \mu^2$

$$= \int_1^3 0.25x^2\,dx + \int_3^4 0.5x^2\,dx - 2.75^2 \ [1 \ mark]$$

$$= \left[\frac{0.25x^3}{3}\right]_1^3 + \left[\frac{0.5x^3}{3}\right]_3^4 - 2.75^2 \ [1 \ mark]$$

$$= \frac{13}{6} + \frac{37}{6} - \left(\frac{11}{4}\right)^2 = \frac{25}{3} - \frac{121}{16}$$

$$= \frac{37}{48} = 0.771 \text{(to 3 d.p.)} \ [1 \ mark].$$

(iii) $P(X < \mu - \sigma) = P\left(X < 2.75 - \sqrt{\dfrac{37}{48}}\right)$
$= P(X < 1.872)$ *[1 mark]*.
Using the above sketch, the area under the p.d.f. between $x = 1$ and $x = 1.872$ is:
$(1.872 - 1) \times 0.25 = 0.218$ (to 3 d.p.) *[1 mark]*.

4 a) $P(0.25 \le X \le 0.75)$
$= P(X \le 0.75) - P(X \le 0.25)$ *[1 mark]*
$= F(0.75) - F(0.25) = \dfrac{27}{32} - \dfrac{5}{32}$
$= \dfrac{11}{16} = 0.6875$ *[1 mark]*

b) $F(0.67) = 0.745$ (3 d.p.) *[1 mark]* and $F(0.68) = 0.758$ (3 d.p.) *[1 mark]*, so the upper quartile Q_3, where $F(Q_3) = 0.75$, is between 0.67 and 0.68 *[1 mark]*.

c) $F(0.5) = 3(0.5)^2 - 2(0.5)^3$ *[1 mark]*
$= 0.75 - 0.25 = 0.5$ *[1 mark]*.

d) (i) Differentiate each bit to find the p.d.f.
[1 mark]

$$f(x) = \begin{cases} 6x - 6x^2 & 0 \le x \le 1 \\ 0 & \text{otherwise} \end{cases}$$

[1 mark for correct p.d.f.]

(ii)

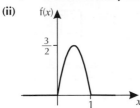

[1 mark]

e)
$$\mu = E(X) = \int_{-\infty}^{\infty} x f(x)\, dx$$
$$= \int_{0}^{1} x(6x - 6x^2)\, dx \ \textit{[1 mark]}$$
$$= \int_{0}^{1} (6x^2 - 6x^3)\, dx = \left[2x^3 - \frac{3}{2}x^4\right]_{0}^{1} \textit{[1 mark]}$$
$$= 2 - \frac{3}{2} = \frac{1}{2} \ \textit{[1 mark]}$$

Chapter 4: Continuous Distributions

1. The Continuous Uniform Distribution

Exercise 1.1 — Continuous uniform distributions

Q1 a) $a = 2$ and $b = 7$, so $\dfrac{1}{b - a} = \dfrac{1}{5} = 0.2$

$\Rightarrow f(x) = \begin{cases} 0.2 & \text{for } 2 \le x \le 7 \\ 0 & \text{otherwise} \end{cases}$

A sketch of the p.d.f. looks like this:

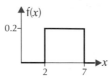

b) $a = -0.5$ and $b = 1.5$, so $\dfrac{1}{b - a} = \dfrac{1}{2} = 0.5$

$\Rightarrow f(x) = \begin{cases} 0.5 & \text{for } -0.5 \le x \le 1.5 \\ 0 & \text{otherwise} \end{cases}$

A sketch of the p.d.f. looks like this:

c) $a = \dfrac{1}{3}$ and $b = 1$, so $\dfrac{1}{b - a} = \dfrac{3}{2} = 1.5$

$\Rightarrow f(x) = \begin{cases} 1.5 & \text{for } \frac{1}{3} \le x \le 1 \\ 0 & \text{otherwise} \end{cases}$

A sketch of the p.d.f. looks like this:

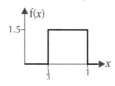

d) $a = 1$ and $b = 100$, so $\dfrac{1}{b - a} = \dfrac{1}{99}$

$\Rightarrow f(x) = \begin{cases} \frac{1}{99} & \text{for } 1 \le x \le 100 \\ 0 & \text{otherwise} \end{cases}$

A sketch of the p.d.f. looks like this:

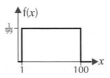

Q2 a) Using the definition of f(x):

$$\frac{1}{b-a} = 0.25 \Rightarrow \frac{1}{k-(-3)} = 0.25$$

$$\Rightarrow \frac{1}{k+3} = 0.25 \Rightarrow k+3 = 4 \Rightarrow k = 1$$

b) Using the definition of f(x):

$$\frac{1}{b-a} = \frac{5}{8} \Rightarrow \frac{1}{7-k} = \frac{5}{8}$$

$$\Rightarrow 7-k = 1.6 \Rightarrow k = 5.4$$

Do these by drawing a sketch if you find it's easier.

Q3 a) Area under f(x) = 1 $\Rightarrow$ (k – 3) × 1 = 1
$\Rightarrow$ k – 3 = 1 $\Rightarrow$ k = 4
So X ~ U[3, 4]

b) Area under f(x) = 1 $\Rightarrow$ (1 – k) × 0.2 = 1
$\Rightarrow$ 1 – k = 5 $\Rightarrow$ k = –4
So X ~ U[–4, 1]

Q4 Y represents the weight of the heavier piece, so it takes values between 400 g and 800 g.
If it weighed less than 400 g, it'd be the lighter piece.

The weight is equally likely to be anywhere within this interval, so Y ~ U[400, 800].

Q5 Since Fred leaves his house at a random time, the time he has to wait for his train is equally likely to be anywhere between 0 minutes and 15 minutes, so T ~ U[0, 15].

Q6 a) The diameter is equally likely to be anywhere between 5.9 cm and 6.3 cm, so D ~ U[5.9, 6.3].

b) $f(x) = \begin{cases} 2.5 & \text{for } 5.9 \le x \le 6.3 \\ 0 & \text{otherwise} \end{cases}$

A sketch of the p.d.f. looks like this:

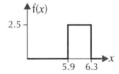

Exercise 1.2 — Finding probabilities

Q1 It's a good idea to sketch the p.d.f.

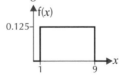

a) P(X > 5) = (9 – 5) × 0.125 = 0.5
b) P(2 < X < 7) = (7 – 2) × 0.125 = 0.625
c) P(X ≤ 2.4) = (2.4 – 1) × 0.125 = 0.175

Q2 Sketch the p.d.f.

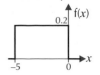

a) P(X ≥ –3) = (0 – (–3)) × 0.2 = 0.6
b) P(–2.4 ≤ X ≤ –1.2) = (–1.2 – (–2.4)) × 0.2 = 0.24
c) P(X > –6) = 1
X can only take values in the range –5 to 0, so it's certain to take a value greater than –6.

Q3 Sketch the p.d.f.

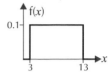

a) P(X > 7) = (13 – 7) × 0.1 = 0.6
b) P(4 < X < 11) = (11 – 4) × 0.1 = 0.7
c) P(X ≥ 10.1) = (13 – 10.1) × 0.1 = 0.29

Q4 Sketching what you know will really help here:

Since the area above x = 3 is 0.5, the area below x = 3 must also be 0.5. So the distribution is symmetrical about x = 3.
This means that k = 3 + 1 = 4.
Or you could use the fact that the area between x = 2 and x = 3 is 0.5 to find the height of the rectangle. Then use height × (k – 3) = 0.5 to find k.

Q5 a) Again, start by sketching what you know.

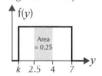

So height of rectangle = 0.25 ÷ (4 – 2.5)
= 0.25 ÷ 1.5
$= \frac{1}{4} \div \frac{3}{2} = \frac{1}{4} \times \frac{2}{3} = \frac{1}{6}$

Which means:

$$(7-k) \times \frac{1}{6} = 1$$

$$\Rightarrow 7-k = 6$$

$$\Rightarrow k = 1$$

b) Y ~ U[1, 7], so Z ~ U[(2 × 1 + 1), (2 × 7 + 1)]
$\Rightarrow$ Z ~ U[3, 15]

The p.d.f. of Z is a rectangle with a width of 12 and a height of $\frac{1}{12}$.

So P(Z < 6) = $(6-3) \times \frac{1}{12} = \frac{3}{12} = \frac{1}{4} = 0.25$

Q6 $X \sim U[2, 7]$ and $Y \sim U[4, 5]$.

For X: $\frac{1}{b-a} = \frac{1}{7-2} = \frac{1}{5} = 0.2$

For Y: $\frac{1}{b-a} = \frac{1}{5-4} = 1$

So a sketch of both p.d.f.s looks like this:

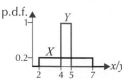

X and Y are independent, so: P($X > 4.5$ and $Y > 4.5$)
= P($X > 4.5$) × P($Y > 4.5$)
= [0.2 × (7 – 4.5)] × [1 × (5 – 4.5)]
= 0.5 × 0.5
= 0.25

Q7 a) The heights are correct to the nearest cm, so the error could be anywhere between –0.5 cm and 0.5 cm. It's equally likely to be anywhere within this interval, so $X \sim U[-0.5, 0.5]$.

b) The p.d.f. of X is a rectangle with a width of (0.5 – (–0.5)) = 1 and therefore a height of $1 \div 1 = 1$.
So P($X > 0.1$) = (0.5 – 0.1) × 1 = 0.4.

Q8 a) The weights are correct to the nearest 0.25 g, so the error could be anywhere between –0.125 g and 0.125 g. It's equally likely to be anywhere within this interval, so $X \sim U[-0.125, 0.125]$.

b) The probability that the recorded weight is inaccurate by at least 0.1 g is given by:
P($X < -0.1$ or $X > 0.1$).
The p.d.f. of X is a rectangle with a width of (0.125 – (–0.125)) = 0.25 and therefore a height of $1 \div 0.25 = 4$.
So P($X > 0.1$) = (0.125 – 0.1) × 4 = 0.1 and, by symmetry, P($X < -0.1$) is also 0.1.
So, P($X < -0.1$ or $X > 0.1$) = 0.1 + 0.1 = 0.2
'X > 0.1' and 'X < −0.1' are mutually exclusive events, so to find the probability of one or the other happening, you add the individual probabilities.

c) Assuming that the errors in the recorded weights of the two chocolate bars are independent of each other, this probability = 0.2 × 0.2 = 0.04.

Exercise 1.3 — The mean and variance

Q1 a) $E(X) = \frac{1+7}{2} = \frac{8}{2} = 4$.

b) $E(X) = \frac{0 + \frac{1}{3}}{2} = \frac{\left(\frac{1}{3}\right)}{2} = \frac{1}{6}$.

c) $E(X) = \frac{-24 + (-6)}{2} = \frac{-30}{2} = -15$.

Q2 a) $\text{Var}(X) = \frac{(5-2)^2}{12} = \frac{9}{12} = \frac{3}{4}$

b) $\text{Var}(X) = \frac{(0.75 - (-0.25))^2}{12} = \frac{1}{12}$

c) $\text{Var}(X) = \frac{(-18 - (-30))^2}{12} = \frac{144}{12} = 12$

Q3 The continuous random variable $X \sim U[3.9, 6.4]$.

$E(X) = \frac{3.9 + 6.4}{2} = 5.15$

$\text{Var}(X) = \frac{(6.4 - 3.9)^2}{12} = \frac{25}{48} = 0.521$ (3 d.p.)

Q4 The continuous random variable $X \sim U[1.7, 4.1]$.

$E(X) = \frac{1.7 + 4.1}{2} = 2.9$

$\text{Var}(X) = \frac{(4.1 - 1.7)^2}{12} = 0.48$

Q5 a) $E(X) = \frac{13 + 17}{2} = 15$

$\text{Var}(X) = \frac{(17 - 13)^2}{12} = \frac{4}{3} = 1.333$ (3 d.p.)

b) $Y \sim U[(2 \times 13) - 9, (2 \times 17) - 9] = U[17, 25]$

$E(Y) = \frac{17 + 25}{2} = 21$

$\text{Var}(Y) = \frac{(25 - 17)^2}{12} = \frac{16}{3} = 5.333$ (3 d.p.)

Or you could say E(Y) = 2E(X) – 9, and Var(Y) = 2²Var(X).

Q6 $E(X) = \frac{3 + k}{2} = 4.5 \Rightarrow 3 + k = 9 \Rightarrow k = 6$.

Q7 a) X represents the error in a measurement to the nearest 10 g. The error in the measurement could be anywhere from –5 g to 5 g. So $X \sim U[-5, 5]$.

b) $E(X) = \frac{-5 + 5}{2} = 0$

$\text{Var}(X) = \frac{(5 - (-5))^2}{12} = \frac{100}{12} = 8.333$ (3 d.p.)

Exercise 1.4 — The cumulative distribution function

Q1 a) $\frac{1}{b-a} = \frac{1}{19-15} = \frac{1}{4} = 0.25$.

So $f(x) = \begin{cases} 0.25 & 15 \leq X \leq 19 \\ 0 & \text{otherwise} \end{cases}$

b) To find the c.d.f., work out $\frac{x-a}{b-a} = \frac{x-15}{4}$

So $F(x) = \begin{cases} 0 & x < 15 \\ \dfrac{x-15}{4} & 15 \leq x \leq 19 \\ 1 & x > 19 \end{cases}$

c) $F(16) = \frac{16 - 15}{4} = \frac{1}{4}$.

Q2 a) $a = 2$ and $b = 10$.

To find the c.d.f., find $\dfrac{x - a}{b - a} = \dfrac{x - 2}{8}$.

So $F(x) = \begin{cases} 0 & x < 2 \\ \dfrac{x - 2}{8} & 2 \le x \le 10 \\ 1 & x > 10 \end{cases}$

b) $P(X < 8.4) = P(X \le 8.4)$

$= F(8.4) = \dfrac{8.4 - 2}{8} = \dfrac{6.4}{8} = 0.8$

Q3 a) $P(X < 24) = P(X \le 24) = F(24) = \dfrac{24 - 22}{7} = \dfrac{2}{7}$

b) To find the p.d.f., differentiate the c.d.f.

For $x < 22$, $f(x) = \dfrac{d}{dx}(0) = 0$

For $22 \le x \le 29$, $f(x) = \dfrac{d}{dx}\left(\dfrac{x - 22}{7}\right) = \dfrac{1}{7}$

For $x > 29$, $f(x) = \dfrac{d}{dx}(1) = 0$

So $f(x) = \begin{cases} \dfrac{1}{7} & 22 \le x \le 29 \\ 0 & \text{otherwise} \end{cases}$

Q4 You can see from how the c.d.f. is defined that $a = 1.7$ and $b = 1.9$.

So $E(X) = \dfrac{1.7 + 1.9}{2} = 1.8$

and $\text{Var}(X) = \dfrac{(1.9 - 1.7)^2}{12} = \dfrac{1}{300}$

Q5 $E(X) = \dfrac{a + b}{2} = 11 \Rightarrow a + b = 22$

$\text{Var}(X) = \dfrac{(b - a)^2}{12} = \dfrac{4}{3} \Rightarrow (b - a)^2 = 16$ so $b - a = \pm 4$

If $b - a = -4$ then $b = a - 4$, which would mean $b < a$. This can't happen, so $b - a = 4 \Rightarrow b = a + 4$.

Putting this into $a + b = 22$ we get $a + (a + 4) = 22 \Rightarrow 2a = 18 \Rightarrow a = 9$. So $a = 9$ and $a + b = 22 \Rightarrow b = 13$.

So the c.d.f. is $F(x) = \begin{cases} 0 & x < 9 \\ \dfrac{x - 9}{4} & 9 \le x \le 13 \\ 1 & x > 13 \end{cases}$

2. Normal Approximations
Exercise 2.1 — Continuity corrections

Q1 a) $P(4.5 < Y < 5.5)$

b) $P(11.5 < Y < 15.5)$

c) $P(Y < 10.5)$

Q2 a) $P(199.5 < Y < 200.5)$

b) $P(Y < 299.5)$

c) $P(Y > 98.5)$

Q3 a) $P(49.5 < Y < 50.5)$

b) $P(Y > 33.5)$

c) $P(47.5 < Y < 49.5)$

Note that this is found by finding $P(47.5 < Y < 48.5)$ + $P(48.5 < Y < 49.5)$ and since Y is continuous, $P(Y = 48.5) = 0$, so you can just write down the whole interval $47.5 < Y < 49.5$.

Q4 a) $P(199.5 < Y < 200.5)$

b) $P(X \ge 650)$ is approximated by $P(Y > 649.5)$.

c) $P(X < 300)$ is approximated by $P(Y < 299.5)$.

Exercise 2.2 — Normal approximation to a binomial distribution

Q1 a) n is large (600) and $p = 0.51 \approx 0.5$, so a normal approximation would be suitable.

b) n is large (100) but $p = 0.98$ is not close to 0.5. It might still be OK if np and nq are > 5. $np = 98$ but $nq = 2$, so a normal approximation would not be suitable.

c) n is large (100) but $p = 0.85$ is not close to 0.5. It might still be OK if np and nq are > 5. $np = 85$ and $nq = 15$, so a normal approximation would be suitable.

d) n is not large (6), so a normal approximation would not be suitable.

Q2 a) $\mu = np = 350 \times 0.45 = 157.5$

$\sigma^2 = npq = 350 \times 0.45 \times 0.55 = 86.625$

b) $\mu = np = 250 \times 0.35 = 87.5$

$\sigma^2 = npq = 250 \times 0.35 \times 0.65 = 56.875$

c) $\mu = np = 70 \times 0.501 = 35.07$

$\sigma^2 = npq = 70 \times 0.501 \times 0.499 = 17.500$ (3 d.p.)

Q3 $X \sim B(200, 0.6)$, so use a normal approximation $Y \sim N(\mu, \sigma^2)$ with

$\mu = np = 200 \times 0.6 = 120$

$\sigma^2 = npq = 200 \times 0.6 \times 0.4 = 48$

So approximate X with $Y \sim N(120, 48)$.

a) Using a continuity correction you're looking for

$P(X < 105) \approx P(Y < 104.5) = P\left(Z < \dfrac{104.5 - 120}{\sqrt{48}}\right)$

$= P(Z < -2.24) = 1 - P(Z \le 2.24) = 1 - 0.9875$

$= 0.0125$

b) Using a continuity correction, you're looking for $P(X = 122) \approx P(121.5 < Y < 122.5)$

$= P\left(\dfrac{121.5 - 120}{\sqrt{48}} < Z < \dfrac{122.5 - 120}{\sqrt{48}}\right)$

$= P(0.22 < Z < 0.36)$

$= P(Z < 0.36) - P(Z \le 0.22) = 0.6406 - 0.5871$

$= 0.0535$

c) Using a continuity correction, you're looking for $P(110 < X < 130) \approx P(110.5 < Y < 129.5)$

$= P\left(\dfrac{110.5 - 120}{\sqrt{48}} < Z < \dfrac{129.5 - 120}{\sqrt{48}}\right)$

$= P(-1.37 < Z < 1.37)$

$= P(Z < 1.37) - P(Z \le -1.37)$

$= P(Z < 1.37) - (1 - P(Z < 1.37))$

$= 2 \times P(Z < 1.37) - 1$

$= 2 \times 0.9147 - 1 = 0.8294$

Q4 $X \sim B(1000, 0.48)$, so use a normal approximation
$Y \sim N(\mu, \sigma^2)$ with
$\mu = np = 1000 \times 0.48 = 480$
$\sigma^2 = npq = 1000 \times 0.48 \times 0.52 = 249.6$
So approximate X with $Y \sim N(480, 249.6)$.

a) Using a continuity correction, you're looking for
$P(X \geq 500) \approx P(Y > 499.5) = P\left(Z > \dfrac{499.5 - 480}{\sqrt{249.6}}\right)$
$= P(Z > 1.23) = 1 - P(Z \leq 1.23) = 1 - 0.8907$
$= 0.1093$

b) Using a continuity correction you're looking for
$P(X < 472) \approx P(Y < 471.5) = P\left(Z < \dfrac{471.5 - 480}{\sqrt{249.6}}\right)$
$= P(Z < -0.54) = 1 - P(Z \leq 0.54) = 1 - 0.7054$
$= 0.2946$

c) Using a continuity correction you're looking for
$P(492 \leq X \leq 502) \approx P(491.5 < Y < 502.5)$
$= P\left(\dfrac{491.5 - 480}{\sqrt{249.6}} < Z < \dfrac{502.5 - 480}{\sqrt{249.6}}\right)$
$= P(0.73 < Z < 1.42) = P(Z < 1.42) - P(Z \leq 0.73)$
$= 0.9222 - 0.7673 = 0.1549$

Q5 a) The normal approximation has
$\mu = np = 80 \times 0.8 = 64$
$\sigma^2 = npq = 80 \times 0.8 \times 0.2 = 12.8$
Note that np = 64 and nq = 16, so this normal
approximation is appropriate.

So approximate X with $Y \sim N(64, 12.8)$.
Using a continuity correction you want to find
$P(X = 70) \approx P(69.5 < Y < 70.5)$
$= P\left(\dfrac{69.5 - 64}{\sqrt{12.8}} < Z < \dfrac{70.5 - 64}{\sqrt{12.8}}\right)$
$= P(1.54 < Z < 1.82) = P(Z < 1.82) - P(Z \leq 1.54)$
$= 0.9656 - 0.9382 = 0.0274$

b) $P(X = 70) = \dbinom{80}{70}(0.8)^{70}(0.2)^{10}$

$= 0.0277$ (to 4 d.p.).

Note that the approximation in part a)
is correct to 2 d.p.

Q6 Let X be the number of times the dice lands on an
even number in the 400 throws.
Then $X \sim B(400, 0.39)$. n is large and p is close to
0.5, so we can use a normal approximation with
$\mu = np = 400 \times 0.39 = 156$
$\sigma^2 = npq = 400 \times 0.39 \times 0.61 = 95.16$
So approximate X with $Y \sim N(156, 95.16)$.
Using a continuity correction, you're looking for
$P(X > 140) \approx P(Y > 140.5) = P\left(Z > \dfrac{140.5 - 156}{\sqrt{95.16}}\right)$
$= P(Z > -1.59) = P(Z < 1.59) = 0.9441$

Q7 a) The binomial distribution could be used to model
this situation, with $n = 1000$ and $p = 0.05$.

b) n is very large and even though p is not close to
0.5, $np = 50 > 5$ and $nq = 950 > 5$, so the normal
distribution is a suitable approximation for this
distribution.

c) The normal approximation has
$\mu = np = 1000 \times 0.05 = 50$
$\sigma^2 = npq = 1000 \times 0.05 \times 0.95 = 47.5$
So approximate X with $Y \sim N(50, 47.5)$.

You're looking for the probability that $X > 75$.
Using a continuity correction, you're looking for
the probability
$P(Y > 75.5) = P\left(Z > \dfrac{75.5 - 50}{\sqrt{47.5}}\right) = P(Z > 3.70)$
$= 1 - P(Z \leq 3.70) = 1 - 0.9999 = 0.0001$

Q8 Work it out for Acme's light bulbs first. Let X_1 be the
number of sampled light bulbs which are faulty on a
given day. Then $X_1 \sim B(200, 0.05)$, so use a normal
approximation $Y_1 \sim N(\mu, \sigma^2)$ with
$\mu = np = 200 \times 0.05 = 10$
$\sigma^2 = npq = 200 \times 0.05 \times 0.95 = 9.5$.
So approximate X_1 with $Y_1 \sim N(10, 9.5)$.
Using a continuity correction, you are looking for the
probability $P(Y_1 > 15.5) = P\left(Z > \dfrac{15.5 - 10}{\sqrt{9.5}}\right)$
$= P(Z > 1.78) = 1 - P(Z \leq 1.78) = 1 - 0.9625$
$= 0.0375$

Now let X_2 be the number of sampled light bulbs
which are faulty at Buildit on a given day.
Then $X_2 \sim B(500, 0.02)$, so use a normal
approximation $Y_2 \sim N(\mu, \sigma^2)$ with
$\mu = np = 500 \times 0.02 = 10$
$\sigma^2 = npq = 500 \times 0.02 \times 0.98 = 9.8$.
So approximate X_2 with $Y_2 \sim N(10, 9.8)$.
Using a continuity correction, you are looking for the
probability $P(Y_2 > 20.5) = P\left(Z > \dfrac{20.5 - 10}{\sqrt{9.8}}\right)$
$= P(Z > 3.35) = 1 - P(Z \leq 3.35) = 1 - 0.9996$
$= 0.0004$.

So Acme is more likely to reject a batch of light bulbs
on any given day.

Exercise 2.3 — Normal approximation to a Poisson distribution

Q1 a) No, because $\lambda = 1$ is not large.

b) Yes, because $\lambda = 103$ is large.

c) No, because $\lambda = 7$ is not large.
Remember that λ should ideally be larger than 10 to
use a normal approximation.

Q2 a) $\mu = 36$ and $\sigma^2 = 36$.

b) $\mu = 99$ and $\sigma^2 = 99$.

c) $\mu = 60$ and $\sigma^2 = 60$.

Q3 $X \sim$ Po(16) can be approximated by $Y \sim$ N(16, 16).

a) Using a continuity correction, you're looking for
$$P(X < 20) \approx P(Y < 19.5) = P\left(Z < \frac{19.5 - 16}{\sqrt{16}}\right)$$
$$= P(Z < 0.88) = 0.8106$$

b) Using a continuity correction, you're looking for
$P(X = 19) \approx P(18.5 < Y < 19.5)$
$$= P\left(\frac{18.5 - 16}{\sqrt{16}} < Z < \frac{19.5 - 16}{\sqrt{16}}\right)$$
$$= P(0.63 < Z < 0.88)$$
$$= P(Z < 0.88) - P(Z \leq 0.63) = 0.8106 - 0.7357$$
$$= 0.0749$$

c) Using a continuity correction, you're looking for
$P(11 < X < 15) \approx P(11.5 < Y < 14.5)$
$$= P\left(\frac{11.5 - 16}{\sqrt{16}} < Z < \frac{14.5 - 16}{\sqrt{16}}\right)$$
$$= P(-1.13 < Z < -0.38) = P(0.38 < Z < 1.13)$$
$$= P(Z < 1.13) - P(Z \leq 0.38)$$
$$= 0.8708 - 0.6480 = 0.2228$$

Q4 $X \sim$ Po(48) can be approximated by $Y \sim$ N(48, 48).

a) Using a continuity correction, you're looking for
$$P(X \geq 50) \approx P(Y > 49.5) = P\left(Z > \frac{49.5 - 48}{\sqrt{48}}\right)$$
$$= P(Z > 0.22) = 1 - P(Z \leq 0.22) = 1 - 0.5871$$
$$= 0.4129$$

b) Using a continuity correction, you're looking for
$$P(X < 45) \approx P(Y < 44.5) = P\left(Z < \frac{44.5 - 48}{\sqrt{48}}\right)$$
$$= P(Z < -0.51) = 1 - P(Z \leq 0.51) = 1 - 0.6950$$
$$= 0.3050$$

c) Using a continuity correction, you're looking for
$P(47 \leq X \leq 51) \approx P(46.5 < Y < 51.5)$
$$= P\left(\frac{46.5 - 48}{\sqrt{48}} < Z < \frac{51.5 - 48}{\sqrt{48}}\right)$$
$$= P(-0.22 < Z < 0.51)$$
$$= P(Z < 0.51) - P(Z \leq -0.22)$$
$$= P(Z < 0.51) - (1 - P(Z < 0.22))$$
$$= 0.6950 - (1 - 0.5871)$$
$$= 0.2821$$

Q5 **a)** The normal approximation to Po(50) is
N(50, 50), so approximate X with $Y \sim$ N(50, 50).
Using a continuity correction you need
$P(X = 49) \approx P(48.5 < Y < 49.5)$
$$= P\left(\frac{48.5 - 50}{\sqrt{50}} < Z < \frac{49.5 - 50}{\sqrt{50}}\right)$$
$$= P(-0.21 < Z < -0.07)$$
$$= P(0.07 < Z < 0.21)$$
$$= P(Z < 0.21) - P(Z \leq 0.07)$$
$$= 0.5832 - 0.5279$$
$$= 0.0553$$

b) Using the Poisson formula,
$$P(X = 49) = \frac{50^{49}e^{-50}}{49!} = 0.0563 \text{ (to 4 d.p.)}$$
The approximation in part a) is accurate to 2 decimal places.

Q6 **a)** The number of hits per hour can be modelled by the Poisson distribution with parameter 156.

b) The normal approximation will be
$Y \sim$ N(156, 156).

(i) The probability that the website gets exactly 160 hits an hour can be approximated by
$P(159.5 < Y < 160.5)$
$$= P\left(\frac{159.5 - 156}{\sqrt{156}} < Z < \frac{160.5 - 156}{\sqrt{156}}\right)$$
$$= P(0.28 < Z < 0.36)$$
$$= P(Z < 0.36) - P(Z \leq 0.28)$$
$$= 0.6406 - 0.6103 = 0.0303$$

(ii) The probability that the website receives more than 180 hits in an hour can be approximated by $P(Y > 180.5) = P\left(Z > \frac{180.5 - 156}{\sqrt{156}}\right)$
$$= P(Z > 1.96) = 1 - P(Z \leq 1.96)$$
$$= 1 - 0.9750 = 0.0250$$

Q7 **a)** The number of babies born on the maternity ward in a day can be modelled by the Poisson distribution with parameter 20. This can be approximated by a normal variable $Y \sim$ N(20, 20). So the probability that exactly 22 babies are born on a particular day can be approximated by
$P(21.5 < Y < 22.5)$
$$= P\left(\frac{21.5 - 20}{\sqrt{20}} < Z < \frac{22.5 - 20}{\sqrt{20}}\right)$$
$$= P(0.34 < Z < 0.56) = P(Z < 0.56) - P(Z \leq 0.34)$$
$$= 0.7123 - 0.6331 = 0.0792$$

b) The number of babies born in a week can be modelled by a Poisson distribution with parameter $20 \times 7 = 140$. So this can be approximated by a normal variable $Y \sim$ N(140, 140). The probability that more than 175 babies are born in a week can be approximated by
$P(Y > 175.5) = P\left(Z > \frac{175.5 - 140}{\sqrt{140}}\right)$
$$= P(Z > 3.00) = 1 - P(Z \leq 3.00) = 1 - 0.9987$$
$$= 0.0013$$

Exercise 2.4 — Choosing a suitable approximation

Q1 **a)** For B(60, 0.1), n is large and p is close to 0 so use a Poisson distribution with $\lambda = np = 6$.

b) For Po(20), λ is large so use a normal distribution with $\mu = 20$ and $\sigma^2 = 20$.

c) For B(200, 0.49), n is large and p is close to 0.5 so use a normal distribution with $\mu = np = 98$ and $\sigma^2 = npq = 49.98$.

d) For B(200, 0.01), n is large and p is close to 0 so use a Poisson distribution with $\lambda = np = 2$.

Q2 a) (i) If a shop sells an average of 220 doughnuts every hour, then the number of doughnuts sold in a particular hour can be modelled by a Poisson distribution with parameter $\lambda = 220$.

(ii) λ is large so a normal distribution can be used to approximate this situation. You'd use a normal distribution with parameters $\mu = 220$ and $\sigma^2 = 220$.

b) (i) 200 people buy doughnuts altogether, and the probability that someone buys a low-fat doughnut is 0.03, so this is a binomial distribution with $n = 200$ and $p = 0.03$.

(ii) n is large and p is close to 0 so this can be approximated by a Poisson distribution with parameter $\lambda = np = 6$.

Q3 a) The number of cheesy oatcakes sold each breaktime can be modelled by a Poisson distribution with parameter $\lambda = 27$.

b) λ is large so this situation can be modelled by a normal distribution with parameters $\mu = 27$ and $\sigma^2 = 27$. Let $Y \sim N(27, 27)$. Then the probability that the cafeteria sells more than 30 cheesy oatcakes one breaktime can be approximated by
$$P(Y > 30.5) = P\left(Z > \frac{30.5 - 27}{\sqrt{27}}\right) = P(Z > 0.67)$$
$$= 1 - P(Z \le 0.67) = 1 - 0.7486 = 0.2514$$

Q4 An unbiased dice has a probability of 0.5 of landing on an even number, so this situation can be modelled by a binomial distribution with $n = 1000$ and $p = 0.5$. n is large and p is exactly 0.5 so a normal approximation can be used with $\mu = np = 500$ and $\sigma^2 = npq = 250$. Let $Y \sim N(500, 250)$. Then the probability of the dice landing on an even number fewer than 480 times can be approximated by
$$P(Y < 479.5) = P\left(Z < \frac{479.5 - 500}{\sqrt{250}}\right) = P(Z < -1.30)$$
$$= 1 - P(Z \le 1.30) = 1 - 0.9032 = 0.0968$$

Review Exercise — Chapter 4

Q1 a) $f(x) = \begin{cases} \frac{1}{4} & 7 \le x \le 11 \\ 0 & \text{otherwise} \end{cases}$

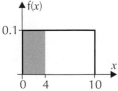

b) $f(y) = \begin{cases} \frac{1}{22} & -4 \le y \le 18 \\ 0 & \text{otherwise} \end{cases}$

Q2 a) First sketch the p.d.f.:

The shaded area represents $P(X < 4)$. This is $4 \times 0.1 = 0.4$.

b) Similarly, $P(X \ge 8) = 2 \times 0.1 = 0.2$.

c) $P(X = 5) = 0$ $[P(X = k) = 0$ for any k and any continuous random variable X.]

d) $P(3 < X \le 7) = 4 \times 0.1 = 0.4$.

Q3 $Y \sim U[5 \times 1 + 2, 5 \times 4 + 2] = U[7, 22]$.

So the p.d.f. is $f(y) = \begin{cases} \frac{1}{15} & 7 \le y \le 22 \\ 0 & \text{otherwise} \end{cases}$

and it looks like this:

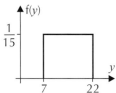

Q4 a) $E(X) = \dfrac{a+b}{2} = \dfrac{4+19}{2} = \dfrac{23}{2}$

$Var(X) = \dfrac{(b-a)^2}{12} = \dfrac{(19-4)^2}{12} = \dfrac{225}{12} = \dfrac{75}{4}$

$F(x) = \begin{cases} 0 & \text{for } x < 4 \\ \dfrac{x-4}{15} & \text{for } 4 \le x \le 19 \\ 1 & \text{for } x > 19 \end{cases}$

b) $Y \sim U[6 \times 4 - 3, 6 \times 19 - 3] = U[21, 111]$, so

$E(Y) = \dfrac{a+b}{2} = \dfrac{21+111}{2} = \dfrac{132}{2} = 66$

$Var(Y) = \dfrac{(b-a)^2}{12} = \dfrac{(111-21)^2}{12} = \dfrac{90^2}{12} = 675$

$G(y) = \begin{cases} 0 & \text{for } y < 21 \\ \dfrac{y-21}{90} & \text{for } 21 \le y \le 111 \\ 1 & \text{for } y > 111 \end{cases}$

Or you could work out E(Y) and Var(Y) using E(Y) = 6E(X) − 3, and Var(Y) = 6²Var(X).

Q5 The error could be anything from –0.5 to 0.5 with equal probability. So $X \sim U[-0.5, 0.5]$.

Q6 a) The p.d.f. of X is a rectangle of height $1 \div 4 = 0.25$, while the p.d.f. of Y is a rectangle of height $1 \div 20 = 0.05$.
$P(X < 6) = (6 - 4) \times 0.25 = 0.5$.
$P(Y > 0) = (12 - 0) \times 0.05 = 0.6$.
So $P(X < 6$ and $Y > 0) = 0.5 \times 0.6 = 0.3$.
You can multiply these probabilities because X and Y are independent random variables.

b) $P(X < 6$ or $Y > 0) = P(X < 6) + P(Y > 0) - P(X < 6$ and $Y > 0) = 0.5 + 0.6 - 0.3 = 0.8$
Remember, for events A and B,
P(A or B) = P(A) + P(B) – P(A and B).

Q7 Let X be the number of minutes the train is delayed. Then $X \sim U[0, 12]$, and its p.d.f. would be a rectangle of height $\frac{1}{12}$.

a) P(late for work) $= P(X > 8) = 4 \times \frac{1}{12} = \frac{1}{3}$

b) P(on time for work) $= P(X \leq 8) = 1 - \frac{1}{3} = \frac{2}{3}$

Since the delays are random, the individual delays are independent and the probabilities can be multiplied.
So P(on time every day) $= \left(\frac{2}{3}\right)^5 = \frac{32}{243}$.

Q8 a) (i) $P(X < 1.8) = P(X \leq 1.8) = F(1.8)$
$= 4(1.8 - 1.75) = 0.2$

(ii) $P(X \geq 1.9) = 1 - P(X < 1.9) = 1 - 4(1.9 - 1.75)$
$= 1 - 0.6 = 0.4$

(iii) $P(1.8 < X < 1.9) = P(X < 1.9) - P(X \leq 1.8)$
$= 4(1.9 - 1.75) - 4(1.8 - 1.75) = 0.4$
Or you could work out part (iii) using:
P(1.8 < X < 1.9) = 1 – P(X < 1.8) – P(X ≥ 1.9)

b) Differentiate each part of the c.d.f.:
For $x < 1.75$, $f(x) = \frac{d}{dx}(0) = 0$
For $1.75 \leq x \leq 2$, $f(x) = \frac{d}{dx}(4(x - 1.75)) = 4$
For $x > 2$, $f(x) = \frac{d}{dx}(1) = 0$
So $f(x) = \begin{cases} 4 & 1.75 \leq x \leq 2 \\ 0 & \text{otherwise} \end{cases}$

Q9 Approximate X using the normal random variable $Y \sim N(45, 24.75)$.

a) $P(X > 50) \approx P(Y > 50.5) = P\left(Z > \frac{50.5 - 45}{\sqrt{24.75}}\right)$
$= P(Z > 1.11)$
$= 1 - P(Z \leq 1.11)$
$= 1 - 0.8665 = 0.1335$

b) $P(X \leq 45) \approx P(Y < 45.5) = P\left(Z < \frac{45.5 - 45}{\sqrt{24.75}}\right)$
$= P(Z < 0.10)$
$= 0.5398$

c) $P(40 < X \leq 47) \approx P(40.5 < Y < 47.5)$
$= P(Y < 47.5) - P(Y \leq 40.5)$
$= P\left(Z < \frac{47.5 - 45}{\sqrt{24.75}}\right) - P\left(Z \leq \frac{40.5 - 45}{\sqrt{24.75}}\right)$
$= P(Z < 0.50) - P(Z \leq -0.90)$
$= P(Z < 0.50) - (1 - P(Z < 0.90))$
$= 0.6915 - 1 + 0.8159 = 0.5074$

Q10 Approximate X using the normal random variable $Y \sim N(25, 25)$.

a) $P(X < 20) \approx P(Y < 20.5)$
$= P\left(Z < \frac{20.5 - 25}{5}\right)$
$= P(Z < -0.9)$
$= 1 - P(Z \leq 0.9)$
$= 1 - 0.8159 = 0.1841$

b) $P(X > 15) \approx P(Y > 15.5)$
$= P\left(Z > \frac{15.5 - 25}{5}\right)$
$= P(Z > -1.90)$
$= P(Z < 1.90) = 0.9713$

c) $P(20 \leq X < 30) \approx P(19.5 < Y < 29.5)$
$= P(Y < 29.5) - P(Y \leq 19.5)$
$= P\left(Z < \frac{29.5 - 25}{5}\right) - P\left(Z \leq \frac{19.5 - 25}{5}\right)$
$- P(Z < 0.90) \quad P(Z \leq -1.10)$
$= P(Z < 0.90) - (1 - P(Z < 1.10))$
$= 0.8159 - 1 + 0.8643 = 0.6802$

Q11 Here $X \sim Po(50)$, and you need to find $P(X > 55)$. λ is large, so approximate X with $Y \sim N(50, 50)$.
$P(X > 55) \approx P(Y > 55.5)$
$= P\left(Z > \frac{55.5 - 50}{\sqrt{50}}\right)$
$= P(Z > 0.78)$
$= 1 - P(Z \leq 0.78)$
$= 1 - 0.7823 = 0.2177$

Exam-Style Questions — Chapter 4

Q1 a) (i) n needs to be large ("as large as possible") *[1 mark]* and p needs to be close to 0.5 *[1 mark]*.

You could also mention that the approximation works well even if p isn't all that close to 0.5, as long as np > 5 and nq > 5.

(ii) A binomial distribution is discrete *[1 mark]*, whereas a normal distribution is continuous. The continuity correction means probabilities can be calculated for the continuous normal distribution that correspond approximately to the discrete binomial probabilities *[1 mark]*.

b) (i) n is large and p is close to 0.5, so use the normal approximation $Y \sim N(60, 24)$ *[1 mark]*.

$P(X \geq 65) \approx P(Y > 64.5)$
$= P\left(Z > \dfrac{64.5 - 60}{\sqrt{24}}\right)$ *[1 mark]*
$= P(Z > 0.92)$
$= 1 - P(Z \leq 0.92)$ *[1 mark]*
$= 1 - 0.8212 = 0.1788$ *[1 mark]*

(ii) $P(50 < X < 62) \approx P(50.5 < Y < 61.5)$
$= P(Y < 61.5) - P(Y \leq 50.5)$ *[1 mark]*
$= P\left(Z < \dfrac{61.5 - 60}{\sqrt{24}}\right) - P\left(Z \leq \dfrac{50.5 - 60}{\sqrt{24}}\right)$
$= P(Z < 0.31) - P(Z \leq -1.94)$ *[1 mark]*
$= P(Z < 0.31) - (1 - P(Z < 1.94))$
$= 0.6217 - (1 - 0.9738) = 0.5955$ *[1 mark]*

All the usual tricks involved there... normal approximation, continuity correction, subtracting values of Φ(z) (the function in your big 'normal distribution table'). They'll all be there on exam day too.

Q2 a) X is equally likely to take any value between 0 and 20, so $X \sim U[0, 20]$ *[1 mark for using a continuous uniform distribution, 1 mark for the correct limits]*

b)

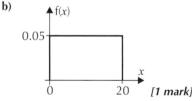

[1 mark]

c) $E(X) = \dfrac{0 + 20}{2} = 10$ *[1 mark]*

$Var(X) = \dfrac{(20 - 0)^2}{12}$ *[1 mark]*

$= \dfrac{400}{12} = 33.3$ (to 3 sig. fig.) *[1 mark]*.

d) (i) $P(X > 5) = (20 - 5) \times 0.05 = 0.75$ *[1 mark]*

(ii) $P(X = 2) = 0$ *[1 mark]*

Remember... P(X = k) = 0 for any value of k if X is a continuous random variable.

Q3 a) The normal approximation is: $Y \sim N(\mu, \sigma^2)$.

$P(X \leq 151) \approx P(Y < 151.5)$ *[1 mark]*
$= P\left(Z < \dfrac{151.5 - \mu}{\sigma}\right) = 0.8944$ *[1 mark]*.

From tables, $\dfrac{151.5 - \mu}{\sigma} = 1.25$.

So $151.5 - \mu = 1.25\sigma$ *[1 mark]*.

$P(X > 127) \approx P(Y > 127.5)$ *[1 mark]*
$= P\left(Z > \dfrac{127.5 - \mu}{\sigma}\right) = 0.9970$ *[1 mark]*.

So $P\left(Z < -\dfrac{127.5 - \mu}{\sigma}\right) = 0.9970$.

$P(Z \leq z) = 0.9970$ means $z = 2.75$.

This tells you that $-\dfrac{127.5 - \mu}{\sigma} = 2.75$,

or $\mu - 127.5 = 2.75\sigma$ *[1 mark]*.

Now you can add your two equations in μ and σ to give $24 = 4\sigma$, or $\sigma = 6$ *[1 mark]*. This then gives $\mu = 144$ *[1 mark]*.

b) You know $\mu = np = 144$ *[1 mark]* and $\sigma^2 = np(1 - p) = 36$ *[1 mark]*. Divide the second equation by the first to give $1 - p = 36 \div 144 = 0.25$, or $p = 0.75$ *[1 mark]*. Then $n = 144 \div 0.75 = 192$ *[1 mark]*.

Q4 a) Let X represent the number of items that the new customer could order per week. Then X follows a Poisson distribution with an average of 40, and so $X \sim Po(40)$ *[1 mark]*.

b) Here, λ is quite large, so X can be approximated by the normal random variable $Y \sim N(40, 40)$ *[1 mark]*.

$P(X > 50) \approx P(Y > 50.5)$
$= P\left(Z > \dfrac{50.5 - 40}{\sqrt{40}}\right)$ *[1 mark]*
$= P(Z > 1.66)$
$= 1 - P(Z \leq 1.66)$
$= 1 - 0.9515 = 0.0485$ *[1 mark]*

c) The probability that the factory will not be able to meet the new customer's order in two consecutive weeks will be $0.0485^2 = 0.00235...$, which is less than 0.01. So the manager should sign the contract *[1 mark for 'yes', with a clear explanation]*.

Q5 a) $a = -2$ and $b = 7$, so the p.d.f. is defined as:

$f(x) = \begin{cases} \dfrac{1}{9} & -2 \leq x \leq 7 \\ 0 & \text{otherwise} \end{cases}$

[1 mark for each part of the p.d.f. correct]

b)

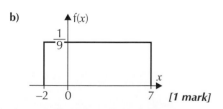

[1 mark]

c) $\dfrac{x-a}{b-a} = \dfrac{x-(-2)}{7-(-2)} = \dfrac{x+2}{9}$ *[1 mark]*

So $F(x) = \begin{cases} 0 & x < -2 \\ \dfrac{x+2}{9} & -2 \leq x \leq 7 \\ 1 & x > 7 \end{cases}$ *[1 mark]*

d) (i) $Y \sim U[3 \times (-2) + 6,\ 3 \times 7 + 6] = U[0, 27]$
[1 mark]

So $E(Y) = \dfrac{0 + 27}{2} = 13.5$ *[1 mark]*

(ii) $Var(Y) = \dfrac{(27-0)^2}{12}$ *[1 mark]*

$= 60.75$ *[1 mark]*

e) (i) $P(Y < 20) = (20 - 0) \times \dfrac{1}{27} = 0.741$ (3 d.p.)
[1 mark]

(ii) $P(10 < Y < 20) = (20 - 10) \times \dfrac{1}{27}$
$= 0.370$ (3 d.p.) *[1 mark]*

Chapter 5: Hypothesis Tests

1. Populations and Samples

Exercise 1.1 — Sampling

Q1 a) Finite.

b) Infinite.
Although there are technically a finite number of people in Australia, counting them precisely would be impossible.

c) Infinite.

d) Finite.

e) Finite.

f) Infinite.

Q2 a) The population is all the members of the book club.

b) A suitable sampling frame would be a numbered list of book club members.

c) A census should be used because all members of the book club should be consulted about the new book. Since it is a local book club, there should be few enough members to ask everyone.

Q3 a) The population is the 1200 students at the school.

b) A suitable sampling frame would be a numbered list of the students in the school.

c) One reason for using a sample is that it would be time-consuming and difficult to test every student in the school. Another reason is that he plans to draw a scatter graph and so he would have a lot of data to process if he did a census.

Q4 a) A list of the unique identification numbers given to the dogs admitted to the sanctuary in 2010 and 2011.

b) There are 108 sampling units.

Q5 Give each house a 3-digit number between 001 and 173 corresponding to its house number. Using a random-number table, choose a starting point on the table and move along it 3 digits at a time. For each 3 digits, see if it is a 3-digit number between 001 and 173. If it is, include the house with that number. Choose the first 40 distinct numbers between 001 and 173 that you come across in the table. Survey the 40 houses which match the numbers you have chosen.

Q6 The sample is not random. For example: The ages of her mother's friends might not be representative of the entire population, or there might be a bias towards either men or women. Pooja's mother might have a group of friends who all have similar opinions on ethically sourced products — this would introduce bias. Similarly, Pooja's mother might have very strong opinions on ethically sourced products and give the questionnaires to people that she knows share her views.

2. Sampling Distributions

Exercise 2.1 — The sampling distribution of a statistic

Q1 **a)** Yes.

   b) No — the mean is unknown.

   c) Yes.

   d) No — the standard deviation is unknown.

Q2 The probability of getting a 1 is 0.25 and the probability of getting a 0 is 0.75.

The possible samples are:

(0, 0, 0), (0, 0, 1), (0, 1, 0), (0, 1, 1),
(1, 0, 0), (1, 0, 1), (1, 1, 0), (1, 1, 1)

(0, 0, 0) gives a mean of 0.

So $P(\overline{X} = 0) = 0.75 \times 0.75 \times 0.75 = \frac{27}{64}$

(0, 0, 1), (0, 1, 0), (1, 0, 0) all give a mean of $\frac{1}{3}$.

So $P\left(X = \frac{1}{3}\right) = P(0,0,1) + P(0,1,0) + P(1,0,0)$

$= (0.75 \times 0.75 \times 0.25)$
$+ (0.75 \times 0.25 \times 0.75)$
$+ (0.25 \times 0.75 \times 0.75)$
$= \frac{27}{64}$

(0, 1, 1), (1, 0, 1), (1, 1, 0) all give a mean of $\frac{2}{3}$.

So $P\left(X = \frac{2}{3}\right) = P(0,1,1) + P(1,0,1) + P(1,1,0)$

$= (0.75 \times 0.25 \times 0.25)$
$+ (0.25 \times 0.75 \times 0.25)$
$+ (0.25 \times 0.25 \times 0.75)$
$= \frac{9}{64}$

(1, 1, 1) gives a mean of 1.

So $P(\overline{X} = 1) = 0.25 \times 0.25 \times 0.25 = \frac{1}{64}$

So the sampling distribution for $\overline{X}$ is:

$\overline{x}$	0	$\frac{1}{3}$	$\frac{2}{3}$	1
$P(\overline{X} = \overline{x})$	$\frac{27}{64}$	$\frac{27}{64}$	$\frac{9}{64}$	$\frac{1}{64}$

Q3 Each sheep in the sample has a probability of $\frac{2}{3}$ of being a 0 and $\frac{1}{3}$ of being a 1. Each sheep picked is an independent trial with a constant probability of being a 1, so it can be modelled by a binomial distribution.

X is just the number of 1's so $X \sim B(3, \frac{1}{3})$.

Q4 40% of the employees like carrot cake, so the probability of an employee in the sample not liking carrot cake is 0.6. So $X \sim B(6, 0.6)$.

Q5 **a)** The 8 possible samples are:
(0, 0, 0), (0, 0, 5), (0, 5, 0), (0, 5, 5),
(5, 0, 0), (5, 0, 5), (5, 5, 0), (5, 5, 5)

Each sample has the sample probability of $0.5 \times 0.5 \times 0.5 = 0.125$.

The median of the samples (0, 0, 0), (0, 0, 5), (0, 5, 0) and (5, 0, 0) is 0
so $P(N = 0) = 0.125 + 0.125 + 0.125 + 0.125$
$= 0.5$

The median of the samples (0, 5, 5), (5, 0, 5), (5, 5, 0), (5, 5, 5) is 5
so $P(N = 5) = 0.125 + 0.125 + 0.125 + 0.125$
$= 0.5$

So the sampling distribution of N is:

n	0	5
$P(N = n)$	0.5	0.5

b) The probability that Tom wins and scores 2 is 0.75 whereas the probability that he loses and scores 0 is 0.25.

The 8 possible samples are:
(0, 0, 0), (0, 0, 2), (0, 2, 0), (0, 2, 2),
(2, 0, 0), (2, 0, 2), (2, 2, 0), (2, 2, 2)

The median of the samples (0, 0, 0), (0, 0, 2), (0, 2, 0) and (2, 0, 0) is 0
so $P(X = 0) = P(0, 0, 0) + P(0, 0, 2) + P(0, 2, 0)$
$\qquad\qquad + P(2, 0, 0)$
$= (0.25 \times 0.25 \times 0.25) + (0.25 \times 0.25 \times 0.75)$
$+ (0.25 \times 0.75 \times 0.25) + (0.75 \times 0.25 \times 0.25)$
$= \frac{5}{32}$

The median of the samples (0, 2, 2), (2, 0, 2), (2, 2, 0) and (2, 2, 2) is 2
so $P(X = 2) = P(0, 2, 2) + P(2, 0, 2) + P(2, 2, 0)$
$\qquad\qquad + P(2, 2, 2)$
$= (0.25 \times 0.75 \times 0.75) + (0.75 \times 0.25 \times 0.75)$
$+ (0.75 \times 0.75 \times 0.25) + (0.75 \times 0.75 \times 0.75)$
$= \frac{27}{32}$

So the sampling distribution of M is:

m	0	2
$P(M = m)$	$\frac{5}{32}$	$\frac{27}{32}$

c) Again the 8 possible samples are:
(0, 0, 0), (0, 0, 2), (0, 2, 0), (0, 2, 2),
(2, 0, 0), (2, 0, 2), (2, 2, 0), (2, 2, 2)

(0, 0, 0) gives a mean of 0.

So $P(\overline{X} = 0) = 0.25 \times 0.25 \times 0.25 = \dfrac{1}{64}$

(0, 0, 2), (0, 2, 0) and (2, 0, 0) give a mean of $\dfrac{2}{3}$.

So $P(\overline{X} = \dfrac{2}{3}) = P(0, 0, 2) + P(0, 2, 0) + P(2, 0, 0)$
$= (0.25 \times 0.25 \times 0.75) + (0.25 \times 0.75 \times 0.25)$
$+ (0.75 \times 0.25 \times 0.25) = \dfrac{9}{64}$

(0, 2, 2), (2, 0, 2) and (2, 2, 0) give a mean of $\dfrac{4}{3}$.

So $P(\overline{X} = \dfrac{4}{3}) = P(0, 2, 2) + P(2, 0, 2) + P(2, 2, 0)$
$= (0.25 \times 0.75 \times 0.75) + (0.75 \times 0.25 \times 0.75)$
$+ (0.75 \times 0.75 \times 0.25) = \dfrac{27}{64}$

(2, 2, 2) gives a mean of 2.

So $P(\overline{X} = 2) = P(2, 2, 2) = 0.75^3 = \dfrac{27}{64}$.

So the sampling distribution of $\overline{X}$ is:

$\overline{x}$	0	$\dfrac{2}{3}$	$\dfrac{4}{3}$	2
$P(\overline{X} = \overline{x})$	$\dfrac{1}{64}$	$\dfrac{9}{64}$	$\dfrac{27}{64}$	$\dfrac{27}{64}$

Q6 Each air guitar is an independent trial with a constant probability of 0.02 of being rejected. Y is just the number of air guitars rejected for their sound quality in a sample of 35, so $Y \sim B(35, 0.02)$.

Q7 Matteo burns meals at an average rate of 5 every 2 hours, so X_i can be modelled by the Poisson distribution Po(2.5). Y is just the number of burnt meals in a sample of 6 hours, so
$Y \sim Po(6 \times 2.5) = Po(15)$.

3. Hypothesis Tests

Exercise 3.1 — Null and alternative hypotheses

Q1 a) The probability that a seed germinates.

b) 0.9

c) Call the probability p.
Then the null hypothesis is $H_0: p = 0.9$.

d) The alternative hypothesis is that the probability has increased, i.e. $H_1: p > 0.9$.

e) The test is one-tailed.

Q2 a) The number of mice caught per day.

b) 1.5.

c) Call the rate λ.
Then the null hypothesis is $H_0: \lambda = 1.5$.

d) The alternative hypothesis is that the rate of mice caught has decreased, i.e. $H_1: \lambda < 1.5$.

e) The test is one-tailed.

Q3 a) The team is interested in the population parameter p, the probability that a teenager has the antibody present.

b) The null hypothesis is that the probability is the same, $H_0: p = 0.35$. The alternative hypothesis is that the probability is different, $H_1: p \neq 0.35$.

c) The test is two-tailed.

Q4 The council want to know if more than 16% of residents are now aware of the grant. Let p be the probability that a resident knows about the grant, then $H_0: p = 0.16$ and $H_1: p > 0.16$.

Q5 The owner wants to know if the average number of jars of chilli chutney sold per week has changed. Let λ be the rate of chilli chutney sold per week. Then $H_0: \lambda = 16$ and $H_1: \lambda \neq 16$.

Q6 Boyd wants to know if the proportion of gym members that watch Australian soaps is higher than the claim of 40%. Let p be the probability that a gym member watches Australian soaps. Then $H_0: p = 0.4$ and $H_1: p > 0.4$.

4. Hypothesis Tests for a Binomial Distribution

Exercise 4.1 — Testing for significance

Q1 a) If Charlotte cannot read minds, she would just be guessing a number between 1 and 5, and so the probability of getting it right would be 0.2. Let p be the probability of Charlotte guessing correctly. Then $H_0: p = 0.2$ and $H_1: p > 0.2$.

b) Let X be the number of times Charlotte guesses correctly in the sample. Then under H_0, $X \sim B(10, 0.2)$.

c) From the tables
$P(X \geq 4) = 1 - P(X \leq 3) = 1 - 0.8791 = 0.1209$
> 0.05. So there is not significant evidence at the 5% level to reject H_0 in favour of Charlotte's claim.

Q2 Let p = the proportion of people who think chicken dinosaurs are good value. Then $H_0: p = 0.45$ and $H_1: p < 0.45$. The significance level $\alpha = 0.05$. Let X be the number of students in the sample who think chicken dinosaurs are good value. Then under H_0, $X \sim B(50, 0.45)$. Now from the tables $P(X \leq 16) = 0.0427 < 0.05$. So there is significant evidence at the 5% level to reject H_0 in favour of Ellen's claim that fewer people think chicken dinosaurs are good value.

Q3 Let p = the proportion of John's pupils who gain distinctions. Then $H_0: p = 0.25$ and $H_1: p \neq 0.25$. The significance level $\alpha = 0.01$ but since it's a two-tailed test, you'll need $\dfrac{\alpha}{2} = 0.005$.
Let X = the number of John's exam candidates who get distinctions.
Then under H_0, $X \sim B(12, 0.25)$. So from the tables
$P(X \geq 6) = 1 - P(X \leq 5) = 1 - 0.9456 = 0.0544 > 0.005$.
So there is not significant evidence at the 1% level to reject H_0 in favour of the alternative hypothesis that the number of distinctions has changed.

Q4 Let p = the proportion of the birds that are rare. Then $H_0: p = 0.15$ and $H_1: p \neq 0.15$. The significance level is $\alpha = 0.1$ but the test is two-tailed so you'll need $\frac{\alpha}{2} = 0.05$.

Let X be the number of rare birds in the sample. Then under H_0, $X \sim B(40, 0.15)$.

Now from the tables, $P(X \leq 2) = 0.0486 < 0.05$.

So there is significant evidence at the 10% level to reject H_0 in favour of the alternative hypothesis that the number of rare birds is different with the new birdseed.

Q5 Let p = the proportion of customers who buy Pigeon Spotter Magazine. Then $H_0: p = 0.1$ and $H_1: p \neq 0.1$. The significance level is $\alpha = 0.05$ but the test is two-tailed so you'll need $\frac{\alpha}{2} = 0.025$. Let X = the number of customers who buy the magazine in the sample. The under H_0, $X \sim B(50, 0.1)$. Now from the tables $P(X \geq 8) = 1 - P(X \leq 7) = 1 - 0.8779 = 0.1221 > 0.025$. So there is not significant evidence at the 5% level to reject H_0 in favour of the alternative hypothesis that the number of customers buying the magazine is different in the new shop.

Q6 Let p = the proportion of clients who pass the driving test first time. Then $H_0: p = 0.7$ and $H_1: p < 0.7$. The significance level is $\alpha = 0.01$. Let X be the number of people in the sample who passed their driving test on their first attempt. Then under H_0, $X \sim B(8, 0.7)$.
You'll need to use the tables to find $P(X \leq 4)$, but the probability is greater than 0.7, so you'll need to do the usual trick for this.

Let Y = the number of people in the sample who didn't pass first time, then $Y \sim B(8, 0.3)$.
From the tables:
$P(X \leq 4) = P(Y \geq 4) = 1 - P(Y \leq 3)$
$= 1 - 0.8059 = 0.1941 > 0.01$
So there is not significant evidence at the 1% level to reject H_0 in favour of H_1, so Hati's claim is not upheld at the 1% level.

Exercise 4.2 — Critical regions

Q1 **a)** Let p = the proportion of pupils reaching the top reading level. So $H_0: p = 0.25$ and $H_1: p > 0.25$. Let X be the number of pupils in the sample that are reaching the top reading level. Then under H_0, $X \sim B(20, 0.25)$.
You're looking for the biggest possible 'low' value x such that
$P(X \geq x) \leq 0.05$. Using the tables,
$P(X \geq 9) = 1 - P(X \leq 8) = 1 - 0.9591 = 0.0409$
$P(X \geq 8) = 1 - P(X \leq 7) = 1 - 0.8982 = 0.1018$
So the critical region is $X \geq 9$.

b) The actual significance level is 0.0409 or 4.09%.

Q2 Let p = the proportion of pupils giving up Miss Cackle's potion-making class after year 9.
So $H_0: p = 0.2$ and $H_1: p < 0.2$. Let X be the number of pupils in the class of 30 that give up potion-making after year 9. Then under H_0, $X \sim B(30, 0.2)$.
You're interested in the low values since you're looking for a decrease.
$P(X \leq 2) = 0.0442$ and $P(X \leq 3) = 0.1227$
This means the critical region is $X \leq 2$.

The actual significance level is 0.0442 or 4.42%.

Q3 Let p = proportion of southern local councils who provide weekly collections.
So $H_0: p = 0.4$ and $H_1: p \neq 0.4$. Let X be the number of southern councils in the sample that offer a weekly collection. Then under H_0, $X \sim B(25, 0.4)$.
Since this is a two-tailed test, you need to find two critical regions, one at each tail.
Lower tail: $P(X \leq 4) = 0.0095$ and $P(X \leq 5) = 0.0294$
The closest probability to 0.025 is 0.0294 so the critical region for this tail is $X \leq 5$.
Upper tail:
$P(X \geq 15) = 1 - P(X \leq 14) = 1 - 0.9656 = 0.0344$
$P(X \geq 16) = 1 - P(X \leq 15) = 1 - 0.9868 = 0.0132$
The closest probability to 0.025 is 0.0344 so the critical region for this tail is $X \geq 15$.
So the critical region is $X \leq 5$ or $X \geq 15$.

The actual significance level is
$0.0344 + 0.0294 = 0.0638$, or 6.38%.

Q4 **a)** Let p = the proportion of people who have booked their summer holiday before February 1st. Then $H_0: p = 0.35$ and $H_1: p < 0.35$. Let X be the number of people in the sample who have booked their holiday. Then under H_0, $X \sim B(15, 0.35)$. Using the tables, $P(X \leq 1) = 0.0142$ and $P(X \leq 2) = 0.0617$. This means the critical region is $X \leq 1$.

b) The actual significance level is 0.0142 or 1.42%.

c) 3 does not lie in the critical region so the result is not significant at the 5% level.

Q5 Let p = the proportion of people reporting an improvement in symptoms. Then $H_0: p = 0.15$ and $H_1: p > 0.15$. Let X be the number of people in the test who report an improvement in symptoms. Then $X \sim B(50, 0.15)$ under H_0.
You're interested in the high values. From the tables:
$P(X \geq 15) = 1 - P(X \leq 14) = 1 - 0.9947 = 0.0053$
$P(X \geq 14) = 1 - P(X \leq 13) = 1 - 0.9868 = 0.0132$
The probability must be less than 0.1 so the critical region is $X \geq 15$.

The actual significance level is 0.0053 or 0.53%.

Q6 Let p = the proportion of five-year-old boys who believe they have magical powers.
Then H_0: $p = 0.05$ and H_1: $p \neq 0.05$. Let X be the number of five-year-old boys in the sample who believe they have magical powers.
Then under H_0, $X \sim B(50, 0.05)$.
The test is two-tailed so you need to consider the upper and lower ends of the binomial distribution.
From the tables:
$P(X \leq 0) = 0.0769$ — this is as close to 0.05 as you can possibly get so the critical region for the lower tail is $X = 0$.
$P(X \geq 6) = 1 - P(X \leq 5) = 1 - 0.9622 = 0.0378$
$P(X \geq 5) = 1 - P(X \leq 4) = 1 - 0.8964 = 0.1036$
So the closest probability to 0.05 is 0.0378 and so the critical region for the higher tail is $X \geq 6$.
So the critical region is $X = 0$ or $X \geq 6$.
The actual significance level is $0.0769 + 0.0378 = 0.1147$

Q7 a) Let p = the proportion of customers the salesman can persuade to get a loyalty card.
Then H_0: $p = 0.6$ and H_1: $p > 0.6$. Let X be the number of customers he persuades in the sample.
Then $X \sim B(12, 0.6)$ under H_0.
This probability is higher than 0.5 so you need to introduce another random variable, Y. Let Y be the number of customers he doesn't persuade, then $Y \sim B(12, 0.4)$ under H_0.
Then you're looking for a value x such that $P(X \geq x) \leq 0.05$, i.e. $P(Y \leq y) \leq 0.05$, where $y = 12 - x$.
$P(Y \leq 1) = 0.0196$ and $P(Y \leq 2) = 0.0834$
So the critical region is $Y \leq 1$, i.e. $X \geq 11$.

b) The actual significance level is 0.0196.

c) 10 doesn't lie in the critical region so this result is not significant at the 5% level.

5. Hypothesis Tests for a Poisson Distribution

Exercise 5.1 — Testing for significance

Q1 a) Let λ be the rate at which noise complaints are received per week. Then H_0: $\lambda = 9$ and H_1: $\lambda < 9$.

b) Now let X be the number of complaints per week. Then under H_0, $X \sim Po(9)$.

c) To test for significance find $P(X \leq 4)$. From the tables $P(X \leq 4) = 0.0550 > 0.05$. So there is not significant evidence to reject H_0.
So there is no evidence at the 5% level to suggest a significant improvement.

Q2 Let λ be the rate that Harriet spills cups of coffee per day. Then H_0: $\lambda = 3$ and H_1: $\lambda > 3$. Let X be the number of cups of coffee Harriet spills in one day. Then under H_0, $X \sim Po(3)$.
From the tables:
$P(X \geq 6) = 1 - P(X \leq 5) = 1 - 0.9161 = 0.0839 < 0.1$.
The result is significant so there is significant evidence at the 10% level to reject H_0 in favour of the alternative hypothesis that Harriet is getting clumsier.

Q3 Let λ be the rate of micro-organisms per sample. Then H_0: $\lambda = 8$ and H_1: $\lambda \neq 8$. Let X be the number of micro-organisms in the sample. Then $X \sim Po(8)$ under H_0. From the tables:
$P(X \geq 15) = 1 - P(X \leq 14) = 1 - 0.9827 = 0.0173$ and $0.0173 < 0.025$ so the result is significant and so there is significant evidence at the 5% level to reject H_0 and to conclude that the abundance of the micro-organisms is different in the second pond.

Q4 Let λ be the rate of Sahdat's headaches per week. Then H_0: $\lambda = 2$ and H_1: $\lambda < 2$. Let X be the number of headaches Sahdat has in 4 weeks. Then $X \sim Po(8)$ under H_0. From the tables, $P(X \leq 3) = 0.0424 < 0.05$. So this is significant evidence at the 5% level to reject H_0 and to conclude that Sahdat's headaches are becoming less frequent.

Q5 Let λ be the rate at which the headmaster uses the word 'excellence' in 20 minutes. Then H_0: $\lambda = 30$ and H_1: $\lambda \neq 30$. Let X be the number of times the headmaster uses the word in 5 minutes. Then under H_0, $X \sim Po(7.5)$. From the tables:
$P(X \geq 15) = 1 - P(X \leq 14) = 1 - 0.9897 = 0.0103$
$0.0103 < 0.025$ so this is a significant result.
So there is significant evidence at the 5% level to reject H_0 in favour of the alternative hypothesis that the headmaster has changed his use of the word.

Q6 Let λ be the rate at which Hayley makes grammatical errors per 10 pages. Then H_0: $\lambda = 37$ and H_1: $\lambda < 37$. Let X be the number of grammatical errors in 1 page. Then $X \sim Po(3.7)$ under H_0.
$P(X \leq 1) = P(X = 0) + P(X = 1)$
$$= \frac{e^{-3.7}(3.7)^0}{0!} + \frac{e^{-3.7}(3.7)^1}{1!} = 0.1162 \text{ (to 4 d.p.)}$$
$0.1162 > 0.01$ so this is not a significant result.
There is not significant evidence at the 1% level to suggest that Hayley's grammar has improved.

Exercise 5.2 — Critical regions

Q1 **a)** λ = the rate at which Lionel finds dandelion plants in his lawn each spring.
$H_0: \lambda = 6$, $H_1: \lambda < 6$. Let X be the number of dandelion plants he digs out this spring.
Then $X \sim \text{Po}(6)$ under H_0.
$P(X \leq 1) = 0.0174$ and $P(X \leq 2) = 0.0620$ so the critical region is $X \leq 1$.

b) The actual significance level is 0.0174 or 1.74%.

Q2 λ = the rate at which callers ring the helpline per day.
$H_0: \lambda = 7$, $H_1: \lambda > 7$. Let X be the number of callers in a day. Then $X \sim \text{Po}(7)$ under H_0.
$P(X \geq 13) = 1 - P(X \leq 12) = 1 - 0.9730 = 0.0270$
$P(X \geq 12) = 1 - P(X \leq 11) = 1 - 0.9467 = 0.0533$
So the critical region is $X \geq 13$.
The actual significance level is 0.0270 or 2.7%.

Q3 **a)** Let λ = the number of left-handed students admitted to the school each year. $H_0: \lambda = 8$ and $H_1: \lambda \neq 8$. Let X be the number of left-handed students in the new year group. Then $X \sim \text{Po}(8)$ under H_0.
Then $P(X \leq 2) = 0.0138$ and $P(X \leq 3) = 0.0424$.
At the lower end, the closest probability to 0.025 is 0.0138 and so the critical region is $X \leq 2$.
$P(X \geq 15) = 1 - P(X \leq 14) = 1 - 0.9827 = 0.0173$
$P(X \geq 14) = 1 - P(X \leq 13) = 1 - 0.9658 = 0.0342$
The closest probability is 0.0173 so the critical region in this tail is $X \geq 15$.
So the critical region is $X \leq 2$ or $X \geq 15$.

b) The actual significance level is $0.0138 + 0.0173 = 0.0311$

c) This result is not significant. There is insufficient evidence at the 5% level to reject H_0. So there is insufficient evidence at the 5% level that the number of left-handed people per year group has changed.

Q4 **a)** Let λ = the rate of 'accidents' per hour.
Then $H_0: \lambda = 2$ and $H_1: \lambda < 2$. Let X be the number of accidents that Ziggy has in a 5-hour period. Then under H_0, $X \sim \text{Po}(10)$.
$P(X \leq 4) = 0.0293$ and $P(X \leq 5) = 0.0671$ so the critical region is $X \leq 4$.

b) The actual significance level is 0.0293 or 2.93%.

c) This result is significant. There is significant evidence at the 5% level to reject H_0 and support the alternative hypothesis that Ziggy has improved.

Q5 Let λ = the rate of sales per week. Then $H_0: \lambda = 35$ and $H_1: \lambda > 35$. Let X be the number of sales in one day. Then under H_0, $X \sim \text{Po}(7)$.
$P(X \geq 15) = 1 - P(X \leq 14) = 1 - 0.9943 = 0.0057$
$P(X \geq 14) = 1 - P(X \leq 13) = 1 - 0.9872 = 0.0128$
So critical region is $X \geq 15$.
The actual significance level is 0.0057 or 0.57%.

6. Hypothesis Tests Involving Approximate Distributions

Exercise 6.1 — Using approximations

Q1 Let p be the probability of Troy missing a putt.
Then $H_0: p = 0.03$ and $H_1: p < 0.03$. Let X be the number of putts Troy misses in 300 practice putts.
Then under H_0, $X \sim \text{B}(300, 0.03)$. n is too large to work with easily here, but p is small so we can approximate X with a Poisson distribution $X \sim \text{Po}(300 \times 0.03) = \text{Po}(9)$. $P(X \leq 4) = 0.0550 > 0.5$. So this result is not significant at the 5% level. So there is no evidence at the 5% level of significance to reject H_0 in favour of the alternative hypothesis that Troy has improved.

Q2 Let λ be the number of times per day that Harpreet loses her mobile signal. Then $H_0: \lambda = 14$ and $H_1: \lambda > 14$. Let X be the number of times she loses her signal in a day. Then $X \sim \text{Po}(14)$ under H_0.
This number is large (bigger than 10) so we can approximate X using $Y \sim \text{N}(14, 14)$.
Apply a continuity correction:
$P(X \geq 22) \approx P(Y > 21.5) = 1 - P(Y \leq 21.5)$
$= 1 - P\left(Z \leq \dfrac{21.5 - 14}{\sqrt{14}}\right) = 1 - P(Z \leq 2.00)$
$= 1 - 0.9772 = 0.0228 < 0.05$.
So this is a significant result. There is significant evidence at the 5% level to reject H_0 and support Harpreet's claim that there has been a significant worsening in her mobile phone signal.

Q3 Let p be the proportion of trees that are home to the rare species of butterfly. $H_0: p = 0.05$ and $H_1: p \neq 0.05$. Let X be the number of trees in the neighbouring wood that are home to the same species of butterfly. Then $X \sim \text{B}(80, 0.05)$ under H_0.
n is large and p is small so we can approximate this with a Poisson distribution, $X \sim \text{Po}(80 \times 0.05) = \text{Po}(4)$.
So $P(X \leq 3) = 0.4335 > 0.025$.
So this result is not significant. There is not significant evidence at the 5% level to reject H_0 and support the alternative hypothesis that the proportion of trees home to the rare butterfly is different in this wood.

Q4 Let p be the proportion of young people who expect to own their own home some day.
Then $H_0: p = 0.7$ and $H_1: p < 0.7$. Let X be the number of young people in the sample that Malcolm used. Then under H_0, $X \sim \text{B}(90, 0.7)$.
n is large but p is close to 0.5 so we can approximate X using:
$Y \sim \text{N}(90 \times 0.7, 90 \times 0.7 \times 0.3) = \text{N}(63, 18.9)$.
Apply a continuity correction:
$P(X \leq 56) \approx P(Y < 56.5) = P\left(Z < \dfrac{56.5 - 63}{\sqrt{18.9}}\right)$
$= P(Z < -1.50) = 1 - P(Z \leq 1.50)$
$= 1 - 0.9332 = 0.0668 > 0.05$.
This result is not significant at the 5% level. So there is no significant evidence at the 5% level to reject H_0 and support the theory that the proportion of young people who expect to own their own home has decreased.

Q5 Let λ be the number of visitors to the safari park on a Sunday. Then H_0: $\lambda = 60$ and H_1: $\lambda < 60$. Let X be the number of visitors to the safari park on the sampled Sunday. Then under H_0, $X \sim \text{Po}(60)$. λ is large so you can approximate X with $Y \sim \text{N}(60, 60)$. Apply a continuity correction:
$P(X \le 46) \approx P(Y < 46.5)$
$= P\left(Z < \dfrac{46.5 - 60}{\sqrt{60}}\right) = P(Z < -1.74) = 1 - P(Z \le 1.74)$
$= 1 - 0.9591 = 0.0409 < 0.05$.
This result is significant. So there is significant evidence at the 5% level to reject H_0 and support the claim that there are fewer visitors on a Sunday.

Q6 Let p be the proportion of eggs that are cracked when they arrive. Then H_0: $p = 0.01$ and H_1: $p > 0.01$. Let X be the number of eggs in the sample of 200 that are cracked. Then $X \sim \text{B}(200, 0.01)$ under H_0. n is large and p is very small, so use a Poisson approximation $X \sim \text{Po}(2)$. Then $P(X \ge 6) = 1 - P(X \le 5) = 1 - 0.9834$
$= 0.0166 < 0.05$.
This result is significant. So there is significant evidence at the 5% level to reject the null hypothesis and support the claim that the proportion of cracked eggs has significantly increased.

Q7 Let p be the proportion of dragons born that are male. Then H_0: $p = 0.52$ and H_1: $p > 0.52$. Let X be the number of males out of 150 dragons born on the remote Scottish island.
Then $X \sim \text{B}(150, 0.52)$ under H_0. n is large and p is close to 0.5, so use a normal approximation, $Y \sim \text{N}(78, 37.44)$.
Apply a continuity correction: $P(X \ge 91)$
$\approx P(Y > 90.5) = 1 - P(Y \le 90.5)$
$= 1 - P\left(Z \le \dfrac{90.5 - 78}{\sqrt{37.44}}\right) = 1 - P(Z \le 2.04)$
$= 1 - 0.9793 = 0.0207 < 0.05$.
This result is significant. So there is significant evidence at the 5% level to reject the null hypothesis and support Charlie's theory that the percentage of dragons born that are male is greater than 52%.

Review Exercise — Chapter 5

Q1 a) All the members of the tennis club.

b) The individual tennis club members.

c) A full membership list.
It might look like I've written the same answer down three times, but there are important differences. Make sure you know exactly what's meant by the three terms tested here.

Q2 a) A census would be more sensible. The results will be more accurate and there are only 8 people in the population, so it wouldn't take long to find out the required information for each person.

b) A sample survey should be done. Testing all 500 toys would take too long, but more importantly it would destroy all the toys.

c) A sample survey is the only option. The population is all the possible dice rolls — there are an infinite number of dice rolls, so you can only examine a sample of them.

Q3 a) A list of all 52 cards, which says the number and the suit of each card.

b) 52.

Q4 Simple random sampling means the sample will not be affected by sampling bias.

Q5 a) Yes

b) No — it contains unknown parameter σ.

c) No — it contains unknown parameter μ.

d) Yes
There's no excuse for getting these ones wrong. You've just got to look for any unknown parameters (they're usually a Greek letter, just to make it even easier) — if you find one, it's not a statistic.

Q6 a) Yes

b) No — the mean μ is unknown.

c) No — the standard deviation is unknown.

d) Yes — the median is just the middle data value.

Q7 a) A two-tailed test should be used — Salma doesn't know if the coin is biased towards heads or tails.
H_0: $p = 0.5$, H_1: $p \ne 0.5$

b) A one-tailed test should be used — the typist is only interested in a decrease in the rate of errors.
H_0: $\lambda = 20$, H_1: $\lambda < 20$

Q8 a) The number (or proportion) of 'successes' in a random sample taken from the distribution.

b) The number of events that occur in a random interval (of time or space).

Q9 a) (i) H_0: $p = 0.2$, H_1: $p < 0.2$, $\alpha = 0.05$ and $x = 2$:
Under H_0, $X \sim \text{B}(20, 0.2)$
$P(X \le 2) = 0.2061$
$0.2061 > 0.05$, so there is insufficient evidence at the 5% level of significance to reject H_0.

(ii) H_0: $p = 0.4$, H_1: $p > 0.4$, $\alpha = 0.01$ and $x = 15$:
Under H_0, $X \sim \text{B}(20, 0.4)$
$P(X \ge 15) = 1 - P(X \le 14) = 1 - 0.9984 = 0.0016$
$0.0016 < 0.01$, so there is sufficient evidence at the 1% level of significance to reject H_0.

b) (i) H_0: $\lambda = 7$, H_1: $\lambda < 7$, $\alpha = 0.05$ and $x = 3$:
Under H_0, $X \sim \text{Po}(7)$
$P(X \le 3) = 0.0818$
$0.0818 > 0.05$, so there is insufficient evidence at the 5% level of significance to reject H_0.

(ii) H_0: $\lambda = 2.5$, H_1: $\lambda > 2.5$, $\alpha = 0.1$ and $x = 4$:
Under H_0, $X \sim \text{Po}(2.5)$
$P(X \ge 4) = 1 - P(X \le 3) = 1 - 0.7576 = 0.2424$
$0.2424 > 0.1$, so there is insufficient evidence at the 10% level of significance to reject H_0.

Q10 a) H_0: $p = 0.3$, H_1: $p < 0.3$, $\alpha = 0.05$
Under H_0, $X \sim B(10, 0.3)$
Critical region = biggest possible set of 'low' values of X with a total probability of ≤ 0.05.
$P(X \leq 0) = 0.0282$, $P(X \leq 1) = 0.1493$, so critical region is $X = 0$.

b) H_0: $\lambda = 6$, H_1: $\lambda < 6$, $\alpha = 0.1$
Under H_0, $X \sim Po(6)$
Critical region = biggest possible set of 'low' values of X with a total probability of ≤ 0.1.
$P(X \leq 2) = 0.0620$, $P(X \leq 3) = 0.1512$, so critical region is $X \leq 2$.

Q11 Let λ be the number of daisies per square metre in the shady area. H_0: $\lambda = 42$ and H_1: $\lambda < 42$.
Let X be the number of daisies found in a square metre in the shade. Then $X \sim Po(42)$ under H_0. λ is large so use a normal approximation $Y \sim N(42, 42)$.
Apply a continuity correction $P(X \leq 30) \approx P(Y < 30.5)$
$= P\left(Z < \dfrac{30.5 - 42}{\sqrt{42}}\right) = P(Z < -1.77)$

$= 1 - P(Z \leq 1.77) = 1 - 0.9616 = 0.0384 < 0.05$

So the result is significant at the 5% level. So there is significant evidence at the 5% level to reject H_0 and support the alternative hypothesis that there are significantly fewer daisies in the shade.

Exam-Style Questions — Chapter 5

Q1 The possible samples are: (1, 1, 1), (1, 1, 2), (1, 2, 1), (2, 1, 1), (2, 2, 1), (2, 1, 2), (1, 2, 2) and (2, 2, 2).
[3 marks for showing that there are 8 possible samples, or 2 marks for showing 4 correct samples, or 1 mark for showing at least 1 correct sample.]

So the median could either be 1 or 2. *[1 mark]*
$P(M = 1) = P(1, 1, 1) + P(1, 1, 2) + P(1, 2, 1)$
$+ P(2, 1, 1)$
$= 0.7^3 + (3 \times 0.7^2 \times 0.3) = 0.784$
$P(M = 2) = P(2, 2, 1) + P(2, 1, 2) + P(1, 2, 2)$
$+ P(2, 2, 2)$
$= (3 \times 0.3^2 \times 0.7) + 0.3^3 = 0.216$
[1 mark for showing that the probabilities of samples giving the same median value should be added, 1 mark for $P(M = 1) = 0.784$ and 1 mark for $P(M = 2) = 0.216$.]
Remember to check that the probabilities you've worked out for the values of the median add up to 1. If not, go back and work out where you've gone wrong.

Q2 a) Binomial *[1 mark]*
'Proportion' should set the binomial bell ringing.

b) (i) Start by stating the hypotheses:
H_0: $p = 0.2$ and H_1: $p > 0.2$
[1 mark for both correct]
X = number of tiramisu orders in sample
Under H_0, $X \sim B(20, 0.2)$ *[1 mark]*
$\alpha = 0.05$
Either:
Use the binomial tables to find the probability of getting a value greater than or equal to 7, under H_0:
$P(X \geq 7) = 1 - P(X \leq 6)$ *[1 mark]*
$= 1 - 0.9133 = 0.0867$ *[1 mark]*
$0.0867 > 0.05$, so the result isn't significant.
[1 mark]
Or:
Use the binomial tables to find the critical region:
$P(X \geq 7) = 1 - P(X \leq 6) = 1 - 0.9133 = 0.0867$
$P(X \geq 8) = 1 - P(X \leq 7) = 1 - 0.9679 = 0.0321$
[1 mark for attempting to find the smallest value of x such that $P(X \geq x) \leq 0.05$.]

$0.0321 < 0.05$, so the critical region is $X \geq 8$ *[1 mark]*. 7 isn't in the critical region, so the result isn't significant. *[1 mark]*

So, there is insufficient evidence at the 5% level of significance to support the chef's theory that the proportion of dessert eaters ordering tiramisu on a Saturday is greater than on weekdays.
[1 mark for a suitable conclusion]

(ii) You're looking for the smallest value of x such that
$P(X \geq x) \leq 0.05$.
You know $X = 7$ isn't significant from part (i).
Try 8: $P(X \geq 8) = 0.0321 < 0.05$,
so the answer is 8 tiramisu orders *[1 mark]*.

Part (ii) here is really just asking for the lower boundary of the critical region. So if you answered part (i) by finding the critical region, you've already worked out the answer. Bonus.

Q3 **a)** First-serve faults must occur randomly (or independently of each other) and at a constant average rate.
[1 mark for saying first-serve faults must occur randomly or independently, and 1 mark for saying first-serve faults must occur at a constant average rate.]

b) $H_0: \lambda = 4$ and $H_1: \lambda < 4$, where λ is the rate of first-serve faults per service game.
X = number of first-serve faults in 5 service games
Under H_0, $X \sim$ Po(20)
$\alpha = 0.05$
X is large so you can approximate it using
$Y \sim$ N(20, 20)
[2 marks for stating the correct normal approximation, or 1 mark for a normal approximation with only one of the mean or variance correct.]

Applying the continuity correction:
$P(X \le 12)$ becomes $P(Y < 12.5)$ *[1 mark]*

$= P\left(Z < \dfrac{12.5 - 20}{\sqrt{20}}\right)$ *[1 mark]*

$= P(Z < -1.68)$
$= 1 - P(Z \le 1.68)$
$= 1 - 0.9535$
$= 0.0465$ *[1 mark]* < 0.05, so the result is significant.
There is evidence at the 5% level of significance to reject H_0 and to say that the rate of first-serve faults has decreased. *[1 mark]*

Q4 **a)** Let X be the test statistic.
Then $X \sim$ Po(6.5) under H_0. *[1 mark]*
$P(X \le 2) = 0.0430$ and $P(X \le 3) = 0.1118$
[1 mark]
So the critical region is $X \le 2$ *[1 mark]*.

b) The probability of rejecting H_0 when it is true is the actual significance level $P(X \le 2) = 0.0430$
[1 mark].

Q5 **a)** **(i)** A survey is a method of collecting data about a population *[1 mark]*.

(ii) A census is a survey in which you collect data from every member of the population
[1 mark].

(iii) A sample consists of just certain members of the population.
[1 mark].

b) **(i)** The sampling units are the individual waterproof cameras *[1 mark]*.

(ii) A suitable sampling frame is a list of unique product codes of the cameras in the batch.
[1 mark].

(iii) If a census was carried out, every camera would be destroyed by water and there would be none left to sell *[1 mark]*.

Q6 **a)** $H_0: p = 0.1$ and $H_1: p \ne 0.1$
X = number of sampled residents against the plan
Under H_0, $X \sim$ B(50, 0.1) *[1 mark]*
It's a two-tailed test, so the critical region is split into two. For the lower end:
$P(X \le 2) = 0.1117$, $P(X \le 1) = 0.0338$ *[1 mark]*, which is the closest value.
For the upper end:
$P(X \ge 10) = 1 - P(X \le 9) = 1 - 0.9755 = 0.0245$,
$P(X \ge 9) = 1 - P(X \le 8) = 1 - 0.9421 = 0.0579$
[1 mark],
which is the closest value.
So CR is $X \le 1$ *[1 mark]* and $X \ge 9$ *[1 mark]*

Watch out for the wording of these questions. You want the probability in each tail to be as close as possible to 0.05 — which means it can be <u>greater</u> than 0.05.

b) The probability of incorrectly rejecting H_0 is the same as the actual significance level.
So, it's $P(X \le 1) + P(X \ge 9)$ *[1 mark]*
$= 0.0338 + 0.0579$
$= 0.0917$ *[1 mark]*

c) The value 4 doesn't lie in the critical region *[1 mark]*, so there is insufficient evidence to reject the claim that the proportion of residents against the plan is 10% *[1 mark]*. *(Allow follow-through for a correct conclusion drawn from an incorrectly calculated critical region in part a).)*

Glossary

Actual significance level
In a **hypothesis test**, the probability of rejecting the **null hypothesis** when it is true.

Alternative hypothesis
The statement that you will accept instead if you decide to reject the **null hypothesis** in a **hypothesis test.** It gives a range of values for the **parameter** and is usually written H_1.

B

Biased sample
A **sample** which does not fairly represent the **population** it is taken from.

Binomial coefficient
The number of orders in which x objects of one type and $(n - x)$ objects of a different type can be arranged.
Equal to $\binom{n}{x} = \dfrac{n!}{x!(n - x)!}$

Binomial distribution B(n, p)
A discrete **probability distribution** which models the number of successes x in n independent trials when the probability of success in each trial is p.

C

Census
A **survey** in which information is collected from every single member of the **population**.

Continuity correction
A correction made in order to approximate a discrete distribution with a continuous distribution.

Continuous random variable
A **random variable** which is measured on a continuous scale. It may take any value in a given range (i.e. with no 'gaps' between possible values).

Continuous uniform distribution
A 'rectangular' continuous **probability distribution** where all values in a given range are equally likely.

Critical region
The set of all values of the **test statistic** that would cause you to reject the **null hypothesis**.

Cumulative distribution function
A function, F(x), giving the probability that a **random variable**, X, will be less than or equal to a particular value, x.

Discrete random variable
A **random variable** with 'gaps' between its possible values.

Expected value
The expected value of a **random variable** is the 'expected' mean of a large number of readings.

Finite population
A **population** for which it is possible and practical to count the members.

Hypothesis
A statement or claim that you want to test.

Hypothesis test
A method of testing a **hypothesis** using observed **sample** data.

Infinite population
A **population** for which it is impossible or impractical to count the members.

Interquartile range
A measure of dispersion given by the difference between the **upper quartile** and the **lower quartile**.

Lower quartile of a continuous random variable
The value that a **random variable** is less than or equal to with probability 0.25. Often written Q_1.

Maximum (of a function f(x))
The highest point on the graph of a function.

Mean of a random variable
The 'expected' mean of a large number of readings.
Also known as the **expected value**.

Median of a continuous random variable
The value that a **random variable** is less than or equal to with probability 0.5. Often written Q_2.

Minimum (of a function f(x))
The lowest point on the graph of a function.

Mode of a continuous random variable
The value at which the **probability density function** reaches its **maximum**.

Mutually exclusive
Events are mutually exclusive (or just 'exclusive') if they have no outcomes in common, and so can't happen at the same time.

Normal distribution
A 'bell-shaped' continuous **probability distribution** where the further from the mean a value is, the less likely it is to occur.

Null hypothesis
A statement which gives a specific value to the **parameter** in a **hypothesis test**. Usually written H_0.

One-tailed test
A **hypothesis test** is 'one-tailed' if the **alternative hypothesis** is specific about whether the **parameter** is greater or less than the value specified by the **null hypothesis**.
E.g. it says $p < a$ or $p > a$ for a **parameter** p and constant a.

Parameter
A quantity that describes a characteristic of a **population**.

Piecewise function
A function $f(x)$ which is defined by different formulas for different ranges of x.

Poisson distribution
A discrete **probability distribution** which models the probability that x events occur in a period of time or space.

Population
The whole group of every single thing (person, animal, item etc.) that you want to investigate in a statistical test.

Probability density function (p.d.f.)
A function $f(x)$ whose integral over a certain range gives the probability of a **continuous random variable** taking a value in that range.

Probability distribution
A description of the possible values a random variable can take, along with a means to find the probability of those values (e.g. a **probability function** or a **p.d.f.**).

Probability function
A function that generates the probabilities of a **discrete random variable** taking each of its possible values.

Random variable
A variable taking different values with specific probabilities.

Sample
A selection of members from a **population**. Information from the sample is used to deduce information about the **population** as a whole.

Sample mean
A **statistic** used to estimate the mean of a **population**. It's the sum of the observed values in a **sample** divided by the **sample** size.

Sampling distribution
The **probability distribution** of a **statistic** — giving all the possible values that the **statistic** can take, along with their probabilities.

Sampling frame
A full list of all the **sampling units**, used to represent the **population** when selecting a **sample**.

Sampling units
The individual members of the **population** that can be sampled.

Significance level (α)
Determines how unlikely the observed value of the **test statistic** needs to be (under H_0) before rejecting the **null hypothesis** in a **hypothesis test**.

Significant result
The observed value of a **test statistic** is significant if, under H_0, it has a probability lower than the **significance level**.

Simple random sampling
A method of selecting a **sample** from a **population** in which every member is equally likely to be chosen and each selection is independent of every other selection.

Standard deviation of a random variable
The 'expected' standard deviation of a large number of readings. Found by taking the square root of the variance.

Standard normal variable, Z
A **random variable** that follows a **normal distribution** with mean 0 and variance 1.

Statistic
A quantity that is calculated using only known observations from a **sample**.

Survey
A way of collecting information about a **population** by questioning people or examining items.

Test statistic
A **statistic** calculated from **sample** data which is used to decide whether or not to reject the **null hypothesis** in a **hypothesis test**.

Two-tailed test
A **hypothesis test** is 'two-tailed' if the **alternative hypothesis** specifies only that the **parameter** doesn't equal the value specified by the **null hypothesis**.
E.g. it says $p \neq a$ for a parameter p and constant a.

Upper quartile of a continuous random variable
The value that a **random variable** is less than or equal to with probability 0.75. Often written Q_3.

Variance of a random variable
The 'expected' variance of a large number of readings.

Z

Z-tables
Tables relating to the **standard normal variable** (Z) — such as the **cumulative distribution function** $\Phi(z)$, and the percentage-points table.

Index

S2 Formula Sheet

These are the formulas you'll be given in the exam, but make sure you know exactly **when you need them** and **how to use them**.

Discrete Distributions

Standard discrete distributions:

Distribution of X	$P(X = x)$	Mean	Variance
Binomial $B(n, p)$	$\binom{n}{x} p^x (1 - p)^{n-x}$	np	$np(1 - p)$
Poisson $Po(\lambda)$	$e^{-\lambda} \dfrac{\lambda^x}{x!}$	λ	λ

Continuous Distributions

For a continuous random variable X having probability density function f:

Expectation (mean): $E(X) = \mu = \int x\,f(x)\,dx$

Variance: $Var(X) = \sigma^2 = \int (x - \mu)^2\,f(x)\,dx$
$$= \int x^2\,f(x)\,dx - \mu^2$$

For a function g(X): $E(g(X)) = \int g(x)f(x)\,dx$

Cumulative distribution function: $F(x_0) = P(X \leq x_0) = \int_{-\infty}^{x_0} f(t)\,dt$

Standard continuous distribution:

Distribution of X	P.D.F.	Mean	Variance
Uniform (Rectangular) on $[a, b]$	$\dfrac{1}{b - a}$	$\dfrac{1}{2}(a + b)$	$\dfrac{1}{12}(b - a)^2$

MES2T61